CHALLENGES

NUMBER FIVE

Senior Problems

based on the
Senior Mathematical Challenge
1997–2016

Andrew Jobbings

United Kingdom
Mathematics Trust

Senior Problems

Published by The United Kingdom Mathematics Trust.

Maths Challenges Office, School of Mathematics, University of Leeds,
Leeds, LS2 9JT, United Kingdom

http://www.ukmt.org.uk

First published 2018

ISBN 978-1-906001-33-9

Printed in the UK for the UKMT by The Charlesworth Press, Wakefield.

http://www.charlesworth.com

Typographic design by Andrew Jobbings of Arbelos.

http://www.arbelos.co.uk

Typeset with LaTeX.

The books published by the United Kingdom Mathematics Trust are grouped into series.

The EXCURSIONS IN MATHEMATICS series consists of monographs which focus on a particular topic of interest and investigate it in some detail, using a wide range of ideas and techniques. They are aimed at high school students, undergraduates and others who are prepared to pursue a subject in some depth, but do not require specialised knowledge.

1. *The Backbone of Pascal's Triangle*, Martin Griffiths
2. *A Prime Puzzle*, Martin Griffiths

The HANDBOOKS series is aimed particularly at students at secondary school who are interested in acquiring the knowledge and skills which are useful for tackling challenging problems, such as those posed in the competitions administered by the UKMT and similar organisations.

1. *Plane Euclidean Geometry: Theory and Problems*, A D Gardiner and C J Bradley
2. *Introduction to Inequalities*, C J Bradley
3. *A Mathematical Olympiad Primer*, Geoff C Smith
4. *Introduction to Number Theory*, C J Bradley
5. *A Problem Solver's Handbook*, Andrew Jobbings
6. *Introduction to Combinatorics*, Gerry Leversha and Dominic Rowland
7. *First Steps for Problem Solvers*, Mary Teresa Fyfe and Andrew Jobbings
8. *A Mathematical Olympiad Companion*, Geoff C Smith

The PATHWAYS series aims to provide classroom teaching material for use in secondary schools. Each title develops a subject in more depth and in more detail than is normally required by public examinations or national curricula.

1. *Crossing the Bridge*, Gerry Leversha
2. *The Geometry of the Triangle*, Gerry Leversha

The PROBLEMS series consists of collections of high-quality and original problems of Olympiad standard.

1. *New Problems in Euclidean Geometry*, David Monk

❖

The CHALLENGES series is aimed at students at secondary school who are interested in tackling stimulating problems, such as those posed in the Mathematical Challenges administered by the UKMT and similar organisations.

1. *Ten Years of Mathematical Challenges: 1997 to 2006*
2. *Ten Further Years of Mathematical Challenges: 2006 to 2016*
3. *Intermediate Problems*, Andrew Jobbings
4. *Junior Problems*, Andrew Jobbings
5. *Senior Problems*, Andrew Jobbings

The YEARBOOKS series documents all the UKMT activities, including details of all the challenge papers and solutions, lists of high scorers, accounts of the IMO and Olympiad training camps, and other information about the Trust's work during each year.

Contents

II More challenging problems

III Remarks and answers

Series Editor's Foreword

This book is part of a series whose aim is to help young mathematicians prepare for competitions at secondary school level. Here the focus is on the questions from the Senior Mathematical Challenge papers. Like other volumes in the Challenges series, it provides cheap and ready access to directly relevant material.

I hope that every secondary school will have these books in its library. The prices have been set so low that many good students will wish to purchase their own copies. Schools wishing to give out large numbers of copies of these books, perhaps as prizes, should note that discounts may be negotiated with the UKMT office.

London, UK GERRY LEVERSHA

About the Author

Andrew Jobbings gained both his BSc and his PhD in mathematics from Durham University. He taught mathematics for 28 years, including 14 years as Head of Department at Bradford Grammar School, before founding the publishing business Arbelos.

With a keen interest in providing mathematics enrichment activities, Andrew devises problems for the UKMT and is involved with many other UKMT projects. He has regularly chaired a problems group for the European Kangaroo contest and gives Royal Institution masterclasses.

Preface

The Senior Mathematical Challenge (SMC) began in 1997, after the UKMT was founded. Prior to that, the equivalent mathematics challenges were organised by the *Mathematical Association*.

Acknowledgements

The problems on the SMC papers are intended to be stimulating as well as challenging—ideally, some problems will raise a smile. That these aims are so admirably fulfilled is a measure of the quality of the problem setters.

Many people have been involved in the SMC since it began, including problem setters, checkers, and teachers in schools. All of them deserve thanks for their help and support over the years of the competition.

Special thanks are due to the various people who have served as Chair of the Problems Group: Tony Gardiner, Howard Groves, Dean Bunnell and Karen Fogden.

I should also particularly like to thank the following, who commented extremely helpfully on a draft version of the book: Mary Teresa Fyfe; Howard Groves; Calum Kilgour; Alan Slomson. There is no doubt that the book has improved immeasurably as a result.

Of course, any remaining mistakes are entirely the responsibility of the author.

Baildon, Shipley, UK   Andrew Jobbings

Introduction

> It is a familiar and significant saying that a problem well put is half-solved.
>
> John Dewey
> *Logic: Theory of Inquiry*

Layout of the book

The Senior Mathematical Challenge (SMC) is a multiple-choice competition with 25 questions.

Problems

This book includes every problem used in the SMC from 1997 to 2016, but these are not given as multiple-choice questions. In most cases the five options have just been removed, but in a few cases, such as question 3 of exercise 1, the problem has been reworded to accommodate the options. In addition, the wording of some problems has been mildly edited.

The problems have been grouped together in two ways: by difficulty; and by topic.

Part I consists of problems appearing earlier on in the SMC papers (up to question 15); these are intended to be more straightforward than the later problems, which are given in part II.

In each of parts I and II, problems broadly based on the same topic have been grouped together into one exercise. In each exercise, the questions are ordered by their position on the original paper. The exercises themselves are roughly ordered by difficulty.

The allocation of problems to topic areas involves a great deal of subjectivity—and is sometimes a little arbitrary—so do not be surprised if you find a problem in an unusual place. Also, the names of the topics may bear little resemblance to anything you have already met; even when you have come across a topic before, the content could well be different to anything you may be used to. The real reason for grouping the problems, of course, is that it is convenient for the author to do so!

To help indicate the degree of difficulty of each question, the number of the question on the original paper is written in the left margin. This is a rough guide only, because the Problem Group's view of the difficulty of a question can be out of line with the outcome. In any case, removing the multiple-choice options may well affect the difficulty.

Remarks

Part III consists of remarks and answers.

Nearly every problem has a remark of some sort. In some cases the results needed for the given method are listed at the start of a remark, using the symbol '☛' to indicate each result.

The remarks are not intended to be 'full written solutions' (so would not get many marks in an Olympiad-style competition), but instead sketch out one method, providing a sequence of pointers so that, hopefully, by reading them you can solve a problem yourself. Sometimes a remark is just a collection of signposts and filling in the gaps may not be straightforward. Several of the remarks refer to non-standard methods.

Though it is not necessary if you are using this book, you may wish to read fuller solutions. These are provided by the UKMT in the solutions booklets, the Yearbooks, and (more recently) the extended solutions.

Note that the methods referred to in the remarks are not based on those given elsewhere: they may be the same; sometimes they are completely different.

Answers

The answer to every problem in the book is given in part III. The answers are upside down, to help you avoid reading them inadvertently.

Of course, the answer to a problem is unimportant in itself, other than as a (potential) check on the validity of the method used. What really matters is that you understand the underlying mathematics.

Using the book

The whole purpose of this book is to provide you with problems to solve. Removing the multiple-choice element means that you actually do need to solve the mathematical problem, rather than use other techniques (such as knowing that exactly one of the options is correct).

Select a problem and have a go. Use pencil and paper to do some calculations, or draw some diagrams, whatever is necessary to make a determined effort to solve the problem. In that way you will properly engage with the problem, and the mathematics contained in it. Do this *before* looking at part III. There are three possible outcomes.

- You do the problem and get it right.

  Well done! Even in this case it is worth reading any remarks: if your approach is the same as the one given, then you can confirm that your method is correct, otherwise, you may well learn something useful!

- You do the problem, but get it wrong.

  After checking that you have read the question correctly, see if knowing the correct answer enables you to find an error, either in your working or your approach. Otherwise, read any remarks and try again.

- You cannot do the problem.

  See if knowing the correct answer helps you to get there. Otherwise, read any remarks and try again. If you still have no joy, then ask someone.

You may find, partway through reading a remark, that you think 'Aha, gotcha, now I see how to do it!'. Then so much the better: stop reading and tackle the problem again. Conversely, you may find a remark too obscure. This is not deliberate (though the remarks are intended to leave you with some work to do). If you do find that you do not understand a remark and still cannot do a problem, try again later, or ask someone else.

As mentioned above, some remarks give a list of useful results. You may not yet have come across all of these; at the very least, try to find out why a result is true, either by proving it yourself, or perhaps by asking someone.

Often there is more than one way to tackle a problem, so your ideas may well differ from the method used in part III. This does not mean that your ideas are not valid—far from it—but it may be worth trying to remember the alternative approach because this could be useful in similar problems. Indeed, one measure of the quality of a problem is the number of different approaches that are possible.

Wait until you are ready before you tackle the harder problems; this applies particularly to the problems in part II.

When faced with unusual or challenging problems, what you need above all is perseverance, the desire to keep trying until some progress is made. Take your time when trying such a problem and keep puzzling away until it yields up its secrets. Success is rarely a question of extra knowledge, more often one of know-how.

In the SMC itself, of course, you are working against the clock. In such circumstances, having the relevant knowledge and know-how at your fingertips—being *fluent* in mathematics—is bound to be helpful. And that is where practice comes in, which brings us back to the purpose of this book.

Finally, suppose that you want to find a particular problem, one that you recall involves 'turnips', say. In that case you should try the index.

Calculators

Calculators are not allowed in the SMC.

In many of these problems a calculator offers no advantage, but many of the more arithmetical questions lose their point if you use a calculator.

You are advised not to use a calculator for any of the problems in the book.

Notation and terminology

You may occasionally find that the book uses notation or terminology that is not familiar to you, such as *km/h* for kilometres per hour, or *average* for what is sometimes called the mean.

Should you have any doubt about notation or terminology, please ask someone.

Part I

Problems

Arithmetic

Exercise 1

1 **1.** What is the value of $2015^2 - 2014 \times 2016$?

1 **2.** What is the value of 98×102?

1 **3.** Which of the following five calculations gives the largest answer?

$2+0+1+3$ $\quad 2\times0+1+3$ $\quad 2+0\times1+3$ $\quad 2+0+1\times3$
$2\times0\times1\times3$

1 **4.** What is the value of $2 \times 2008 + 2008 \times 8$?

1 **5.** What is the value of 2005 plus 2005 thousandths, written as a decimal?

1 **6.** Which of the following five calculations does not give the same answer as the other four?

$2+4\times2$ $\quad (-24)\div(-2)$ $\quad -3-(-15)$ $\quad 24\times(0.5)$
$(-7)+19$

2 **7.** A giant thresher shark weighing 1250 pounds, believed to be the heaviest ever caught, was landed by fisherman Roger Nowell off the Cornish coast in November 2007. The fish was sold by auction at Newlyn Fish Market for £255.

Which of the following is roughly the cost per pound?

5p 20p 50p £2 £5

2 **8.** A dictionary defines one billion to be either one million million or one thousand million.

What is the difference between these two numbers, written in digits rather than words?

2 **9.** When written in decimal form, $\frac{1}{81}$ is $0.012\,345\,679\,012\,3\ldots$.

What is the value of $\frac{2}{81}$ correct to six decimal places?

3 **10.** The price of my favourite soft drink has gone up by leaps and bounds over the past ten years.

In four of those years it has leapt up by 5p each year, whilst in the other six years it has bounded up by 2p each year.

Ten years ago the drink cost 70p. How much does it cost now?

3 **11.** What is the value of $1^6 - 2^5 + 3^4 - 4^3 + 5^2 - 6^1$?

3 **12.** What is the value of $\sqrt{\frac{1}{2^6} + \frac{1}{6^2}}$?

3 **13.** What is the value of $2006 \times 2008 - 2007 \times 2007$?

3 **14.** The symbol $\boxtimes$ is defined by $a \boxtimes b = \sqrt{ab+4}$.

What is the value of $(2 \boxtimes 6) \boxtimes 8$?

4 **15.** According to one astronomer, there are a hundred thousand million galaxies in the universe, each containing a hundred thousand million stars.

As a power of ten, how many stars is that altogether?

4 **16.** What is the value of $\sqrt{2^4 + \sqrt{3^4}}$?

5 **17.** Two hundred T-shirts have been bought for a Fun Run at a cost of £400 plus VAT at $17\frac{1}{2}$%. The cost of entry for the run is £5 per person.

What is the minimum number of entries needed in order to cover the total cost of the T-shirts?

5 **18.** One of the oldest sporting events in the world is the Kiplingcotes Derby, a horse race which has been held in the East Yorkshire Wolds almost every year since 1519.

Each rider pays a fee of £4.25 to enter the race. The first prize in the race is the sum of £50, but the second prize is the total of the entry fees minus an administration cost of 25p per rider.

In 2000, eighteen riders competed in the Kiplingcotes Derby.

How much greater than the first prize was the second prize?

6 **19.** What symbol should replace $\heartsuit$ to make the following equation true?

$$1 \times 2 \times (3 \heartsuit 4 + 5) \times (6 \times 7 + 8 + 9) = 2006.$$

6 **20.** The average of seven consecutive odd integers is 21.

What is the sum of the first, third, fifth and seventh of these integers?

7 **21.** Which of the following five expressions has the smallest value?

2016^{-1} $\quad 2016^{-\frac{1}{2}}$ $\quad 2016^{0}$ $\quad 2016^{\frac{1}{2}}$ $\quad 2016^{1}$

8 **22.** When the following five numbers are arranged in numerical order, which one is in the middle?

$4\sqrt{15}$ $\quad 5\sqrt{10}$ $\quad 7\sqrt{5}$ $\quad 9\sqrt{3}$ $\quad 11\sqrt{2}$

9 **23.** The symbol $\diamond$ is defined by $x \diamond y = x^y - y^x$.

What is the value of $(2 \diamond 3) \diamond 4$?

9 **24.** What is the value of $\dfrac{61^2 - 39^2}{51^2 - 49^2}$?

10 **25.** Which of the following five expressions has the largest value?

$\sqrt{1999}$ $\quad 1\sqrt{999}$ $\quad 19\sqrt{99}$ $\quad 199\sqrt{9}$ $\quad 1999\sqrt{0}$

11 **26.** What is the median of the following five numbers?

$9\sqrt{2}$ $\quad 3\sqrt{19}$ $\quad 4\sqrt{11}$ $\quad 5\sqrt{7}$ $\quad 6\sqrt{5}$

11 **27.** Which of the following five numbers has the largest value?

$9^{(9^9)}$ $\quad 999$ $\quad 9^{99}$ $\quad (9^9)^9$ $\quad 99^9$

12 **28.** Which of the following five numbers is equal to

$$1+2(1+2(1+2(1+2(1+2(1+2(1+2(1+2(1+2(1+2(1+2))))))))))?$$

$2^{10}+1$ $\quad 2^{11}-1$ $\quad 2^{11}+1$ $\quad 2^{12}-1$ $\quad 2^{12}+1$

Divisibility and remainders

Exercise 2

1 **1.** Which of the following five fractions is *not* an integer?

$$\frac{2011+0}{1} \qquad \frac{2011+1}{2} \qquad \frac{2011+2}{3} \qquad \frac{2011+3}{4} \qquad \frac{2011+4}{5}$$

1 **2.** Beatrix keeps counting back eleven years at a time from 2003. At which of the following five years does she arrive?

1505 1605 1705 1805 1905

1 **3.** What is the remainder when $743\,589 \times 301\,647$ is divided by 5?

2 **4.** Which of the following five integers is *not* a multiple of 15?

135 315 555 785 915

2 **5.** Exactly one of the following five integers is divisible by 11. Which one?

$$10^7 - 11 \qquad 10^7 - 1 \qquad 10^7 \qquad 10^7 + 1 \qquad 10^7 + 11$$

4 **6.** The year 2010 is one in which the sum of its digits is a factor of the year itself.

After 2010, when was this next the case?

4 **7.** What is the remainder when $123\,456\,789 \times 987\,654\,321$ is divided by 6?

5 **8.** How many integers between 1 and 2014 are multiples of both 20 and 14?

6 **9.** What is the largest four-digit palindromic integer which is divisible by 15?

7 **10.** How many integers between 1 and 2007 are divisible by 2 but not by 7?

9 **11.** Which of the following five numbers is divisible by 9?

$10^{2014}+5 \qquad 10^{2014}+6 \qquad 10^{2014}+7 \qquad 10^{2014}+8 \qquad 10^{2014}+9$

9 **12.** What is the remainder when the 2008-digit integer $222\ldots22$ is divided by 9?

10 **13.** Consider all positive three-digit integers formed by using *different* digits from 0, 1, 2, 3 and 5.

How many of these integers are divisible by 6?

13 **14.** How many positive two-digit integers have remainder 1 when divided by 3 and remainder 2 when divided by 4?

13 **15.** Which of the following is divisible by 3 for every integer n?

$n^3-n \qquad n^3-1 \qquad n^3 \qquad n^3+1 \qquad n^3+n$

14 **16.** A square is divided by 6. Which of the following five integers could not be the remainder?

0 1 2 3 4

Time, dates and units

Exercise 3

1 **1.** A candle burns for 100 hours. I light it at midday on a Sunday.
On which day of the week does it burn out?

2 **2.** Little John claims he is 2 m 8 cm and 3 mm tall.
What is this height in metres?

2 **3.** One morning in 2007 Sam told Pat "I am getting married today, aged 30."
From this information, Pat may correctly deduce that Sam was born in which of the following years?

1976 or 1977   1977   1978   1979   1977 or 1978

2 **4.** What is the largest number of Sundays that there can be in any one year?

3 **5.** 31 December 1997 was a Wednesday.
How many Wednesdays were there in 1997?

4 **6.** Steve travelled 150 miles on a motorbike and used 10 litres of petrol.

How many miles per gallon did Steve achieve on his journey, to the nearest 10?

[1 gallon $\approx$ 4.5 litres.]

5 **7.** 1 January 2006 was a Sunday.

Which day of the week occurred most frequently in *2007*?

5 **8.** In 1998 a newspaper reported that

> The world record for remembering the value of π to the greatest number of decimal places is 40 000 places, which took the record holder 17 hours and 21 minutes to recite.

What was the average number of decimal places recited per minute, to one significant figure?

7 **9.** According to research in 2014, global sea levels could rise 36.8 cm by the year 2100 as a result of melting ice.

How many millimetres is that per year, to one significant figure?

7 **10.** A ball is dropped out of a classroom window onto the playground 29 feet 3 inches below.

Every time the ball hits the ground it bounces to two thirds of its previous height.

What is the greatest height to which it rises following the third bounce?

[There are 12 inches in 1 foot.]

8 **11.** A furlong is 220 yards long and a yard is 36 inches. A chain is 44 cubits long and a cubit is 54 barleycorns. There are 10 chains in a furlong.

How many barleycorns are there in one inch?

10 **12.** In 1954, a total of 6 527 mm of rain fell at Sprinkling Tarn and this set a UK record for annual rainfall. The tarn has a surface area of 23 450 m^2.

Which of the following is roughly the number of million litres of water that fell on Sprinkling Tarn in 1954?

15	150	1500	15 000	150 000

10 **13.** As a power of ten, roughly how many seconds are there in a day?

12 **14.** Mr and Mrs Stevens were married on a Saturday in July 1948.

On what day of the week did their diamond wedding anniversary fall in 2008?

12 **15.** One day the White Rabbit said to me

> Two days ago, Alice was still thirteen, but her sixteenth birthday will be next year.

What is the date of Alice's birthday?

13 **16.** Which of the following is the exact number of seconds in the last six complete weeks of 2007?

9!	10!	11!	12!	13!

[The notation $n!$ *means the* factorial *of* n*, which is* $n \times (n-1) \times \cdots \times 2 \times 1$.

For example, $6!$ *means* $6 \times 5 \times 4 \times 3 \times 2 \times 1$.*]*

Fractions and percentages

Exercise 4

1 **1.** What is 20% of 30%?

1 **2.** What is the value of $\frac{2007}{9} + \frac{7002}{9}$?

1 **3.** The promotion

AMAZING! 20% OFF ALL OUR BEDFRAMES

appears on the cover of the 2006 brochure of a well-known furniture company.

When 20% is taken off the length of a bedframe originally 2.10 m long, what is the resulting length of the bedframe?

2 **4.** On a Monday, all prices in Isla's shop are 10% more than normal. On Friday all prices in Isla's shop are 10% less than normal.

James bought a book on Monday for £5.50.

What would be the price of another copy of this book on Friday?

2 **5.** Jack and Jill went up the hill to fetch a pail of water.

Having filled the pail completely, Jack fell down, spilling $\frac{2}{3}$ of the water, before Jill caught the pail. She then tumbled down the hill, spilling $\frac{2}{5}$ of the remainder of the water.

What fraction of the original pail of water was left?

3 **6.** When Louise had her first car, 50 litres of petrol cost £40. When she filled up the other day, she noticed that 40 litres of petrol cost £50.

What was the percentage increase in the cost of petrol over this time, to the nearest whole number?

3 **7.** What is the average of the five numbers 1^5, 2^4, 3^3, 4^2 and 5^1?

4 **8.** After I had spent $\frac{1}{5}$ of my money and then spent $\frac{1}{4}$ of what was left, I had £15 remaining.

How much did I start with?

4 **9.** I need to buy 12 films for my camera before my holiday. They normally cost £4.50 each, but a number of shops have "special offers".

Which of the following five deals is the best?

One fifth off all prices! Two for the price of four!
Buy two, get one free! 30% price cut!
Pay only three-quarters of the normal price!

6 **10.** According to a newspaper report, the average forecourt price of petrol was 73.3 pence per litre for unleaded petrol. The price before tax, however, was 15.2 pence per litre.

What was the percentage increase from the price before tax to the average forecourt price, to one significant figure?

6 **11.** Our ancient Ancient History teacher's copy of Homer's *Odyssey* cost 40p in 1974. A similar edition in 1999 cost £5.

What percentage increase is that?

7 **12.** Which of the following five fractions has the largest value?

$$\frac{\left(\frac{1}{2}\right)}{\left(\frac{3}{4}\right)} \qquad \frac{1}{\left(\frac{\left(\frac{2}{3}\right)}{4}\right)} \qquad \frac{\left(\frac{\left(\frac{1}{2}\right)}{3}\right)}{4} \qquad \frac{1}{\left(\frac{2}{\left(\frac{3}{4}\right)}\right)} \qquad \frac{\left(\frac{1}{\left(\frac{2}{3}\right)}\right)}{4}$$

7 **13.** Mary's height increased by 30% between her fifth birthday and her tenth birthday. It increased by 20% between her tenth birthday and her fifteenth birthday.

By what percentage did her height increase between her fifth birthday and her fifteenth birthday?

8 **14.** The entries to the Senior Mathematical Challenge grew from 87 400 in 2007 to 92 690 in 2008.

To the nearest whole number, what percentage increase is that?

8 **15.** Matt black paint absorbs 97% of light, the remainder being reflected.

Scientists have developed a new superblack coating, "10 times blacker" than matt black paint, meaning that it reflects $\frac{1}{10}$ of the light reflected by matt black paint.

What percentage of light does the new coating absorb?

9 **16.** According to a newspaper headline, 'Glaciers in the French Alps have lost a quarter of their area in the past 40 years'.

To the nearest 10%, what is the approximate percentage reduction in the length of the side of a square when it loses one quarter of its area, thereby becoming a smaller square?

9 **17.** In a sale, a shopkeeper reduced the advertised selling price of a dress by 20%. This resulted in a profit of 4% over the cost price of the dress.

What percentage profit would the shopkeeper have made had the dress been sold at the original selling price?

9 **18.** What is the value of the expression

$$\left(1+\frac{1}{2}\right)\left(1+\frac{1}{3}\right)\left(1+\frac{1}{4}\right)\cdots\left(1+\frac{1}{2004}\right)\left(1+\frac{1}{2005}\right)?$$

9 **19.** Mary received a 10% pay rise, and Margaret received a 5% pay rise. This gave them both salaries of £23 100 per year.

Before they received these pay rises, how much more did Margaret earn per year than Mary?

10 **20.** Which one of the following five fractions *cannot* be expressed as $\frac{1}{m} + \frac{1}{n}$, where m and n are different positive integers?

$$\frac{3}{4} \quad \frac{3}{5} \quad \frac{3}{6} \quad \frac{3}{7} \quad \frac{3}{8}$$

10 **21.** The digit a is positive.

What is the value of $\frac{0.a}{0.\dot{a}}$?

11 **22.** Note that $\frac{1647}{8235} = \frac{1}{5}$.

Start with $\frac{1647}{8235}$. First delete one digit from the numerator and one digit from the denominator to give a fraction $\frac{A}{B}$ that is equal to the fraction you started with.

Then delete one digit from the new numerator A and one digit from the new denominator B to give a fraction $\frac{C}{D}$ that is equal to $\frac{A}{B}$.

What is the value of $D - C$?

12 **23.** At Ulan Bator market yesterday, you could buy a white elephant or 99 wild geese for the same number of Tugriks (the Mongolian currency).

Today, the price of a white elephant has fallen by 10% and the price of a wild goose has risen by 10%.

How many wild geese are now worth the same as one white elephant?

13 **24.** A trapezium has height h and parallel sides of length a and b, as shown alongside.

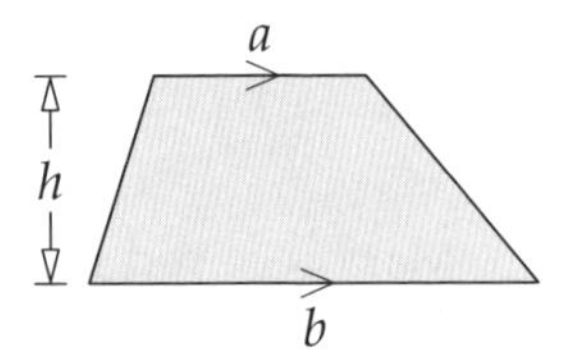

The height h is increased by 10%, and the sides a and b are both decreased by 10%.

What is the percentage change in the area of the trapezium?

Angles

Exercise 5

2 **1.** The diagram shows an equilateral triangle, a square and a regular pentagon that all share a common vertex.

What is the value of θ?

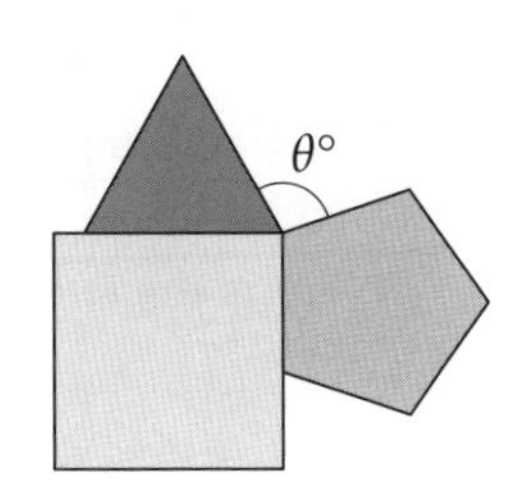

3 **2.** The diagram shows an equilateral triangle touching two straight lines.

What is the sum of the four marked angles?

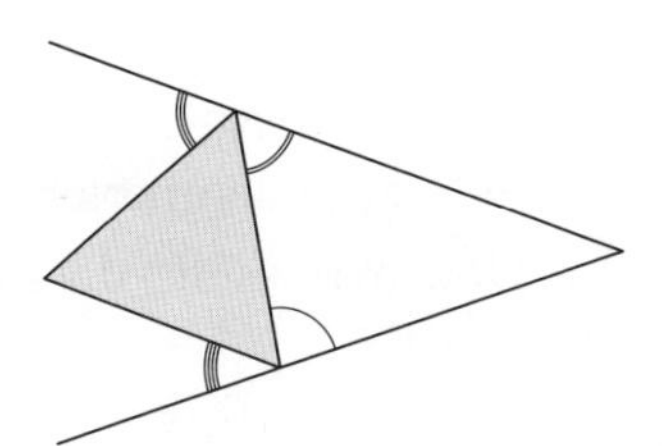

3 **3.** The diagram shows two overlapping squares.

What is the value of $x + y$?

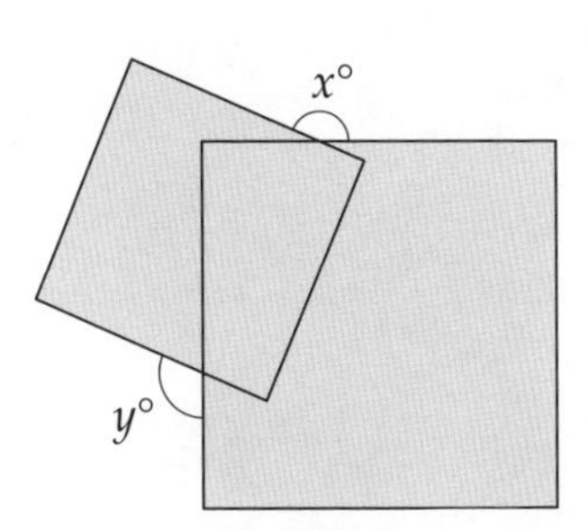

4 **4.** Alex draws a scalene triangle. One of the angles is equal to 80°.

Which of the following could be the value of the difference between the other two angles in Alex's triangle?

0°	60°	80°	100°	120°

4 **5.** The diagram shows a square *PQRS* and a regular hexagon *QPTUVW*.

What is the size of $\angle PST$?

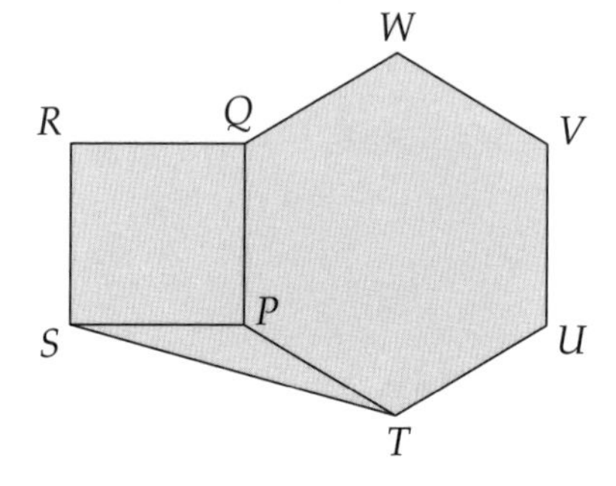

5 **6.** The diagram shows a regular hexagon inside a rectangle.

What is the sum of the four marked angles?

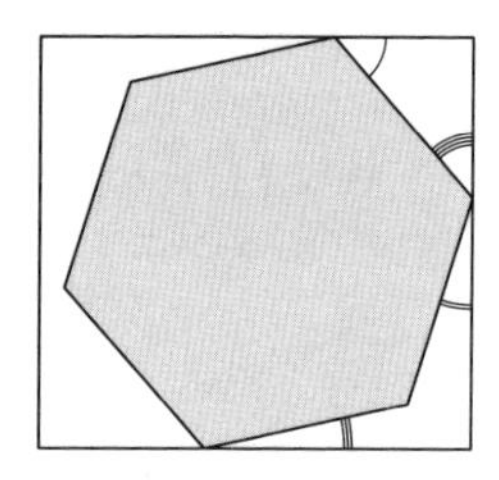

7 **7.** The size of each exterior angle of a regular polygon is one quarter of the size of an interior angle.

How many sides does the polygon have?

8 **8.** In the diagram, $AB = AF$ and ABC, AFD, BFE and CDE are all straight lines.

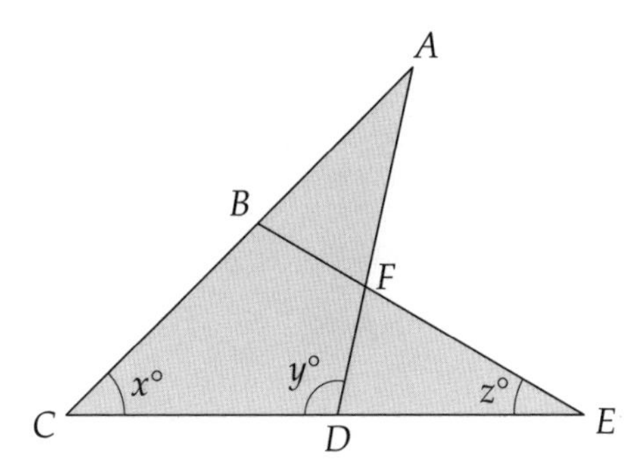

Which of the following five expressions is equal to z, whatever the values of x and y?

$\frac{y-x}{2}$ $\quad y-\frac{x}{2}$ $\quad \frac{y-x}{3}$ $\quad y-\frac{x}{3}$ $\quad y-x$

12 **9.** A circle touches the sides of triangle PQR at the points S, T and U, as shown below. Also, $\angle PQR = \alpha°$, $\angle QRP = \beta°$ and $\angle UST = \gamma°$.

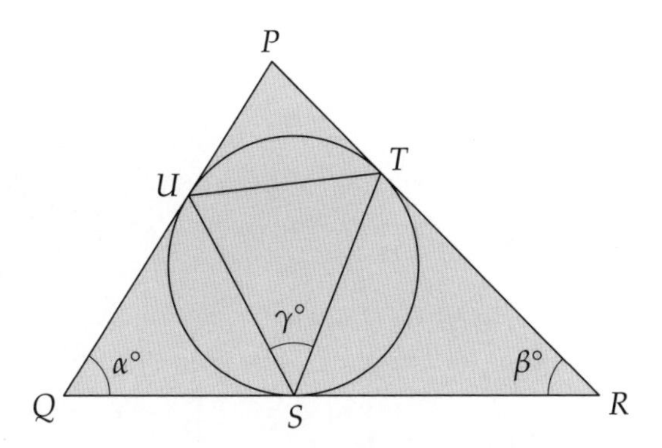

Which of the following five expressions is equal to γ, whatever the values of α and β?

$\frac{1}{2}(\alpha+\beta)$ $\quad 180-\frac{1}{2}(\alpha+\beta)$ $\quad 180-(\alpha+\beta)$ $\quad \alpha+\beta$
$\frac{1}{3}(\alpha+\beta)$

12 **10.** $ABCDEFGH$ is a regular octagon. The point P lies inside the octagon so that triangle ABP is equilateral.

What is the size of angle CPA?

13 **11.** In the diagram, what is the sum of the marked angles at P, Q, R, S and T?

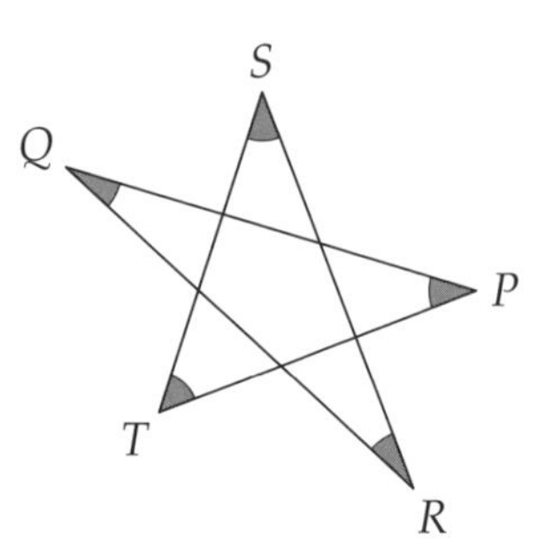

15 **12.** The diagram shows three rectangles and three straight lines.

What is the value of

$$p + q + r?$$

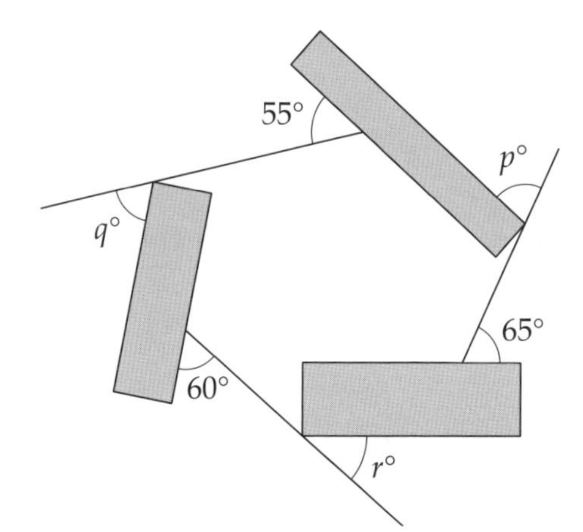

Digits

Exercise 6

1 **1.** How many times does the digit 9 appear in the answer to

$$987\,654\,321 \times 9?$$

1 **2.** What is the digit d in the following crossnumber?

Across	Down
1. A cube	1. One less than a cube
3. A cube	

1	2
3	d

[A crossnumber is like a crossword, except that all the answers are numbers instead of words, with one digit in each cell, and no answer starting with the digit zero.]

3 **3.** What is the 'tens' digit when the value of $2013^2 - 2013$ is calculated?

4 **4.** What is the units digit of 3^{2011}?

4 **5.** In the subtraction alongside, P, Q, R and S are digits.

What is the value of $P + Q + R + S$?

$$\begin{array}{r} 8\ Q\ 0\ S \\ -\ P\ 0\ R\ 2 \\ \hline 2\ 0\ 0\ 8 \end{array}$$

5 **6.** All the digits 2, 3, 4, 5 and 6 are placed in the grid, one in each cell, to form a three-digit square across and a three-digit square down.

What is the value of the digit d?

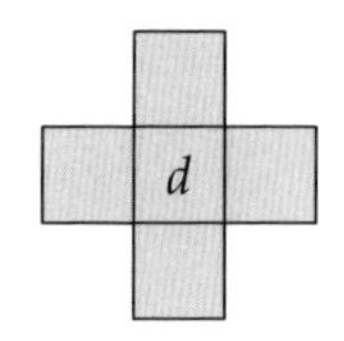

5 **7.** All six digits of three positive two-digit integers are different.

What is the largest possible sum of three such integers?

6 **8.** In the addition sum shown alongside, each of the letters T, H, I and S represents a non-zero digit.

What is the value of $T + H + I + S$?

$$\begin{array}{cccc} T & H & I & S \\ + & & I & S \\ \hline 2 & 0 & 1 & 4 \end{array}$$

7 **9.** When completed, the following crossnumber has a different non-zero digit in each cell.

What digit is d?

Across
1. A cube
3. A sum of two squares

Down
1. A square
2. A prime

1	2
3	d

[A crossnumber is like a crossword, except that all the answers are numbers instead of words, with one digit in each cell, and no answer starting with the digit zero.]

9 **10.** How many integers from 12 to 12 345 inclusive have digits that are consecutive and in increasing order, reading from left to right?

10 **11.** Let N be the smallest positive integer whose digits add up to 2012.

What is the leftmost digit of $N + 1$?

10 **12.** The digits 1, 2, 3, 4, 5, 6, 7, 8, and 9 are to be written in the cells so that every row and every column of three cells has a total of 13.

Two digits have already been entered.

What is the value of d?

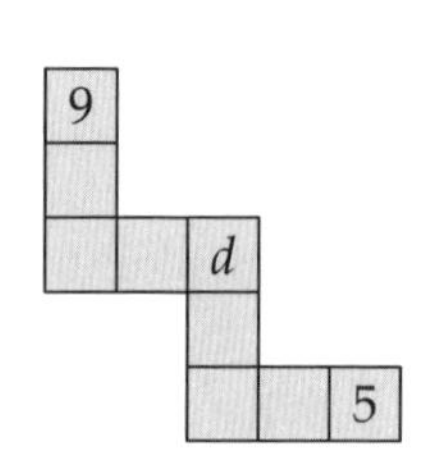

10 **13.** The digits 1 to 8 are to be inserted in the cells of the grid shown alongside, one in each, so that any two digits which are adjacent to each other in the sequence 1 to 8 are not in adjacent cells. (Two cells meeting along an edge or at a corner are considered to be adjacent.)

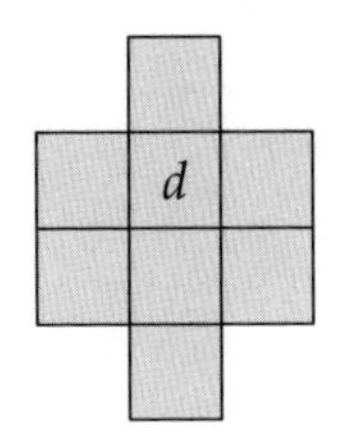

Which one of the following digits could be d?

4	5	6	7	8

12 **14.** How many two-digit integers N have the property that the sum of N and the integer formed by reversing the digits of N is a square?

13 **15.** The value of $1^{2004} + 3^{2004} + 5^{2004} + 7^{2004} + 9^{2004}$ is calculated using a powerful computer.

What is the units digit of the correct answer?

15 **16.** Sam correctly calculates the value of $5^8 \times 8^5$.

How many digits does Sam's answer contain?

15 **17.** The diagram represents the addition of three positive three-digit integers that between them use all the digits from 1 to 9.

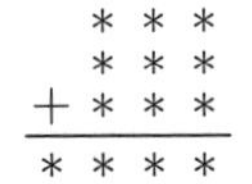

Which of the following five numbers cannot be obtained as the answer?

1500	1503	1512	1521	1539

Algebra

Exercise 7

1 **1.** The sum of five consecutive even integers is 60.

What is the smallest of the five integers?

2 **2.** What is the sum of all the solutions of the equation $6x = \frac{150}{x}$?

2 **3.** Suppose that x and y satisfy the equations

$$\begin{aligned} 6x - y &= 21 \\ \text{and} \quad 6y - x &= 14. \end{aligned}$$

What is the value of $x - y$?

2 **4.** The average of five consecutive integers is 10.

What is the sum of the second and fourth of these integers?

3 **5.** Milly and Molly are each given a 100 g ice-lolly. They start eating their lollies at the same time, but Milly eats hers twice as fast as Molly.

When Molly has three times as much of her lolly left as has Milly, what fraction of her lolly has Milly eaten?

3 **6.** Anakin Skywalker and Obi-Wan Kenobi each has some coins in his pocket. If Anakin gave Obi-Wan Kenobi one coin then Obi-Wan Kenobi would have twice as many coins as Anakin, but if Obi-Wan Kenobi gave Anakin one coin, they would each have the same number of coins.

Altogether, how many coins do they have?

5 **7.** The integer n is the average of 17, 23 and $2n$.

What is the value of n?

5 **8.** Suppose that x and y satisfy the equations

$$\begin{aligned} x(y+2) &= 100 \\ \text{and} \quad y(x+2) &= 60. \end{aligned}$$

What is the value of $x - y$?

5 **9.** The first two pairs of scales shown below are perfectly balanced.

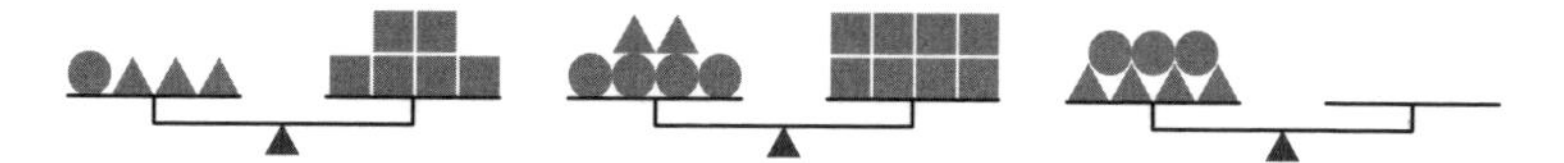

How many squares will be needed on the right of the third pair of scales so that they also balance?

6 **10.** Rebecca went swimming yesterday.

After a while she had covered one fifth of her intended distance. After swimming six more lengths of the pool, she had covered one quarter of her intended distance.

How many lengths of the pool did she intend to complete?

7 **11.** Suppose that

$$\begin{aligned} x + y + z &= 1, \\ x + y - z &= 2 \\ \text{and} \quad x - y - z &= 3. \end{aligned}$$

What is the value of xyz?

8 **12.** Which of the following five expressions is equivalent to

$$(x+y+z)(x-y-z)?$$

$x^2-y^2-z^2$	$x^2-y^2+z^2$	$x^2-xy-xz-z^2$
$x^2-(y+z)^2$	$x^2-(y-z)^2$	

8 **13.** The difference between two numbers is one quarter of their sum.

What, numerically, is the ratio of the smaller number to the larger number?

8 **14.** Two numbers differ by 9 and have sum 99.

What, numerically, is the ratio of the larger number to the smaller?

9 **15.** Pascal, Newton, Galileo and Fermat all took the same test. The average score of all four candidates was 16; Pascal and Newton had an average of 16, Pascal and Fermat had an average of 13, while Newton and Fermat had an average of 18.

What was Galileo's score?

10 **16.** The positive integer n is between 1 and 20. Milly adds up all the integers from 1 to n inclusive. Billy adds up all the integers from $n+1$ to 20 inclusive.

Their totals are the same.

What is the value of n?

10 **17.** A rectangle has area $120\,\text{cm}^2$ and its perimeter has length 46 cm.

What is the length of each of the diagonals?

10 **18.** Sam and Pat were counting their money. They discovered that if Sam gave Pat £5, then Pat would have 5 times as much as Sam, but if Pat gave Sam £5, then Sam would have 5 times as much as Pat.

How much did they have altogether?

11 **19.** In the grid below each of the middle four cells is to be filled by the average of the numbers in the two adjacent cells.

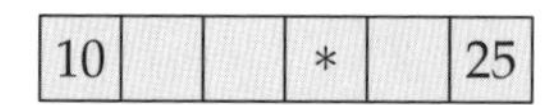

10			$*$		25

What number should go in the cell marked $*$?

11 **20.** Three consecutive even integers are such that the sum of four times the smallest and twice the largest exceeds three times the second by 2006.

What is the sum of the digits of the smallest integer?

11 **21.** Suppose that $x = \frac{1}{y}$, where x and y are unequal and non-zero.

Which of the following is equal to $\left(x + \frac{1}{x}\right)\left(y - \frac{1}{y}\right)$ whatever the value of x?

$y^2 - x^2$ $\quad x^2 - y^2$ $\quad 2y$ $\quad 2x$ $\quad 0$

12 **22.** Karen has three times the number of cherries that Lionel has, and twice the number of cherries that Michael has. Michael has seven more cherries than Lionel.

How many cherries do Karen, Lionel and Michael have altogether?

13 **23.** Suppose that $x - \frac{1}{x} = y - \frac{1}{y}$ and that $x \neq y$.

What is the value of xy?

13 **24.** Suppose that $x = \left(\frac{1}{4}\right)^{\frac{1}{2}}$.

What is the value of x^{-x}?

14 **25.** Suppose that $\frac{3x + y}{x - 3y} = -1$.

What is the value of $\frac{x + 3y}{3x - y}$?

15 **26.** The equation $x^2 + ax + b = 0$, where a and b are different, has solutions $x = a$ and $x = b$.

How many such equations are there?

14 **27.** Heather and Rachel each has some pennies.

Heather has more than Rachel. In fact, the number of pennies that Heather has is the square of the number that Rachel has.

The total number of pennies they have between them makes a whole number of pounds.

What is the smallest this total could be?

Miscellany 1

Exercise 8

1 **1.** The sum of the lengths of the perimeters of N squares, each of area $1\,\text{cm}^2$, is equal to the length of the perimeter of a single square of area $4\,\text{cm}^2$.

What is the value of N?

2 **2.** Which of the following five networks is *not* traversable?

[A traversable *network is one that can be drawn without taking the pen off the paper and without going over any line more than once.]*

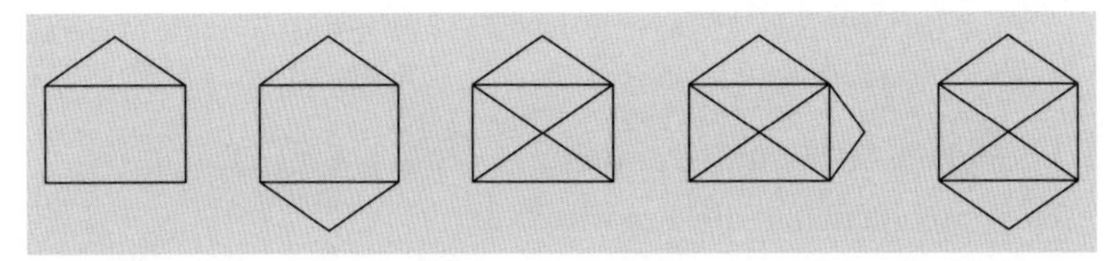

3 **3.** The diagram shows a circle with radius 1 that rolls without slipping around the inside of a square with sides of length 5.

The circle rolls once around the square, returning to its starting point.

What distance does the centre of the circle travel?

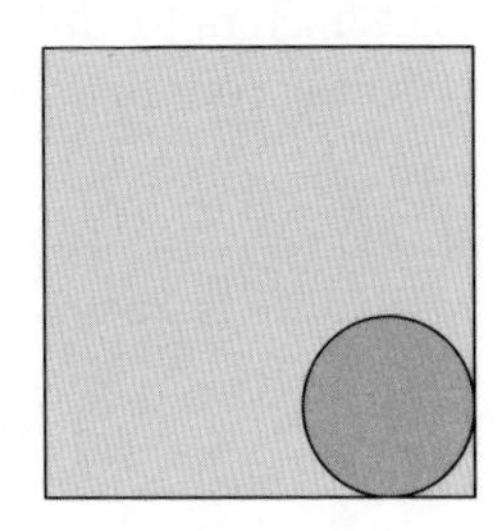

3 **4.** Peri the winkle starts at the point $(1,1)$. Each day Peri crawls from point (x,y) to point $(y,x+y)$, so that at the end of the first day Peri has reached $(1,2)$.

Where is Peri at the end of the sixth day?

3 **5.** Which of the following five shapes is *not* the net of a pyramid?

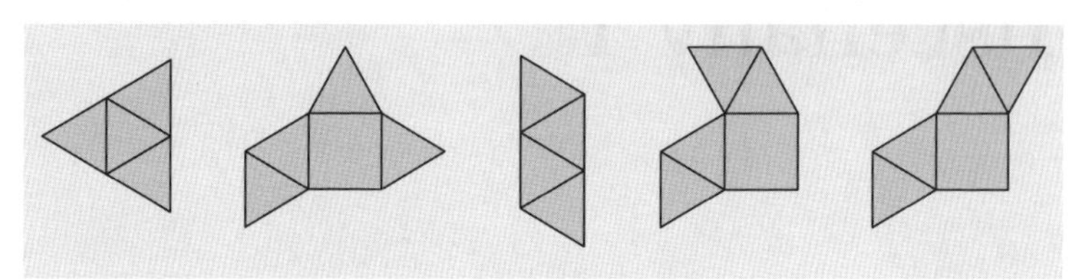

3 **6.** The *integer part* of a positive number is the part before the decimal point; the *decimal part* is the part after the decimal point. For example, the integer part of 3.72 is 3 and the decimal part is 0.72.

Which one of the following five numbers has decimal part equal to exactly one eighth of the integer part?

0.05 1.15 2.25 3.35 4.45

4 **7.** Timmy Riddle was selling toffee apples at the school fête. When I asked him what they cost he said:

> One toffee apple costs the smallest amount that cannot be paid exactly using four or fewer standard British coins.

I bought as many toffee apples as I could get for £1.

How much change did I receive?

5 **8.** Which of the following five expressions has a different value from the other four?

2^8 4^4 $8^{\frac{8}{3}}$ 16^2 $32^{\frac{6}{5}}$

6 **9.** The numbers 5, 6, 7, 8, 9, 10 are to be placed, one in each of the circles in the diagram, so that the sum of the numbers in each pair of touching circles is prime.

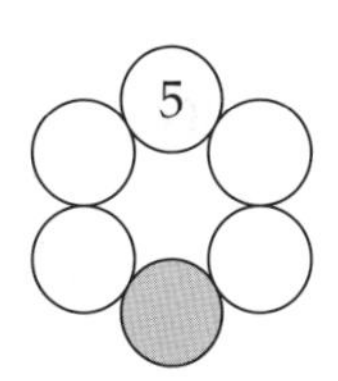

The number 5 is placed in the top circle, as shown.

When the diagram is complete, which number is in the shaded circle?

7 **10.** Two sides of a triangle have lengths 4 cm and 5 cm. The third side has length n cm, where n is a positive integer.

How many different values can n have?

6 **11.** The following box lists the measurements of five different rectangles. The list includes two pairs of similar rectangles, while one rectangle differs in shape from all the others.

Which is the odd one out?

240×120 300×180 55×110 320×200 210×350

7 **12.** Climbers use ropes of different diameters. A 50 m rope that is 9 mm in diameter weighs about 2.7 kg.

Which of the following is roughly the weight of a 50 m rope made of the same material, but of diameter 11 mm?

2.7 kg 3.3 kg 4 kg 4.9 kg 6 kg

7 **13.** The first six volumes of the *Encyclopedia of Mathematicians* are arranged in alphabetical order on my shelf from left to right.

The six volumes contain names beginning A–Ba, Be–Ca, Ce–Ei, Ek–Fe, Fee–Fi and Fo–Fum.

Ignoring the covers, which of the following encyclopedia entries could be on a page 'next to' the page with the entry for Einstein?

Abel Bernoulli Cantor Euler Fibonacci

8 **14.** The diagrams below show four types of tile, each of which is made up of one or more equilateral triangles.

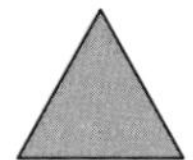 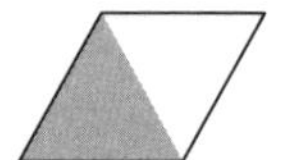 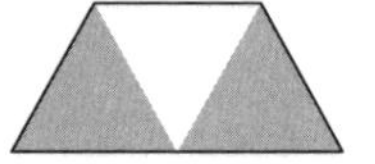 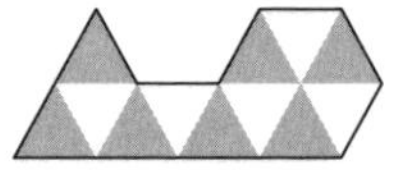

For how many of these four types of tile can three identical copies of the tile be placed together, without gaps or overlaps, to make an equilateral triangle?

8 **15.** The diagram shows three right-angled triangles.

What is the value of x?

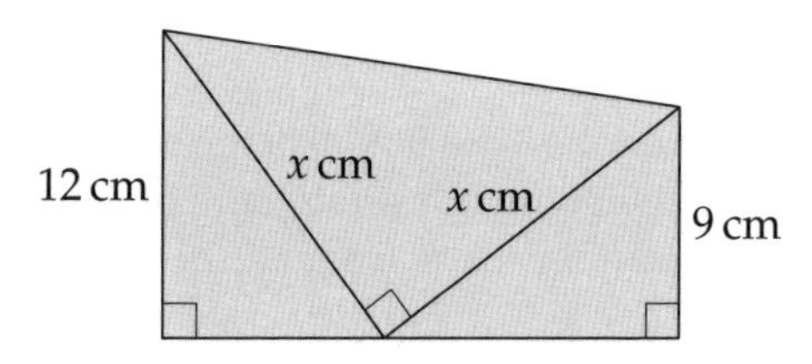

8 **16.** A teacher gave a test to 20 students. Marks on the test ranged from 0 to 10 inclusive. The average of the first twelve papers marked was 6.5.

From this information, what may be deduced about the average for the whole group?

9 **17.** A square $PQRS$ has sides of length s. The point T is the midpoint of QR and U is the foot of the perpendicular from T to the diagonal QS.

What is the length of TU in terms of s?

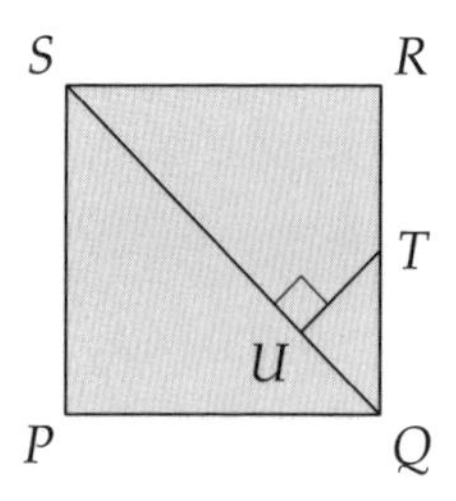

10 **18.** A square is cut into 37 squares, of which 36 have area $1\,\text{cm}^2$.

What is the length of a side of the original square?

10 **19.** The diagram shows a triangular piece of paper that has been folded once to produce a shape with the outline of a pentagon.

A *rectangular* piece of paper is folded once.

What is the smallest value of n (greater than four) for which it is not possible to create a polygon with n sides in the same way?

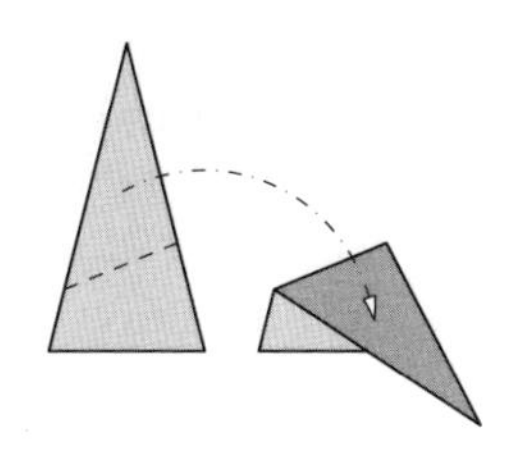

10 **20.** A square piece of wood, with sides of length 8 cm, is painted grey and fixed to a table. An identical square, painted white, is placed on the table alongside the grey square and has a point P marked one quarter of the way along a diagonal, as shown alongside.

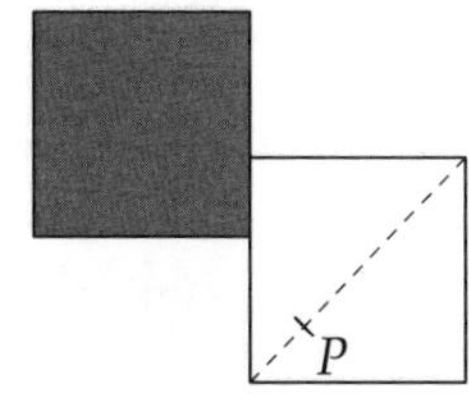

Whilst keeping the same orientation on the table and always remaining in contact with the grey square, the white square now slides once around the grey square.

Through what distance does P move?

11 **21.** For what value of x is $\sqrt{2} + \sqrt{2} + \sqrt{2} + \sqrt{2}$ equal to 2^x?

12 **22.** The diagram shows a right-angled triangle divided into three parts.

What is the value of $a + b$?

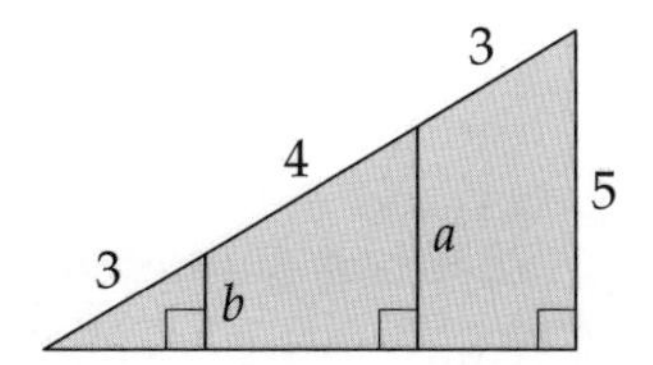

13 **23.** A cube is placed with one face on square 1 in the maze shown alongside, so that it completely covers the square with no overlap. The upper face of the cube is covered in wet paint.

13	12	11	10	9
14	23	22	21	8
15	24	25	20	7
16	17	18	19	6
1	2	3	4	5

The cube is then 'rolled' around the maze, rotating about an edge each time, until it reaches square 25. It leaves paint on all of the squares on which the painted face lands, but on no others.

The cube is removed on reaching the square 25.

What is the sum of the numbers on the squares that are now marked with paint?

14 **24.** An equilateral triangle with sides of length 4 cm is cut into smaller equilateral triangles, each of whose sides has length equal to a whole number of centimetres.

Which one of the following cannot be the number of smaller triangles obtained?

4   8   12   13   16

14 **25.** In the diagram, P, Q, R, S and T are vertices of a regular polygon. The sides PQ and TS are extended to meet at X, as shown alongside, and $\angle QXS = 140°$.

How many sides does the polygon have?

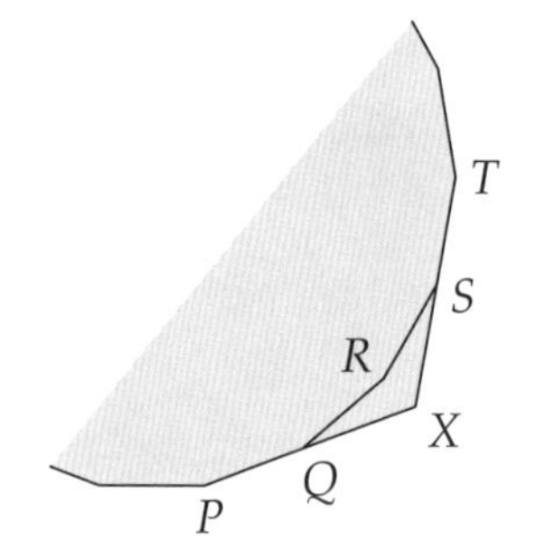

14 **26.** Which of the following five straight lines should be omitted to leave four lines that determine a square?

$y + x = 3$ $y = x - 1$ $y + x = 1$ $y = x + 1$ $y + x = 2$

14 **27.** The diagram shows a square and two equilateral triangles. All the sides have length 1.

What is the length of XY?

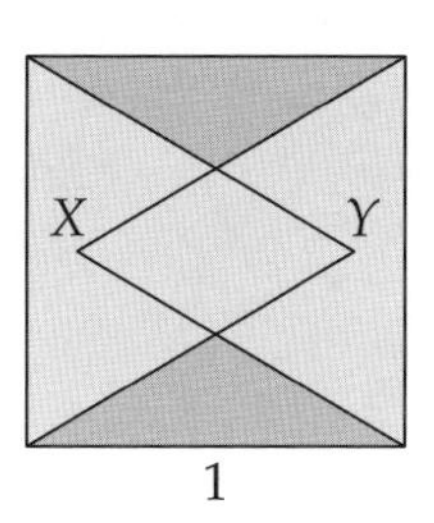

15 **28.** A sequence of positive integers $t_1, t_2, t_3, t_4, \ldots$ is defined by $t_1 = 13$ and

$$t_{n+1} = \begin{cases} \frac{1}{2}t_n \text{ if } n \text{ is even;} \\ 3t_n + 1 \text{ if } n \text{ is odd.} \end{cases}$$

What is the value of t_{2008}?

Primes

Exercise 9

1 **1.** Which of the following five integers *cannot* be written as the sum of two primes?

1 **2.** How many primes are less than 20?

5 **3.** The positive integers w, x, y and z are prime and $wxyz$ equals 2002. What is the value of $w^2 + x^2 + y^2 + z^2$?

5 **4.** *Goldbach's conjecture* states that every even integer greater than two is the sum of two primes. However, the same is not true for every odd integer.

Which of the following five odd integers is *not* the sum of two primes?

13 33 43 53 73

[At the time of writing, Goldbach's conjecture has not been proved.]

6 **5.** Pat's age in years is prime. Twenty years ago, as a teenager, Pat's age was also prime.

How old is Pat?

11 **6.** A *Mersenne prime* is a prime of the form $2^p - 1$, where p is also prime. One of the following five integers is *not* a Mersenne prime. Which one is it?

$2^2 - 1$ $2^3 - 1$ $2^5 - 1$ $2^7 - 1$ $2^{11} - 1$

12 **7.** Let the *primorial* of a positive integer be the product of all the primes less than or equal to that number. For example, the primorial of 6 is $2 \times 3 \times 5 = 30$.

For how many different positive integers is the primorial equal to 210?

15 **8.** For how many positive integers n is $4^n - 1$ prime?

15 **9.** What is the smallest prime that is equal to the sum of three different primes and is also equal to the sum of two primes?

15 **10.** Three people each think of a positive integer that is the product of two different primes.

Which of the following could be the product of the three integers that they think of?

120 144 240 3000 12 100

Counting

Exercise 10

2 **1.** The diagram shows six regions.

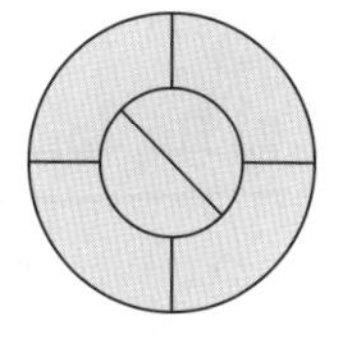

Each of the regions is to be painted a single colour, so that no two regions sharing a side have the same colour.

What is the smallest number of colours required?

3 **2.** The diagram shows a regular hexagon divided up into six equilateral triangles.

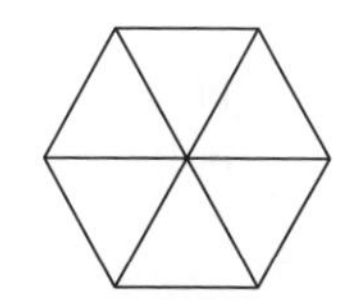

How many quadrilaterals are there in the diagram?

4 **3.** A route on the 3×3 board shown alongside consists of a number of steps.

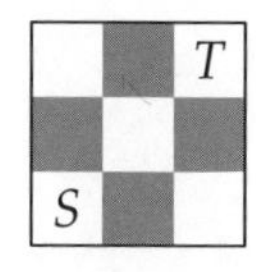

Each step is from one cell to an adjacent cell of a different colour.

How many different routes are there from cell S to cell T that pass through every other cell exactly once?

6 **4.** A bag contains hundreds of glass marbles, each one a single colour—either red, orange, green or blue. There are more than two marbles of each colour.

Marbles are taken randomly from the bag, one at a time, and not replaced.

How many marbles need to be taken from the bag in order to ensure that at least three marbles of the same colour have been taken?

6 **5.** The diagram shows six small squares.

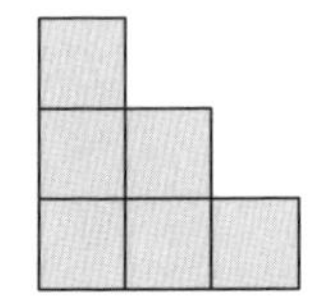

At least one of these is to be shaded black so that the resulting diagram has exactly one axis of symmetry.

In how many different ways can this be done?

6 **6.** How many differently-shaped triangles exist in which the lengths of the sides are different integers, and the length of the perimeter of the triangle is less than 13?

6 **7.** The engineering company *Sparks and Tensor* has a complicated system of conveyor belts in its factory.

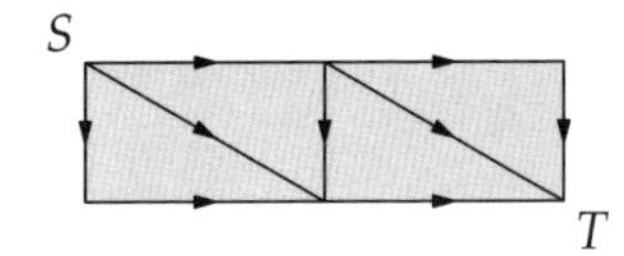

Components travel along these belts in the directions shown by the arrows.

How many different routes are there from S to T along the conveyor belts?

8 **8.** Figure 1 shows the three different ways of dividing a 2×3 grid of squares into 1×2 rectangles.

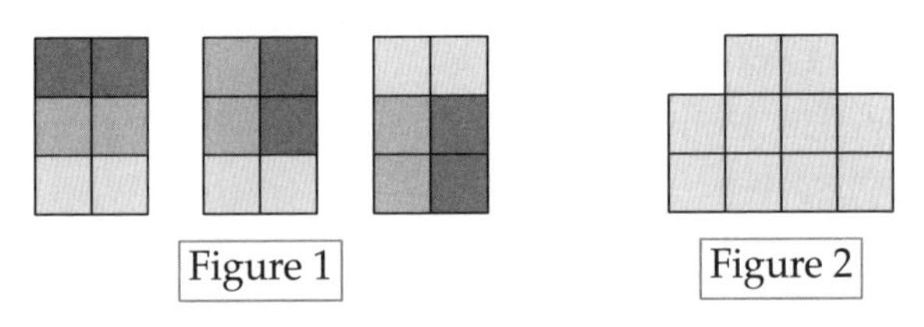

Figure 1 Figure 2

How many ways are there of dividing the shape in Figure 2 into 1×2 rectangles?

7 **9.** There are 120 different arrangements of the five letters in the word ANGLE. All 120 are listed in alphabetical order starting with AEGLN and finishing with NLGEA

Which position in the list does ANGLE occupy?

7 **10.** A mini-sudoku is a 4×4 grid in which the digits 1, 2, 3 and 4 are contained once and once only in each row, column and 2×2 block indicated.

How many different ways are there of completing the mini-sudoku shown alongside?

			4
		3	
	2		
1			

8 **11.** Points are drawn on the sides of a square, dividing each side into n equal parts (so, in the example shown alongside, $n = 4$).

The points are joined in the manner indicated, to form several small squares (24 in the example, shown shaded) and some triangles.

How many small squares are formed when $n = 7$?

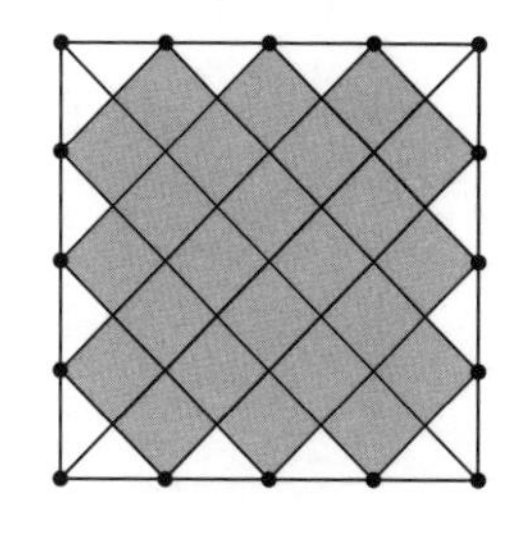

8 **12.** The diagram shows eight small squares.

Six of these squares are to be shaded black so that the black squares form the net of a cube.

In how many different ways can this be done?

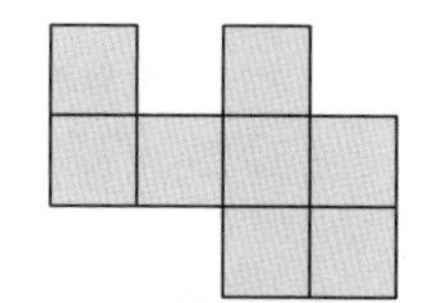

8 **13.** The diagram shows four sets of parallel lines, containing two, three, four and five lines respectively.parallel line

How many points of intersection are there?

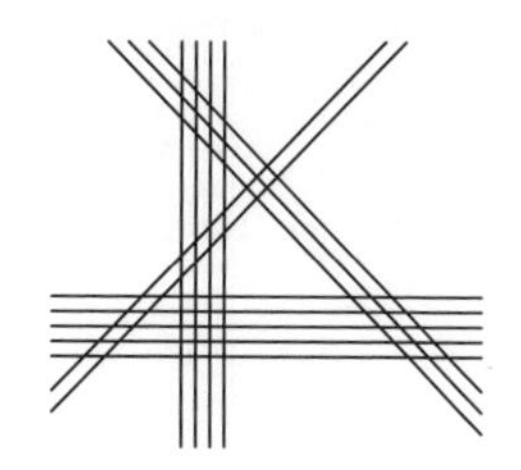

9 **14.** Four different straight lines are drawn in the plane.

The number of points where two or more lines intersect is counted.

Which of the following could *not* be the number of such points?

1	2	3	4	5

11 **15.** Rahid has a large number of cubic building blocks. Each block has edges of length 4 cm, 6 cm or 10 cm.

Rahid makes little towers built from three blocks stacked on top of each other.

How many different heights of tower can he make?

11 **16.** In how many different ways can I circle letters in the grid shown alongside so that there is exactly one circled letter in each row and exactly one circled letter in each column?

A	B	C	D	E
F	G	H	I	J
K	L	M	N	O
P	Q	R	S	T
U	V	W	X	Y

12 **17.** As a special treat, Sammy is allowed to eat five sweets from his very large jar, which contains many sweets of each of three flavours: lemon, orange and strawberry.

He wants to eat his five sweets in such a way that no two consecutive sweets have the same flavour.

In how many ways can he do this?

12 **18.** The number 3 can be expressed as the sum of one or more positive integers in four different ways, shown in the box.

3	$1+2$	$2+1$	$1+1+1$

In how many ways can the number 5 be so expressed?

13 **19.** The diagram represents a maze. The only moves allowed are to go from one cell to the next across an edge, and it is not allowed to revisit a cell.

How many different routes are there through the maze?

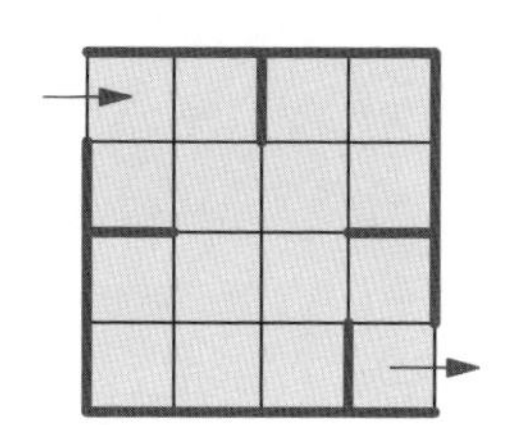

13 **20.** The diagram shows five discs connected by five line segments.

The discs are to be coloured so that discs which are connected by a line segment have different colours. Three colours are available.

In how many different ways is it possible to colour all five discs?

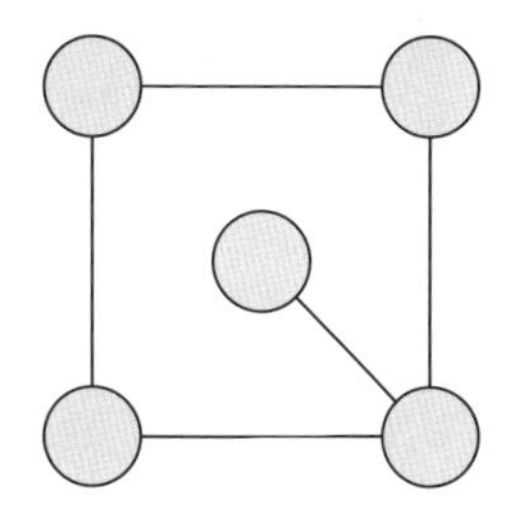

15 **21.** The DIAGRAM shown alongside is made from seven small squares.

Some of these squares are to be shaded black so that:

(i) at least two squares are shaded black;
(ii) two squares meeting along a side or at a vertex are not both shaded black.

How many ways are there to do this?

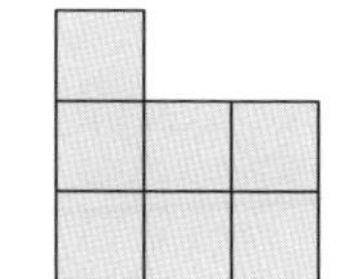

15 **22.** The diagram shows a 3×2 grid.

How many different hexagons are there, each whose vertices is one of the grid points?

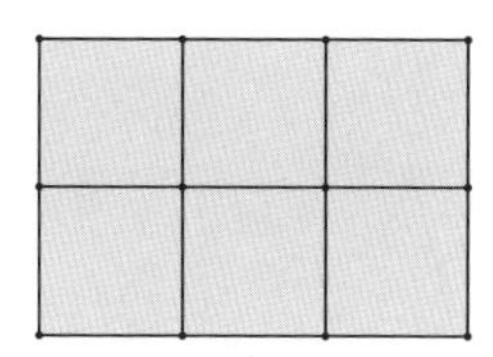

Areas

Exercise 11

2

1. Triangle PQR has a right angle at Q. The points S, T and U divide the side QR into four equal parts.

Which of the following five statements about triangles PQS, PST, PTU and PUR is true?

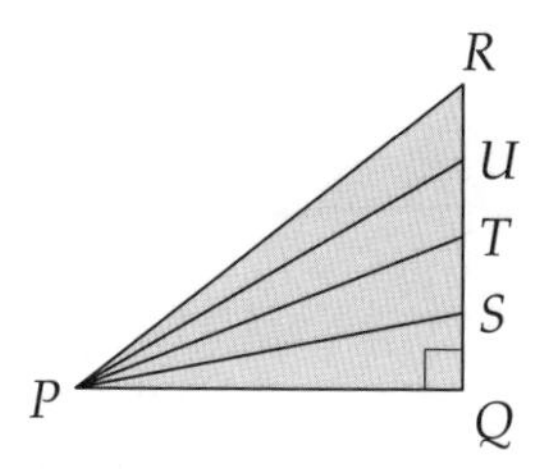

Triangle PQS has biggest area. Triangle PST has biggest area.
Triangle PTU has biggest area. Triangle PUR has biggest area.
All four triangles have the same area.

3

2. The lengths of the diagonals of a rhombus are 2 cm and 3 cm.

What is the area of the rhombus?

4

3. The diagram shows two squares, with sides of length 1 and 3, that have the same centre and corresponding sides parallel.

What fraction of the larger square is shaded?

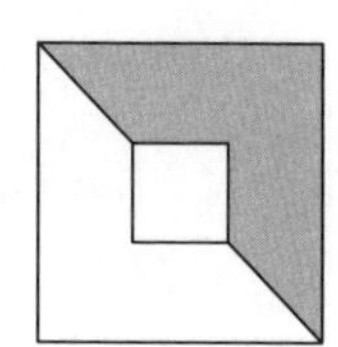

5 **4.** The diagram shows a rectangle $ABCD$. The point P is the midpoint of DA, and Q lies on BC so that BQ is one third of BC.

What fraction of the area of the rectangle is the area of the quadrilateral $ABQP$?

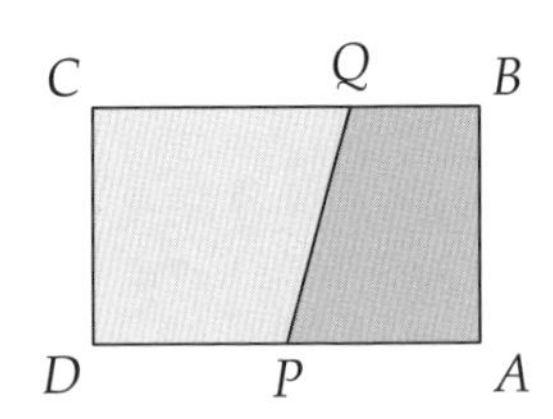

5 **5.** The perimeter of a square has the same length as that of a $4\,\text{cm} \times 2\,\text{cm}$ rectangle.

What is the area of the square?

6 **6.** The diagram shows a square and a right-angled triangle. The sides of the square have length 3, and the perpendicular sides of the triangle have lengths 3 and 4.

What is the area of the shaded region?

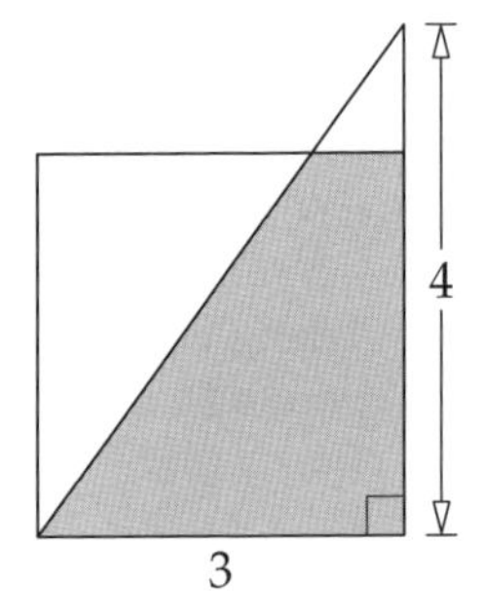

7 **7.** Each of the three regular hexagons in the diagram has the same size. Let X, Y and Z be the total area of each shaded region, as indicated.

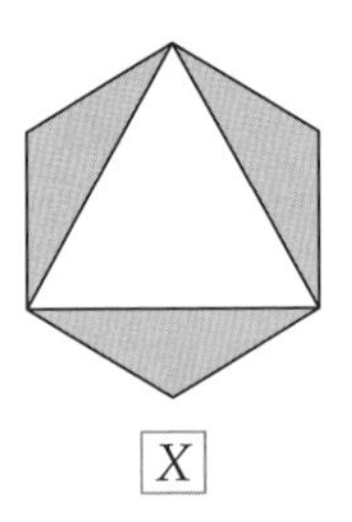
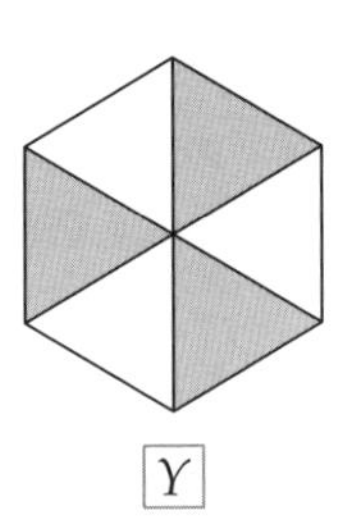
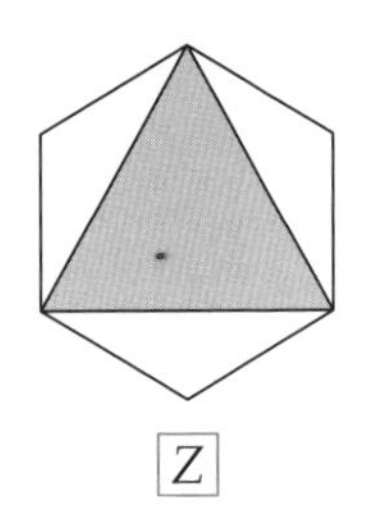

X Y Z

Which of the following five statements is true?

X is equal to Y, but not to Z.

Y is equal to Z, but not to X.

Y is equal to Z, but not to X.

X is equal to Y and to Z.

X, Y and Z are all different.

8 **8.** The right-angled triangle shown in the top diagram alongside has a base that is 4 times its height.

Four such triangles are placed so that their hypotenuses form the boundary of a large square, as shown.

What is the side-length of the shaded square in the diagram, in terms of h?

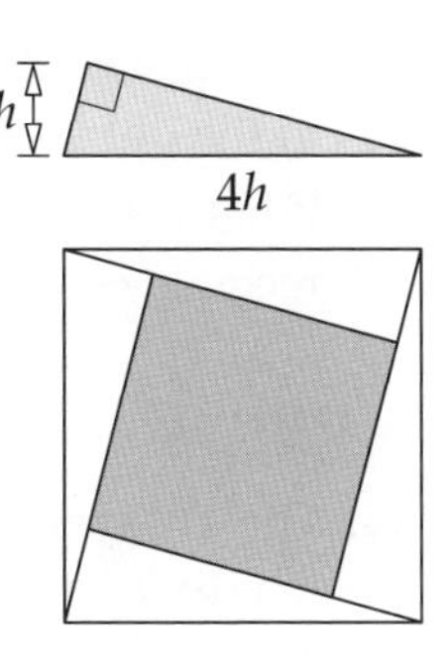

8 **9.** The diagram shows a regular hexagon $PQRSTU$ with area 60.

What is the area of the kite $PQRT$?

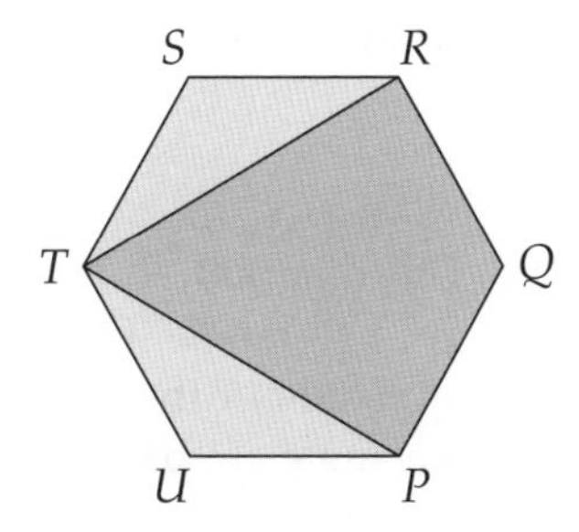

10 **10.** A triangle has two sides of length 5.

What length should be chosen for the third side of the triangle so as to maximise the area of the triangle?

9 **11.** When forest trees are planted 1 metre apart in a particular repeating pattern, covering a large area of ground, the density of trees is about 10 000 per hectare.

Some trees are planted 2 metres apart in the same pattern.

Approximately how many trees per hectare are there now?

11 **12.** $PQRSTU$ is a regular hexagon and V is the midpoint of ST.

What fraction of the area of $PQRSTU$ is the area of triangle PQV?

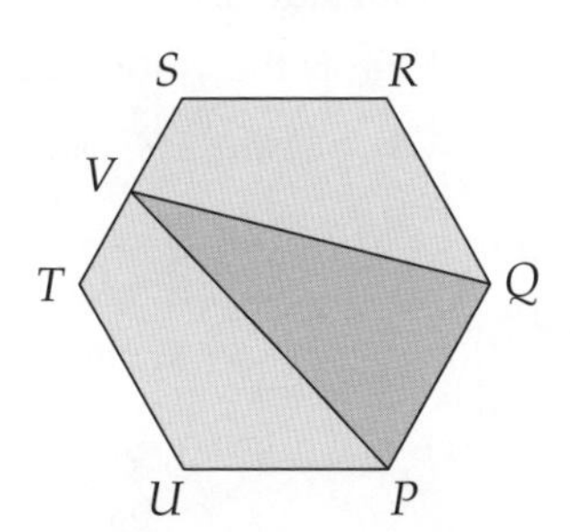

11 **13.** The distance between two neighbouring dots in the dot lattice is 1.

What is the area of the region where the two rectangles overlap?

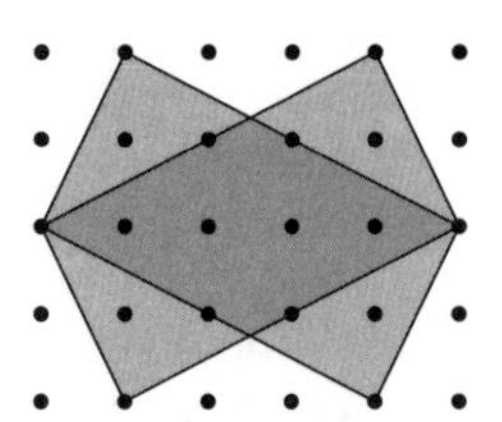

12 **14.** The diagram shows a square with sides of length 1, divided into four rectangles whose areas are equal.

What is the value of x?

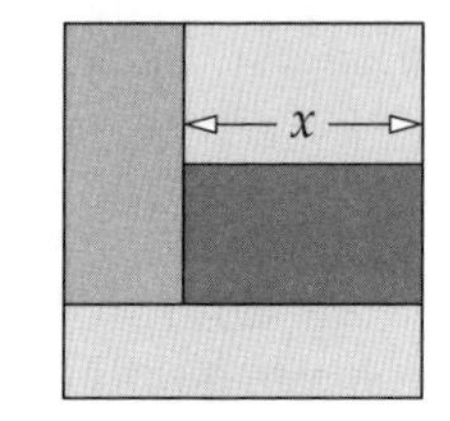

12 **15.** The diagram shows a 2×2 square and a 3×1 rectangle. One vertex of the square lies on a side of the rectangle. The sides of the rectangle are parallel to the diagonals of the square.

What is the area of the shaded triangle?

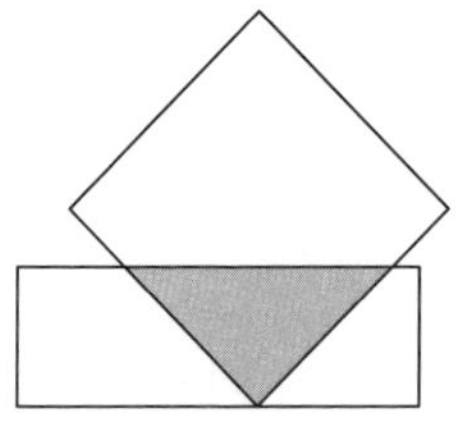

13 **16.** Two square pieces of card, each $3\,\text{cm} \times 3\,\text{cm}$, are attached by a single pin to a board. The pin passes through a point one third of the way along the diagonal of each square and the squares overlap exactly.

The bottom card is now fixed and the top card is rotated through $180°$.

What is the area of overlap of the cards in this new position?

14 **17.** The area of the triangle shown alongside is 88.

What is the value of y?

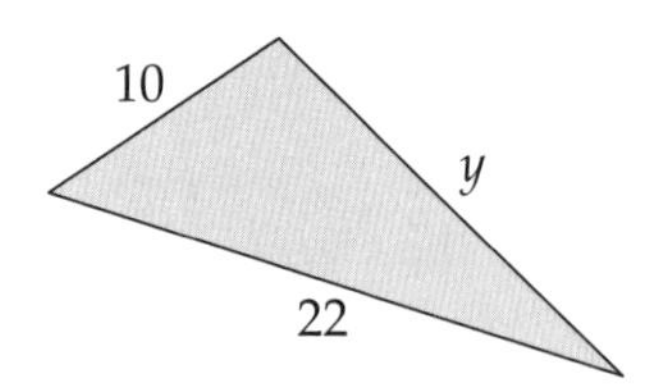

14 **18.** The diagram shows a rectangle $PQRS$ in which $QR = 2 \times PQ$. The point T lies on PR so that QT is perpendicular to PR.

What, numerically, is the ratio of the area of the triangle PQT to the area of the rectangle $PQRS$?

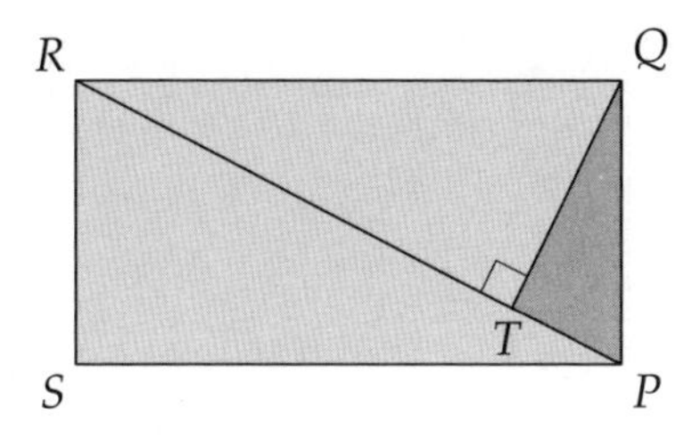

15 **19.** The diagram shows a square $PQRS$. The points U and V are the midpoints of the sides SP and RS respectively. The line segments PV and RU meet at T.

What fraction of the area of the square $PQRS$ is the area of the quadrilateral $PQRT$?

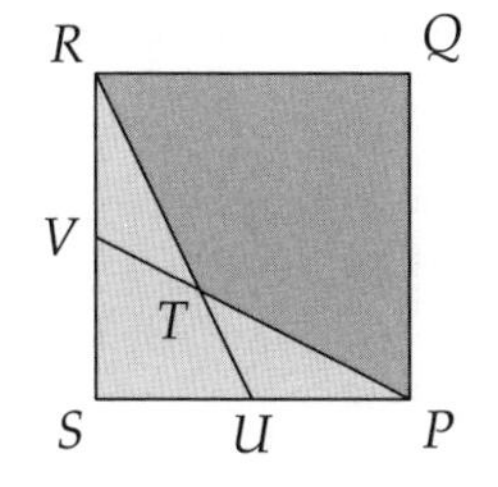

Integers

Exercise 12

1

1. Three different positive integers add up to 12.

How large could the largest of the three integers be?

2

2. What is the smallest possible value of $20p + 10q + r$ when p, q and r are *different* positive integers?

2

3. The number 2005 is the sum of five consecutive positive integers.

Which of the following integers is one of them?

395	400	405	410	415

4

4. A pieman sells pies at 4p for 5, or 1p each. Simon simply buys 2004 pies.

What is the least amount he could pay?

4

5. In the Hackey Hockey league, a team scores 5 points for a win, 2 for a draw and 0 if it loses.

The captain of the Hickey Hockey Club remembers a season when the club played 20 games in this league and scored 21 points, but does not recall any of the details.

What is the smallest possible number of games the club could have lost that season?

6 **6.** Granny and her granddaughter Gill both had their birthday yesterday.

Today, Granny's age in years is even and 15 times that of Gill. In 4 years' time Granny's age in years will be the square of Gill's age in years.

How many years older than Gill is Granny today?

5 **7.** Last year Rachel took part in a swimathon. Every day for nine weeks she swam the same number of lengths, either in a 25 m indoor pool or a 20 m outdoor pool.

Later she discovered that she had swum the same total distance in each pool.

On how many days did Rachel swim in the indoor pool?

6 **8.** Cheryl finds a bag of two-pence and five-pence coins. There are 50 coins inside and the value of the contents is £1.81.

How many more five-pence coins are there inside the bag than two-pence coins?

6 **9.** Observe that $18 = 4^2 + 1^2 + 1^2 + 0^2$.

How many of the first fifteen positive integers can be written as the sum of the squares of four integers?

7 **10.** In a 'ninety-nine' shop, all items cost a whole number of pounds and 99 pence.

Susanna spent £65.76. How many items did she buy?

7 **11.** Consider the two arithmetic sequences

$$\begin{aligned} &1998, 2005, 2012, \ldots \\ \text{and}\quad &1996, 2005, 2014, \ldots . \end{aligned}$$

What is the next number *after* 2005 that appears in both sequences?

7 **12.** A gardener decided to plant a bed with rose bushes, with the aid of an apprentice. The bed is in the shape of an isosceles triangle.

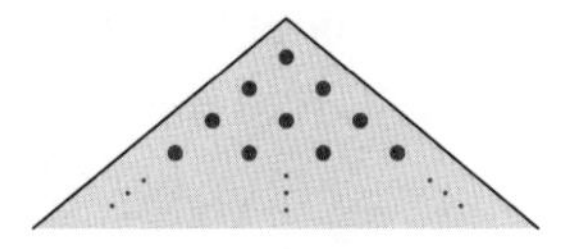

He planted the first row with 101 bushes along the 'base', then the apprentice planted the next row with 100 bushes. They continued in this way, planting alternate rows, until the whole bed was planted.

The gardener planted the last row, which contained 1 bush.

How many more bushes did the gardener plant than the apprentice?

8 **13.** An examination paper is made by taking 5 large sheets of paper, folding the pile in half and stapling it. The pages are then numbered in order from 1 to 20.

What is the sum of the three page numbers that are on the same sheet of paper as page number 5?

9 **14.** What is the smallest positive integer that is *not* a factor of 50!?

[The notation n! means the factorial *of n, which is* $n \times (n-1) \times \cdots \times 2 \times 1$.

For example, 6! *means* $6 \times 5 \times 4 \times 3 \times 2 \times 1$.*]*

10 **15.** The digits from 1 to 9 are to be written in the nine cells of the 3×3 grid shown alongside, one digit in each cell.

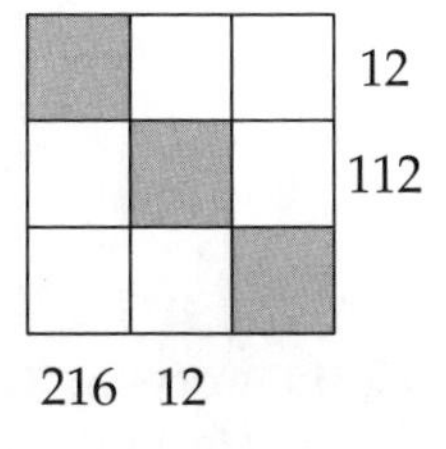

The numbers shown outside the grid are the products of the digits in the corresponding row or column. So the products are known for the first two rows and the first two columns.

What is the product of the digits in the shaded cells?

10 **16.** Frank's teacher asks him to write down five integers such that the median is one more than the mean, and the mode is one greater than the median. Frank is also told that the median is 10.

What is the smallest possible integer that Frank could include in his list?

11 **17.** Suppose that a and b are positive integers.

Which of the following five equations could be true?

$a - b = a \div b$ $\quad a + b = a \div b$ $\quad a - b = a \times b$ $\quad a + b = a - b$

$\sqrt{a+b} = \sqrt{a} + \sqrt{b}$

12 **18.** What is the smallest square that has 2016 as a factor?

12 **19.** The positive integer n is a multiple of 7, and $\sqrt{n}$ is between 15 and 16.

What is the number of possible values of n?

12 **20.** Observe that $2000 = 2^4 \times 5^3$.

What is the number of the next year after 2000 that is equal to $a^b \times c^d$, where a, b, c and d, perhaps in a different order, are 2, 3, 4 and 5?

13 **21.** Positive integers m and n are such that $2^m + 2^n = 1280$.

What is the value of $m + n$?

13 **22.** Last year Noel bought a number of identically-priced Christmas cards. The total cost was £15.60.

In a gesture of seasonal goodwill the shopkeeper gave him one extra card free, and this reduced the average cost per card by exactly 1p.

How many cards could Noel have bought with £5 at their original price?

14 **23.** I am trying to do a rectangular jigsaw puzzle. The puzzle was made by starting with a rectangular picture and then cutting it into 1000 pieces by sawing along the lines of a (wiggly!) rectangular grid.

I start by separating out all the edge and corner pieces.

Which of the following four numbers could *not* possibly be the number of corner and edge pieces of such a jigsaw?

126 $\quad$ 136 $\quad$ 216 $\quad$ 316

15 **24.** For how many integers n is $\dfrac{n}{100 - n}$ also an integer?

15 **25.** The number 2003 is prime.
How many squares are factors of 2003^{2003}?

15 **26.** For how many integer values of n does the equation $x^2 + nx - 16 = 0$ have integer solutions?

Rates

Exercise 13

4 **1.** An attempt by two men to sit in every one of the 72 000 seats in Cardiff's Millennium Stadium to raise money for charity ended in painful failure, despite the fact that they wore tracksuits made of man-made fibre to help them slide from seat to seat.

Before the pain stopped them, they had managed 64 000 seats between them in 27 hours.

On average, how many seconds did each man take per seat, to one significant figure?

5 **2.** A notice on Morecambe promenade reads:

It would take 20 million years to fill Morecambe Bay from a bath tap.

Assuming that the flow from the bath tap is 6 litres a minute, which of the following is the approximate number of litres in Morecambe Bay implied by the notice?

6×10^{10} $\quad$ 6×10^{11} $\quad$ 6×10^{12} $\quad$ 6×10^{13} $\quad$ 6×10^{14}

6 **3.** Dean runs up a mountain road at 8 km/h. It takes him one hour to get to the top.

He runs down the same road at 12 km/h.

How many minutes does it take him to run down the mountain?

7 **4.** A newspaper headline read

> Welsh tortoise recaptured 1.8 miles from home after 8 months on the run.

Assuming the tortoise travelled in a straight line, how many minutes (to the nearest ten minutes) did the tortoise take on average to 'run' one foot?

[1 *mile* = 5280 *feet*.]

8 **5.** Travelling at an average speed of 100 km/h, a train took 3 hours to travel to Birmingham. Unfortunately the train waited just outside the station, which reduced the average speed for the whole journey to 90 km/h.

For how many minutes was the train waiting?

8 **6.** A van travels from Newcastle to South Shields at an average speed of 30 mph and returns by the same route at an average speed of 40 mph.

What is the van's average speed for the whole journey?

11 **7.** Sam can mow a lawn in 3 hours. Mel takes 4 hours to mow the same lawn, and Chris takes 6 hours to do the same.

One day they work with a lawn mower each, and do not get in the way of each other.

How many minutes do they take to mow the lawn together?

13 **8.** Two entrants in a school's sponsored run adopt different tactics. Angus walks for half the time and runs for the other half, whilst Bruce walks for half the distance and runs for the other half.

Both competitors walk at 3 mph and run at 6 mph. Angus takes 40 minutes to complete the course.

How many minutes does Bruce take?

13 **9.** Rosie the road-runner recently ran in two road races. The second race was 20% further in distance than the first race and Rosie's average speed was 20% slower in the second race.

By what percentage was her time for the second race greater than that for the first?

15 **10.** Professor Rosseforp runs to work every day.

On Thursday he ran 10% faster than his usual average speed. As a result, his journey time was reduced by x minutes.

In terms of x, how many minutes did the journey take on Wednesday?

15 **11.** A jogger runs a certain distance at V m/s, and then walks half that distance at U m/s.

The total time for the two stages is T seconds.

What is the total distance travelled in terms of T, U and V?

Circles

Exercise 14

4 **1.** In the diagram, the smaller circle touches the larger circle and also passes through its centre.

What fraction of the area of the larger circle is outside the smaller circle?

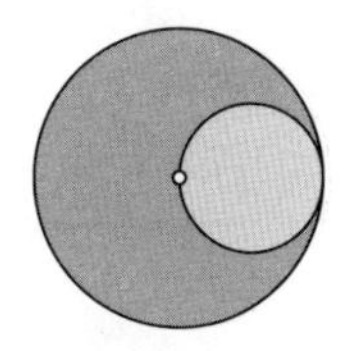

4 **2.** The smaller circle touches the larger circle, and goes through the centre of the larger circle.

What fraction of the area of the larger circle is outside the smaller circle?

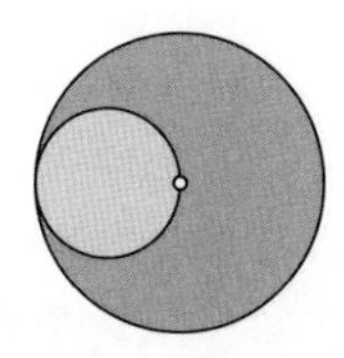

5 **3.** Boris Biker entered the Tour de Transylvania with an unusual bicycle whose back wheel is larger than the front. The radius of the back wheel is 40 cm, and the radius of the front wheel is 30 cm.

The smaller wheel made 120 000 revolutions on the first stage of the race.

How many revolutions did the larger wheel make?

9 **4.** The 80 spokes of the giant wheel *The London Eye* are made from four miles of cable.

Which of the following is roughly the length of the circumference of the wheel?

50 m	100 m	500 m	750 m	900 m

10 **5.** The diagram shows seven circles of equal radius that fit snugly in the larger circle.

What is the ratio of the unshaded area to the shaded area, numerically?

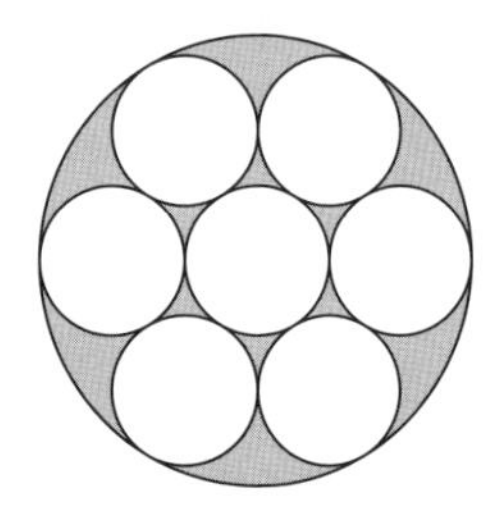

10 **6.** Steve Fossett completed the first solo balloon circumnavigation of the world on 2 July 2002, after $13\frac{1}{2}$ days.

Assuming the balloon travelled along a circle of diameter 12 750 km, which of the following was roughly the average speed of the balloon?

12 km/h	40 km/h	75 km/h	120 km/h	300 km/h

11 **7.** The diagram shows a circle with centre O, and a triangle OPQ.

The side PQ is a tangent to the circle. The area of the circle is equal to the area of the triangle.

What, numerically, is the ratio of the length of PQ to the length of the circumference of the circle?

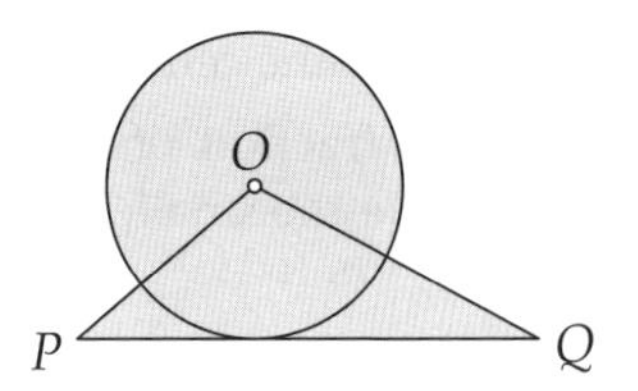

11 **8.** The diagram shows two concentric circles with radii r and $2r$ respectively.

What, numerically, is the ratio of the total shaded area to the total unshaded area?

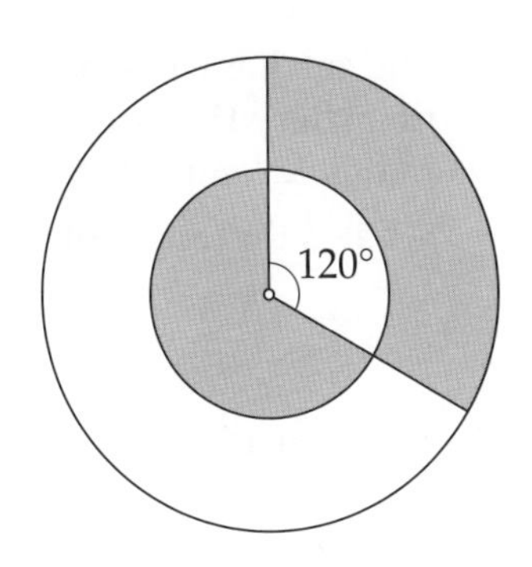

13 **9.** Five square tiles are put together side by side. A quarter-circle is drawn on each tile to make a continuous curve as shown alongside. Each of the two smallest tiles has sides of length 1.

What is the total length of the curve?

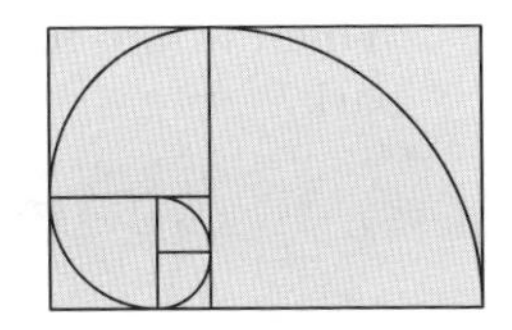

14 **10.** The point O is the centre of both circles and the shaded area is one-sixth of the area of the outer circle.

What is the value of x?

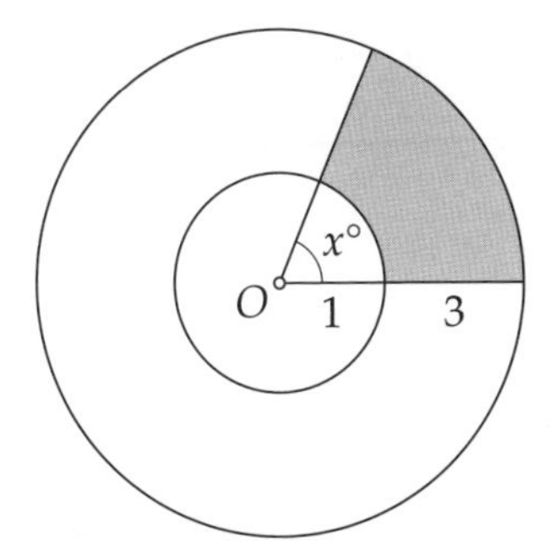

14 **11.** A circular disc of diameter d rolls without slipping around the inside of a ring of internal diameter $3d$, as shown in the diagram.

When the centre of the inner disc returns to its original position for the first time, how many times will the inner disc have turned about its centre?

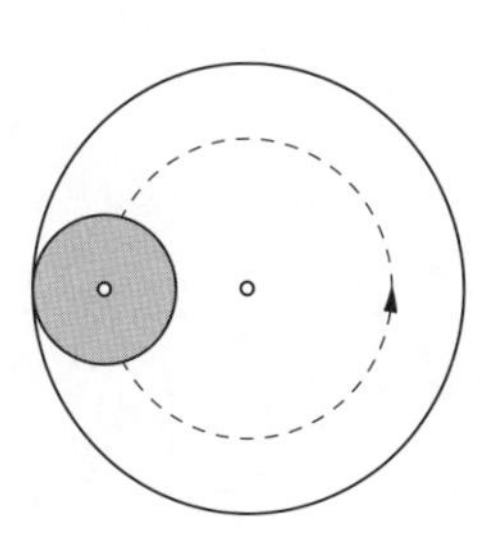

14 **12.** The smaller circle has radius 10; AB is a diameter. The larger circle has centre A, radius 12, and cuts the smaller circle at C.

What is the length of the chord BC?

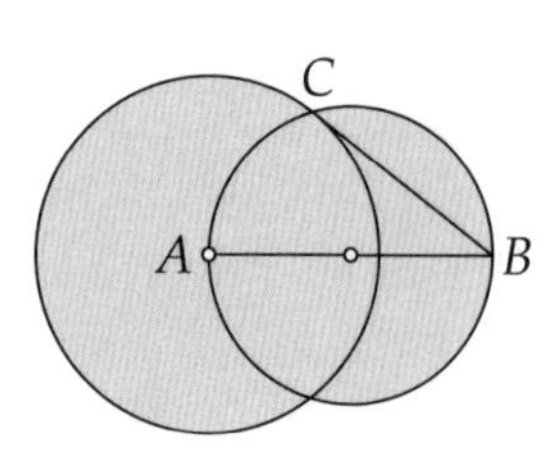

15 **13.** The trunk of a monkey-puzzle tree has diameter 40 cm. As a protection from fire, the trunk of the tree has a bark that makes up 19% of its volume.

Which of the following roughly gives the average thickness of the bark?

0.4 cm	1.2 cm	2 cm	2.8 cm	4 cm

Three dimensions

Exercise 15

5 **1.** Eight unit cubes are arranged to form a $2 \times 2 \times 2$ cube, as shown alongside.

What is the largest number of unit cubes that can be removed from this arrangement so that the resulting shape has the same surface area as the original?

7 **2.** The base of a pyramid has n edges.

In terms of n, what is the difference between the number of edges the pyramid has and the number of faces the pyramid has?

9 **3.** Sam has a large collection of $1 \times 1 \times 1$ cubes, each of which is either red or yellow.

Sam makes a $3 \times 3 \times 3$ block from twenty-seven cubes, so that no cubes of the same colour meet face-to-face.

What is the difference between the largest number of red cubes that Sam can use and the smallest number?

9 **4.** The points P, Q and R are three vertices of a cube, as shown alongside.

What is the cosine of the angle PQR?

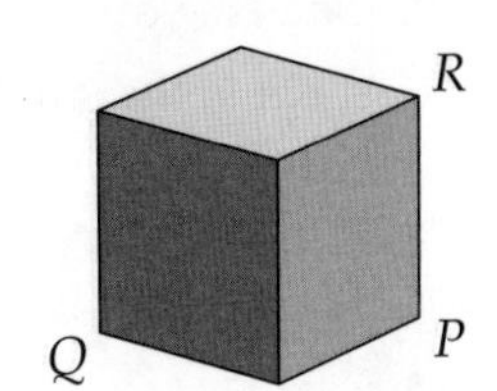

11 **5.** Coco is making clown hats from a circular piece of cardboard.

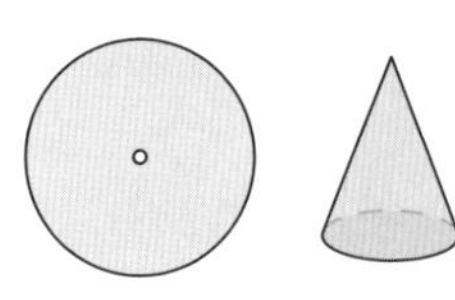

The length of the circumference of the base of each hat is equal to the slant length of the hat, which in turn is equal to the radius of the piece of cardboard.

What is the maximum number of hats that Coco can make from the piece of cardboard?

11 **6.** A $4 \times 4 \times 4$ cube has three $2 \times 2 \times 4$ holes drilled symmetrically all the way through, as shown alongside.

What is the surface area of the resulting solid?

11 **7.** A sculpture is made from 12 wooden cylinders, each of height 2 cm. They are glued together as shown alongside.

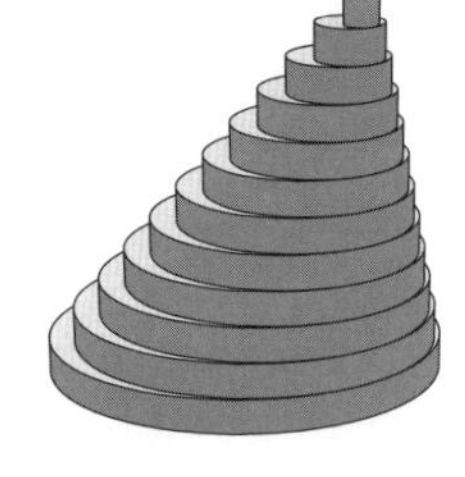

The diameter of the top cylinder is 2 cm and each of the other cylinders has a diameter 2 cm more than the one immediately above it.

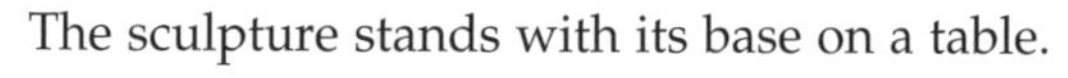

The sculpture stands with its base on a table.

What is the total surface area of the sculpture, excluding the base?

11 **8.** In a fit of madness, the bee Zerk left the hive and flew 1 m due North, then 1 m due East, then 1 m vertically up. She then made a beeline for the hive, flying directly home in a straight line.

How far did she fly altogether?

12 **9.** One face of a solid polyhedron is a regular hexagon.

What is the smallest possible number of edges the polyhedron could have?

13 **10.** Each of the five nets P, Q, R, S and T is made from six squares. The front and back of each square have the same colour. Net P is folded to form a cube.

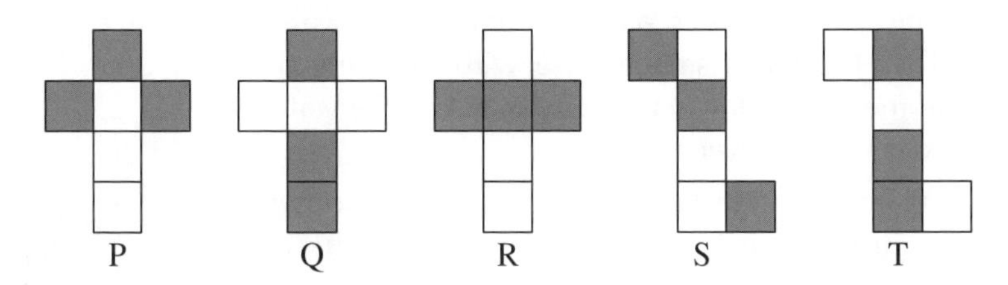

How many of the nets Q, R, S and T can be folded to produce a cube that looks the same as that produced by P?

14 **11.** The points L, M and N are midpoints of the edges of a cube, as shown alongside.

What is the value of angle LMN?

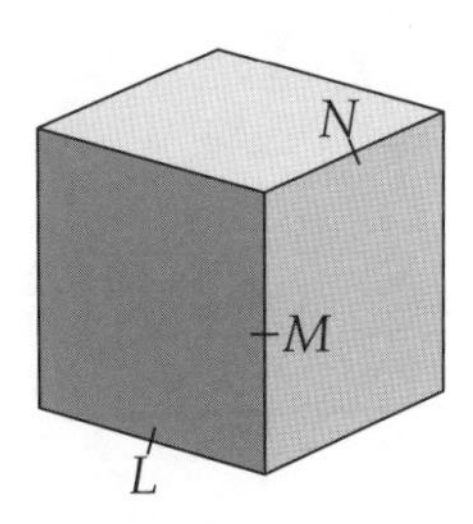

14 **12.** The diagram shows a triangular prism with three rectangular faces.

Which of the following five shapes cannot be obtained as the cross-section (in any direction) of this solid?

triangle	rectangle	trapezium
pentagon	hexagon	

15 **13.** Each of two vases has the shape of a cylinder. The larger vase has a diameter of 20 cm. The smaller vase has a diameter of 10 cm and a height of 16 cm.

The larger vase is partially filled with water. Then the empty smaller vase, with the open end at the top, is slowly pushed down into the water, which flows over its rim.

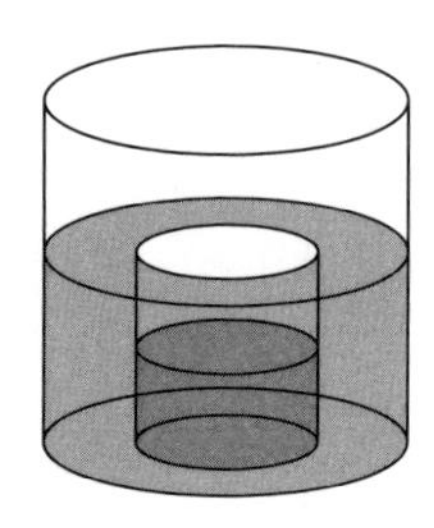

When the smaller vase is pushed down completely, it is half full of water, as shown alongside.

What was the original depth of the water in the larger vase?

Reasoning

Exercise 16

2 **1.** The headteacher is informed that, in a class of thirty pupils, there are twenty-two pupils who are right-handed and there are fourteen girls.

What may the headteacher deduce about the smallest possible number of girls who are right-handed?

4 **2.** Susan is taller than Sophie, but shorter than Sandra. Stephanie is taller than Sarah, but shorter than Susan.

Who is the tallest of these five girls?

6 **3.** In the village of Much-Pedling-in-the-Marsh, one third of the children can swim, two thirds can ride a bicycle and one seventh can both swim and ride a bicycle (though not necessarily at the same time). There are fewer than 40 children in Much-Pedling-in-the-Marsh.

How many of the children in the village can neither swim nor ride a bicycle?

9 **4.** Pierre said, "Just one of us is telling the truth".
Qadr said, "What Pierre says is not true".
Ratna said, "What Qadr says is not true".
Sven said, "What Ratna says is not true".
Tanya said, "What Sven says is not true".

How many of them were telling the truth?

9 **5.** The statement

If n is prime then $n^2 + 2$ is also prime.

is not true. Which of the following four integers is a counterexample?

3 5 6 9

12 **6.** The statement

If n is prime, then $n! + 1$ is also prime.

is not true. Which of the following five integers is a counterexample?

1 2 3 4 5

[The notation $n!$ *means the* factorial *of* n*, which is* $n \times (n-1) \times \cdots \times 2 \times 1$.
For example, $6!$ *means* $6 \times 5 \times 4 \times 3 \times 2 \times 1$.*]*

13 **7.** The Knave of Hearts tells only the truth on Mondays, Tuesdays, Wednesdays and Thursdays. He tells only lies on all the other days.

The Knave of Diamonds tells only the truth on Fridays, Saturdays, Sundays and Mondays. He tells only lies on all the other days.

On one day last week, they both said, "Yesterday I told lies."

On which day of the week was that?

14 **8.** The statement in the next box is false.

If n is not prime then $n - 2$ is not prime.

Which of the following five values of n is a counterexample?

6 11 27 33 51

15 **9.** The four statements in the following box refer to a mother and her four daughters.

Alice is the mother.

Carol and Ella are both daughters.

Beth is the mother.

One of Alice, Diane or Ella is the mother.

One statement is true; three statements are false.

Who is the mother?

16 **10.** Andrew states that:

Every composite integer of the form $8n + 3$, where n is an integer, has a prime factor of the same form.

Which of the following five integers is an example showing that Andrew's statement is false?

19 33 85 91 99

17 **11.** A survey of the food preferences of pupils at a school discovered that 70% of the pupils like pears, 75% like oranges, 80% like bananas and 85% like apples.

What is the smallest possible percentage of pupils who like all four of these fruits?

18 **12.** What is the greatest number of the following five statements about the numbers a and b that can be true at the same time?

$$\frac{1}{a} < \frac{1}{b} \qquad a^2 > b^2 \qquad a < b \qquad a < 0 \qquad b < 0$$

21 **13.** Each of the Four Musketeers made a statement about the four of them, as follows.

d'Artagnan: "Exactly one is lying."

Athos: "Exactly two of us are lying."

Porthos: "An odd number of us is lying."

Aramis: "An even number of us is lying."

What are the possibilities for the number of them that were lying (with the others telling the truth)?

24 **14.** The Queen of Hearts had some tarts, but they were eaten.

Precisely one of the following five statements about the tarts and the Knaves of Clubs, Diamonds and Spades is true. Which one?

None of the three Knaves ate any tarts.

The Knave of Clubs ate some tarts.

Only one of the three Knaves ate any tarts.

At least one of the Knave of Diamonds and the Knave of Spades ate no tarts.

More than one of the three Knaves ate some tarts.

Part II

More challenging problems

Trigonometry

Exercise 17

12 **1.** Which of the following five expressions has the greatest value?

$\cos 50°$	$\sin 50°$	$\tan 50°$	$\dfrac{1}{\sin 50°}$	$\dfrac{1}{\cos 50°}$

14 **2.** The parallel sides of a trapezium have lengths $2x$ and $2y$ respectively. The diagonals are equal in length, and a diagonal makes an angle θ with the parallel sides, as shown alongside.

What is the length of each diagonal in terms of x, y and θ?

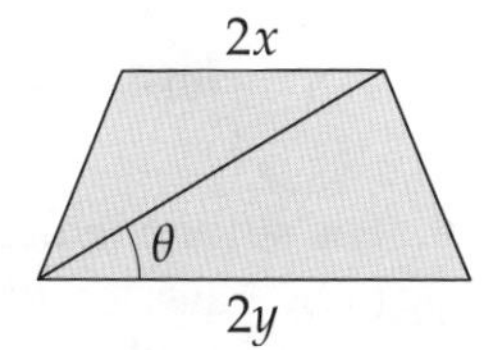

14 **3.** The diagram shows five touching circles each with radius 1. Their centres are at the vertices of a regular pentagon.

Which of the following five expressions is equal to the radius of the circle through the points of contact P, Q, R, S and T?

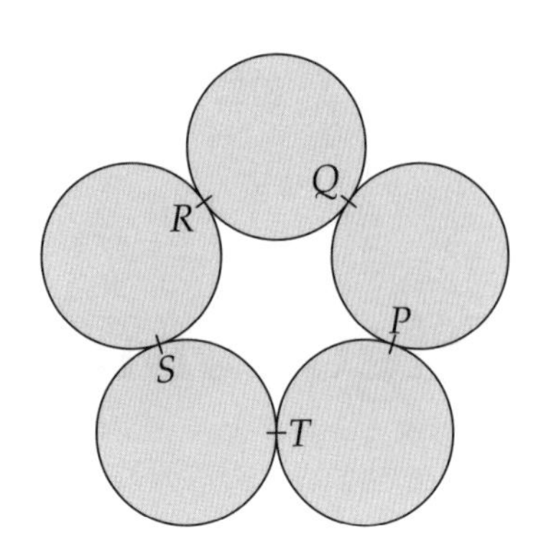

$\tan 18°$	$\tan 36°$	$\tan 45°$
$\tan 54°$	$\tan 72°$	

15 **4.** Triangle ABC is isosceles with $CA = AB$, and the point D is the midpoint of AB. Suppose that $\angle BCD = \angle BAC$. Let $\angle BAC = \theta$.

What is the value of $\cos\theta$?

16 **5.** The angles of a right-angled triangle are α and β, with $\alpha < \beta$, as shown alongside.

How many different values are there among the following four expressions?

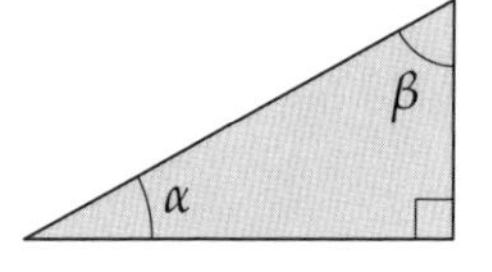

$\sin\alpha\sin\beta$	$\sin\alpha\cos\beta$	$\cos\alpha\sin\beta$	$\cos\alpha\cos\beta$

17 **6.** The sides of equilateral triangle PQR have length 1. The lines PT and PU trisect the angle RPQ, the lines RS and RT trisect the angle QRP, and the lines QS and QU trisect the angle PQR.

Which of the following five expressions is equal to the length of each side of the equilateral triangle STU?

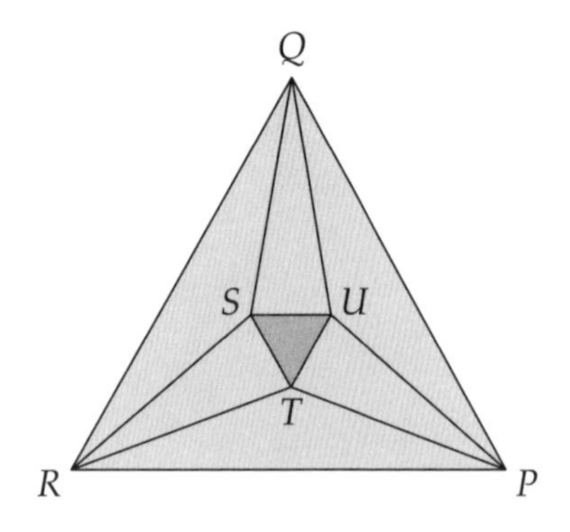

$\dfrac{\cos 80°}{\cos 20°}$	$\frac{1}{3}\cos 20°$	$\cos^2 20°$	$\frac{1}{6}$	$\cos 20°\cos 80°$

18 **7.** The diagram shows two squares, with sides of length $\frac{1}{2}$, inclined at an angle 2α to one another.

In terms of α, what is the value of x?

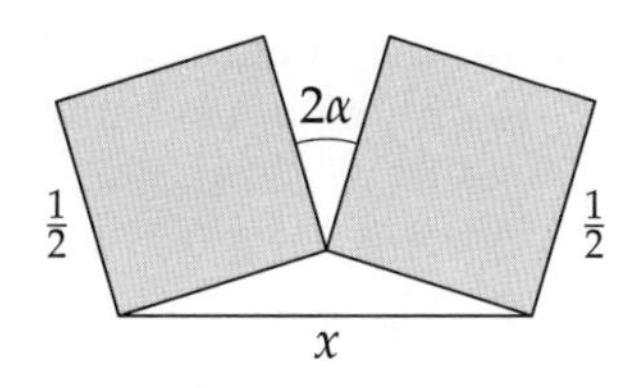

19 **8.** Suppose that $\cos\theta = \frac{1}{2}$.

Which one of the following cannot be equal to $\sin 2\theta$?

$\sin\theta$	$\dfrac{1}{2}$	$-\dfrac{\sqrt{3}}{2}$	$\dfrac{\sqrt{3}}{2}$	$2\cos\theta\sin\theta$

21 **9.** The diagram shows ten equal discs that lie between two concentric circles—an inner circle and an outer circle. Each disc touches two neighbouring discs and both circles. The inner circle has radius 1.

Which of the following five expressions is equal to the radius of the *outer* circle?

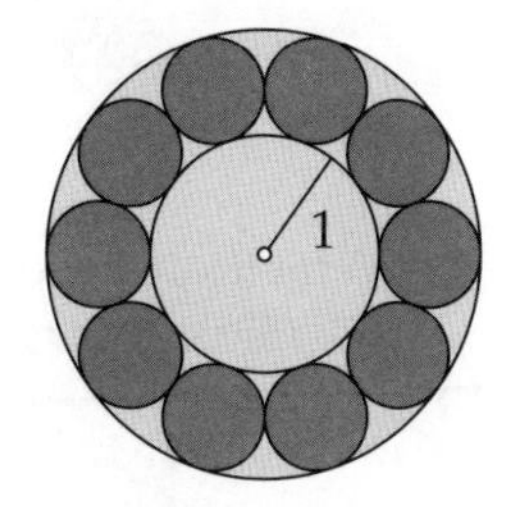

$2\tan 36^\circ$	$\dfrac{\sin 36^\circ}{1-\sin 36^\circ}$	$\dfrac{1+\sin 18^\circ}{1-\sin 18^\circ}$	$\dfrac{2}{\cos 18^\circ}$	$\dfrac{9}{5}$

22 **10.** In the diagram, DFC and BFE are straight lines, and $\angle ABE = 10°$, $\angle EBC = 70°$, $\angle DCA = 50°$, $\angle BCD = 20°$ and $\angle FED = \alpha°$.

Which of the following five expressions is equal to $\tan\alpha°$?

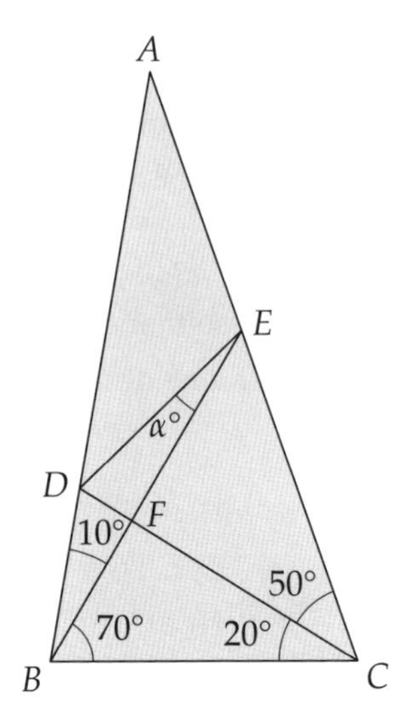

$\dfrac{\tan 10° \tan 20°}{\tan 50°}$ $\dfrac{\tan 10° \tan 20°}{\tan 70°}$

$\dfrac{\tan 10° \tan 50°}{\tan 70°}$ $\dfrac{\tan 20° \tan 50°}{\tan 70°}$

$\dfrac{\tan 10° \tan 70°}{\tan 50°}$

22 **11.** Which of the following five expressions is equal to $\sin^3 x + \cos^3 x$ whatever the value of x?

$\sin 3x + \cos 3x$ 1 $(\sin x + \cos x)(1 - \sin x \cos x)$

$(\sin x + \cos x)^3$ $(\sin x + \cos x)(2 \sin x \cos x + 1)$

24 **12.** The diagram shows two straight lines PR and QS crossing at O.

What is the value of x?

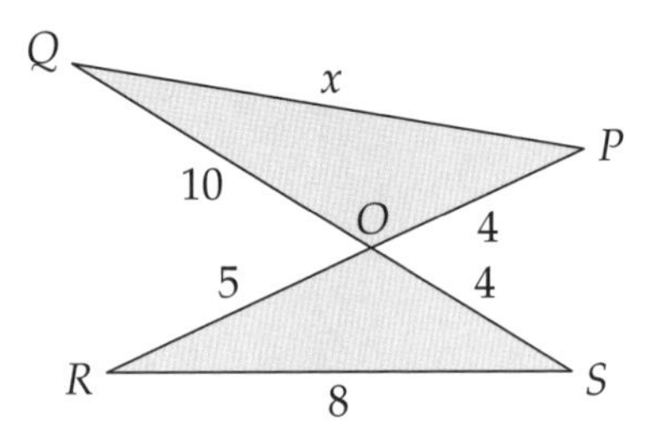

Graphs and coordinates

Exercise 18

9 **1.** A square has vertices at the points $(0,0)$, $(1,0)$, $(1,1)$ and $(0,1)$.

Graphs of the following equations are drawn on the same set of axes as the square.

$$x^2 + y^2 = 1 \qquad y = x + 1 \qquad y = -x^2 + 1 \qquad y = x \qquad y = \frac{1}{x}$$

How many of the graphs pass through exactly two of the vertices of the square?

14 **2.** The straight line with equation $y = 3x + 4$ is reflected in the line with equation $y = -x$.

What is the equation of the image line?

16 **3.** The diagram shows the ellipse whose equation is $x^2 + y^2 - xy + x - 4y = 12$. The ellipse cuts the y-axis at points A and C and cuts the x-axis at points B and D.

What is the area of the inscribed quadrilateral $ABCD$?

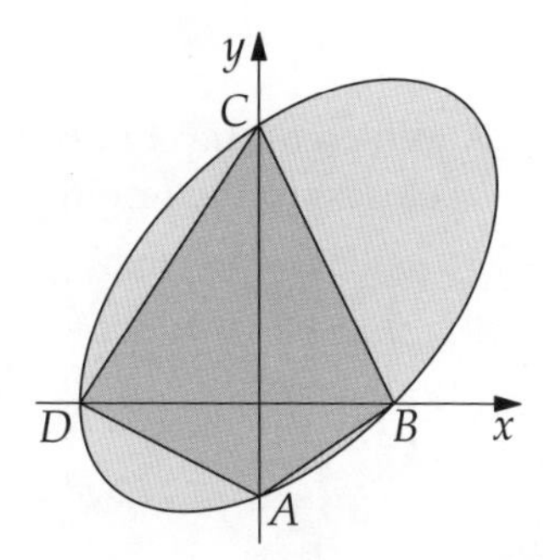

17 **4.** A trapezium is bounded by four straight lines, the equations of which are:

$x = 0 \qquad x = 4 \qquad 4y = 3x + 8 \qquad y = k$, where $k < 2$

For what value of k is the numerical value of the length of the perimeter of the trapezium equal to the numerical value of the area of the trapezium?

17 **5.** The diagram shows the graph of $y = |f(x)|$. The graph of $y = f(x)$ is a continuous curve.

How many different possibilities are there for the graph of $y = f(x)$?

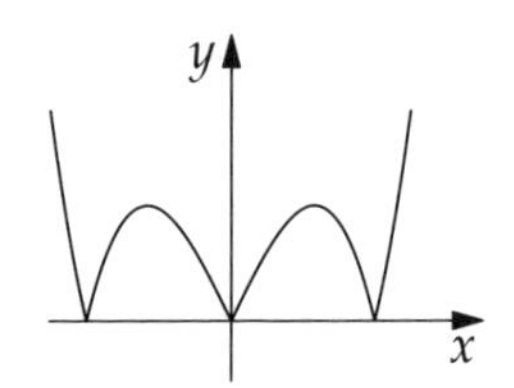

18 **6.** Which of the following five graphs shows the curve with equation $y^2 = x(2 - x)$?

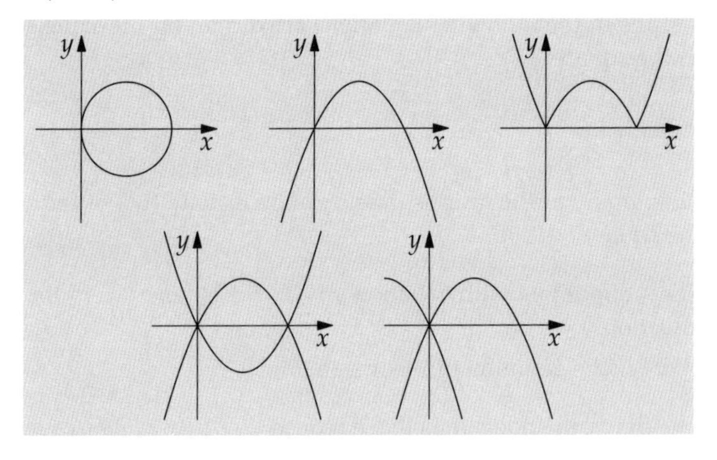

18 **7.** Which of the curves or lines with the following five equations comes closest to the origin?

$y = x - 4 \qquad x^2 + y^2 = 4 \qquad y = \frac{4}{x} \qquad y = x^2 + 4 \qquad y = x^4 - 4$

18 **8.** The curve with equation

$$y = x^2 - 6x + 11,$$

shown alongside, is rotated through 180° about the origin.

What is the equation of the new curve?

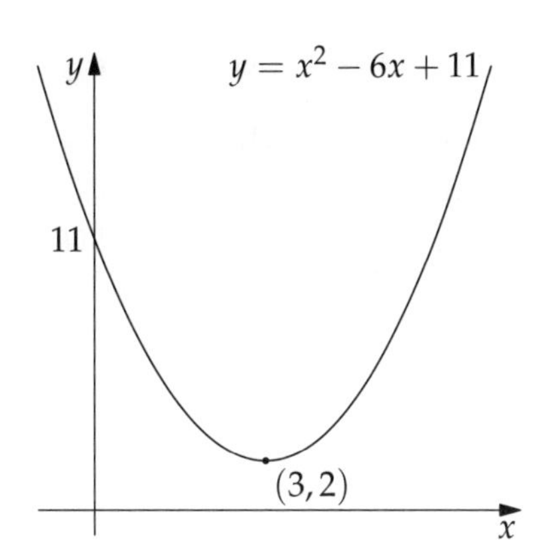

18 **9.** The diagram shows part of the graph of a 'curve'.

Which of the following four equations could be the equation of the 'curve'?

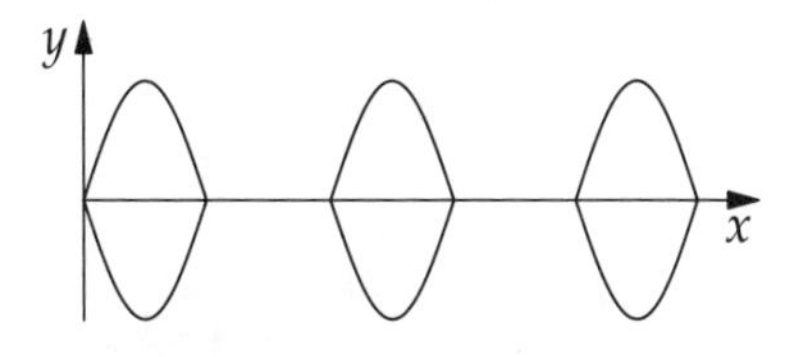

$y = \sin x$ $\quad |y| = \sin x$ $\quad y = |\sin x|$ $\quad |y| = |\sin x|$

19 **10.** The diagram alongside shows the graph of $y = |x|$. Which of the following five graphs is the graph of $y = x|x|$?

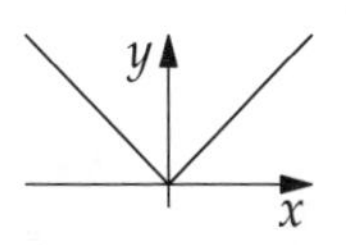

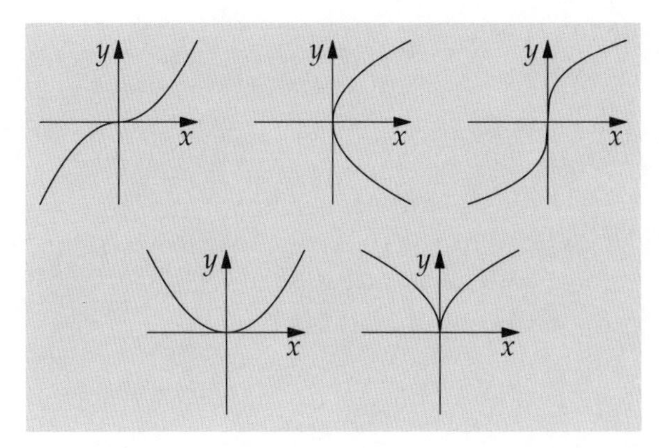

19 **11.** The diagram shows the graph of $\frac{1}{y}$ plotted against $\sqrt{x}$. The graph is a straight line. Which of the following five equations could be the equation connecting y and x?

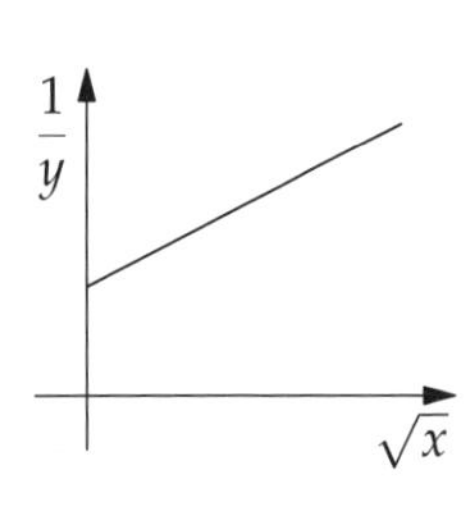

$$y^2 = \frac{1}{x-1} \qquad y^2 = \frac{1}{x^2+1} \qquad y^2 = x - 1$$
$$y^2 = \frac{1}{x - 2\sqrt{x} + 1} \qquad y^2 = \frac{1}{x + 2\sqrt{x} + 1}$$

20 **12.** Which of the following five graphs could be the graph of $y = \sin(x^2)$?

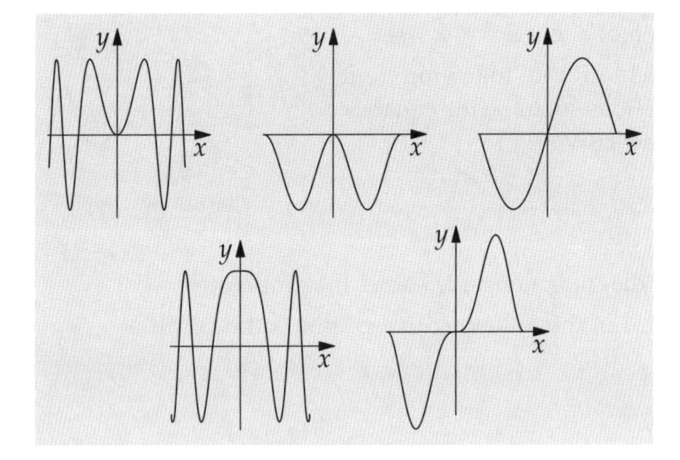

21 **13.** Fiona wants to draw a shape on a grid of squares, part of which is shown alongside.

The perimeter of the shape has to pass through all four of the points P, Q, R and S.

Which of the following three shapes can she draw?

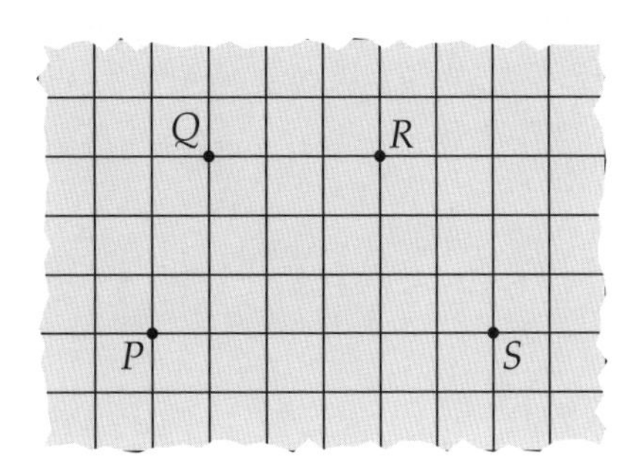

a circle a square
an equilateral triangle

25 **14.** What is the area of the polygon formed by all points (x, y) in the plane that satisfy the inequality

$$\Big||x| - 2\Big| + \Big||y| - 2\Big| \leq 4?$$

25 **15.** The straight line with equation $y = x$ is an axis of symmetry of the curve with equation $y = \dfrac{px + q}{rx + s}$, where p, q, r and s are all non-zero.

Which of the following five equations is true whatever the non-zero values of p, q, r and s?

$p + q = 0$ $r + s = 0$ $p + r = 0$ $p + s = 0$ $q + r = 0$

Probability

Exercise 19

13 **1.** The cards in a set of 36 are numbered 1 to 36.

The cards are shuffled and four cards are dealt.

What is the probability that the four cards are dealt in descending order?

14 **2.** Six students who share a house all speak exactly two languages.

Helga speaks only English and German.
Ina speaks only German and Spanish.
Jean-Pierre speaks only French and Spanish.
Karim speaks only German and French.
Lionel speaks only French and English.
Mary speaks only Spanish and English.

Two of the students are chosen at random. What is the probability that they speak a common language?

16 **3.** The probability of a single ticket winning the jackpot in the National Lottery in 1998 was

$$\frac{6}{49} \times \frac{5}{48} \times \frac{4}{47} \times \frac{3}{46} \times \frac{2}{45} \times \frac{1}{44}.$$

I bought one ticket every week in 1998. I should have expected to win the jackpot once every T years.

Which of the following is roughly the value of T?

one hundred	twenty thousand
one hundred thousand	one quarter of a million
one million	

20 **4.** There are 10 girls in a mixed class. When two pupils from the class are selected at random to represent the class on the School Council, the probability that both are girls is 0.15.

How many boys are in the class?

20 **5.** A point P is chosen at random inside a square $QRST$.

What is the probability that $\angle RPQ$ is acute?

22 **6.** A bag contains m blue and n yellow marbles.

One marble is selected at random from the bag and its colour is noted. It is returned to the bag and k other marbles of the same colour are added to the bag. A second marble is now selected at random from the bag.

What is the probability that the second marble is blue?

22 **7.** Triangle ABC has $\angle ABC = 90°$ and $\angle BCA = 30°$. A point P inside the triangle is chosen at random.

What is the probability that P is nearer to AB than to CA?

23 **8.** Tom and Geri have a competition.

Initially, each player has one attempt at hitting a target. If one player hits the target and the other does not then the successful player wins. If both players hit the target, or if both players miss the target, then each has another attempt, with the same rules applying.

The probability of Tom hitting the target is always $\frac{4}{5}$ and the probability of Geri hitting the target is always $\frac{2}{3}$.

What is the probability that Tom wins the competition?

More algebra

Exercise 20

16 **1.** Suppose that x and y are positive, and satisfy the equations

$$\begin{aligned} x^4 - y^4 &= 2009 \\ \text{and} \quad x^2 + y^2 &= 49. \end{aligned}$$

What is the value of y?

16 **2.** Suppose that x, y and z satisfy the equations

$$\begin{aligned} x + y + 2z &= 850, \\ x + 2y + z &= 950 \\ \text{and} \quad 2x + y + z &= 1200. \end{aligned}$$

What value is the average of x, y and z?

16 **3.** Five peaches, three oranges and two melons cost £3.18. Four peaches, eight oranges and three melons cost £4.49.

How much more expensive is a peach than an orange?

17 **4.** The equation

$$a^3 + b^3 + c^3 = (a+b+c)^3 - 3(a+b+c)(ab+bc+ca) + kabc$$

is true for all a, b and c.

What is the value of k?

17 **5.** The ratio of Jon's age to Jan's age is 3 : 1. Three years ago the ratio was 4 : 1.

In how many years time will the ratio be 2 : 1?

17 **6.** Which of the following is equal to $(x-1)(x^4+1)(x^2+1)(x+1)$ whatever the value of x?

$x^8 - 1$ $\quad$ $x^8 + x^6 + x^4 + x^2 + 1$ $\quad$ $x^8 + 1$

$x^8 + x^7 + x^6 + x^5 + x^4 + x^3 + x^2 + x + 1$ $\quad$ $x^8 - x^6 + x^4 - 1$

17 **7.** For each real number x, except 0, 1 and -1, define $f(x)$ by

$$f(x) = \frac{x-1}{x+1}.$$

What is the value of $f^6(x)$, that is, $f(f(f(f(f(f(x))))))$?

18 **8.** Suppose that x and y satisfy the equations

$$\frac{1}{x} + \frac{1}{y} = \frac{1}{2}$$

$$\text{and} \quad x + y = 20.$$

What is the value of $x^2y + xy^2$?

19 **9.** Three squares are arranged as shown alongside so that their bases lie on a straight line. Also, the vertices P, Q and R lie on a straight line.

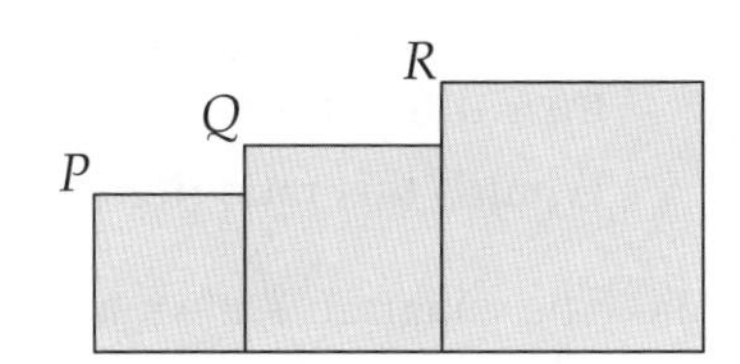

The middle square has sides that are 8 cm longer than the sides of the smallest square.

The largest square has sides of length 50 cm.

What are the two possible values for the length of the sides of the smallest square?

19 **10.** Hamish and his friend Ben live in villages that are 51 miles apart.

During the summer holidays, they agreed to ride a bicycle towards each other along the same main road. Starting at noon, Hamish cycled at x mph. Starting at 2 pm, Ben cycled at y mph.

They met at 4 pm. If they had both started at noon, they would have met at 2.50 pm.

What is the value of y?

19 **11.** An engineer is directed to a faulty signal, one quarter of the way into a tunnel. Whilst there, he is warned of a train heading towards the tunnel entrance.

The engineer can run at 10 mph and can either run back to the tunnel entrance or forward to the exit. In either case, the engineer and the front of the train would reach the entrance or exit together.

What is the speed of the train, in mph?

19 **12.** The integers S, M and C satisfy the equations

$$S \times M \times C = 240,$$
$$S \times C + M = 46$$
$$\text{and} \quad S + M \times C = 64.$$

What is the value of $S + M + C$?

20 **13.** The ratio of two positive numbers is equal to the ratio of their sum to their difference.

What is this ratio numerically?

21 **14.** The diagram shows a triangle XYZ.

The sides XY, YZ and ZX have lengths 4, 3 and 2 respectively.

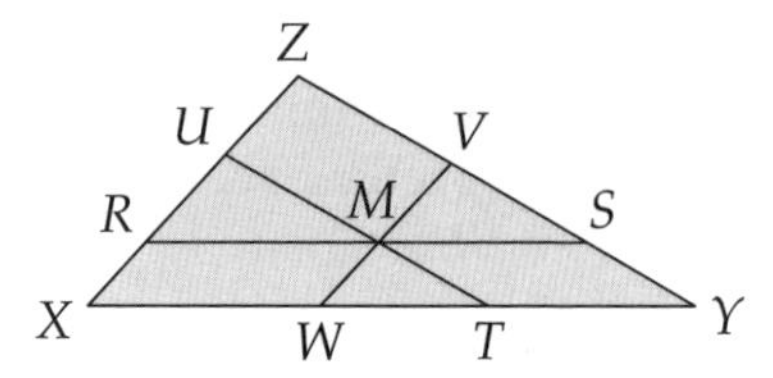

The lines RMS, TMU and VMW are drawn parallel to the sides of triangle XYZ so that WT, SV and UR are of equal length.

What is the length of UR?

22 **15.** The positive integers m and n satisfy the equation $x^2 - mx - n = 0$.

Which of the following five expressions could not be equal to x^3, whatever the value of x?

$4x + 3$ $\quad 8x + 5$ $\quad 8x + 7$ $\quad 10x + 3$ $\quad 26x + 5$

22 **16.** Suppose that $0 < b < a$ and $a^2 + b^2 = 6ab$.

What is the value of $\dfrac{a+b}{a-b}$?

23 **17.** What is the minimum value of $x^2 + y^2 + 2xy + 6x + 6y + 4$?

23 **18.** How many distinct pairs (x, y) of real numbers satisfy the equation

$$(x + y)^2 = (x + 3)(y - 3)?$$

24 **19.** Suppose that $x^2 - 3x + 1 = 0$.

What is the value of $x^2 + \left(\dfrac{1}{x}\right)^2$?

25 **20.** How many distinct pairs (x, y) of real numbers satisfy the equation

$$(x + y)^2 = (x + 4)(y - 4)?$$

More circles

Exercise 21

16 **1.** The quadrilateral $PQRS$ is inscribed in a circle with diameter PR. The lengths of PQ, QR and RS are 60, 25 and 52 respectively.

What is the length of SP?

16 **2.** In triangle PQR, angle P is $90°$, $PQ = 15\,\text{cm}$ and $QR = 17\,\text{cm}$.

Circular arcs are drawn with centres at P, Q and R so that each arc touches the other two arcs, as shown alongside.

What is the radius of the arc with centre Q?

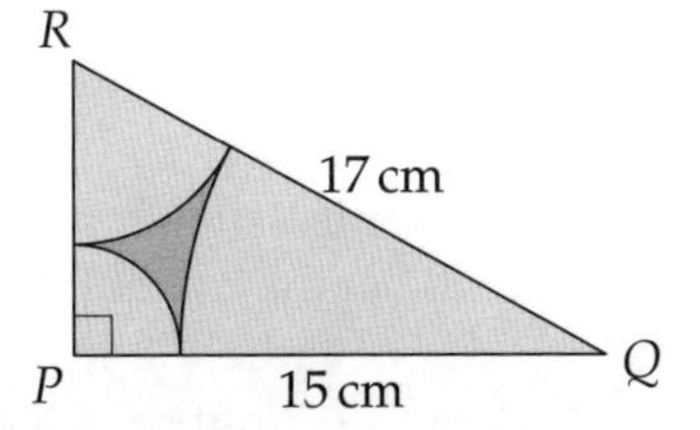

16 **3.** Three circles touch, as shown in the diagram. Each of the two larger circles has radius 1 and the smaller circle has radius $\sqrt{2} - 1$.

What is the length of the perimeter of the shaded region?

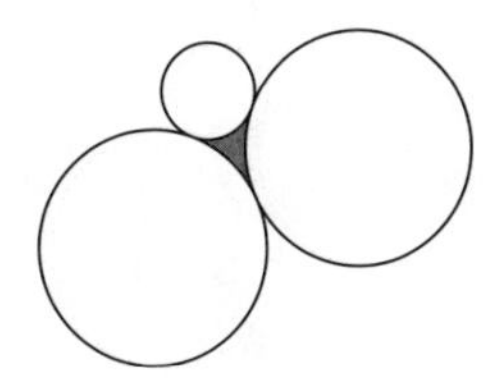

16 **4.** A roll of adhesive tape is wound round a central cylindrical core of radius 3 cm.

The outer radius of a roll containing 20 m of tape is 4 cm.

To the nearest centimetre, what is the outer radius of a roll containing 80 m of tape?

16 **5.** In the diagram AA' and BB' are arcs of concentric circles with centre O, and $\angle A'OA = x^\circ$.

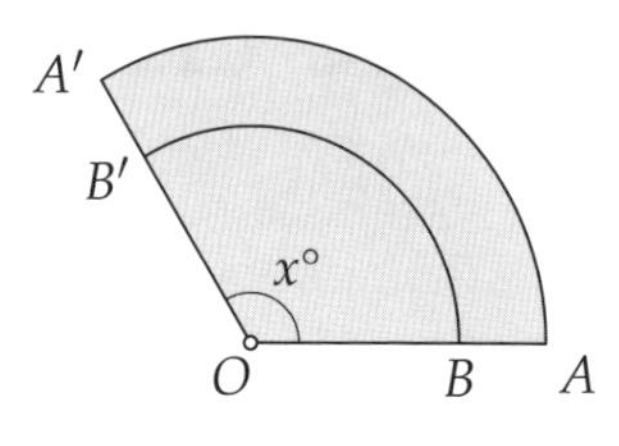

The length of the arc AA' is equal to the total distance from A to A' via the arc BB'.

What is the value of x?

17 **6.** The diagram shows eight circles of two different sizes. The circles are arranged in concentric pairs so that the centres form a square. Each larger circle touches one other larger circle and two smaller circles. The larger circles have radius 1.

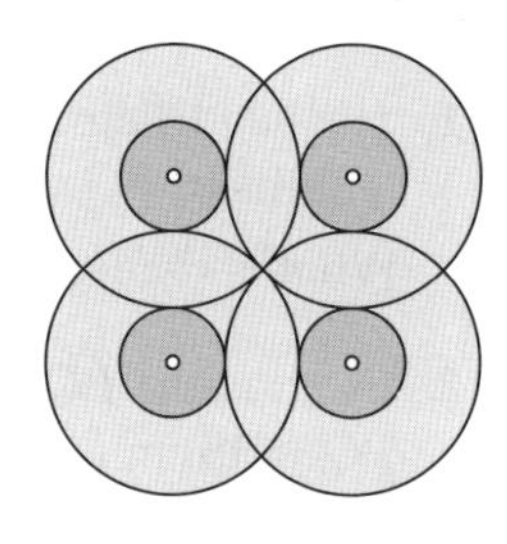

What is the radius of each smaller circle?

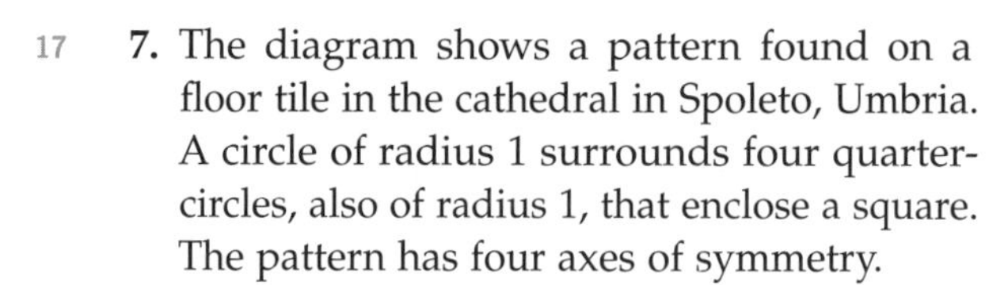

17 **7.** The diagram shows a pattern found on a floor tile in the cathedral in Spoleto, Umbria. A circle of radius 1 surrounds four quarter-circles, also of radius 1, that enclose a square. The pattern has four axes of symmetry.

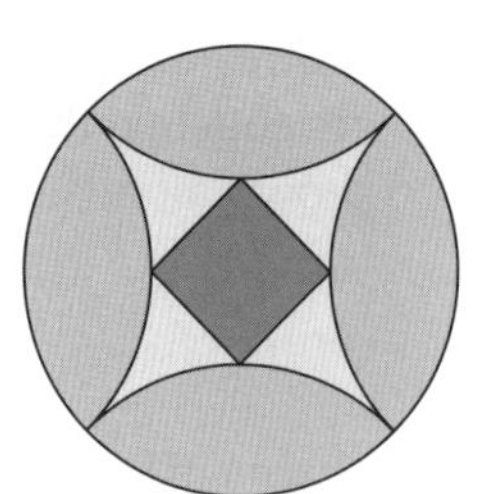

What is the length of each side of the square?

18 **8.** In the diagram, the line PQ is a tangent at N to the circle through points L, M and N. The lengths LM and LN are equal. The line LM, when extended, meets the tangent PQ at the point R. Angle PNL is $\theta°$ and angle LRP is $\phi°$.

What is ϕ in terms of θ?

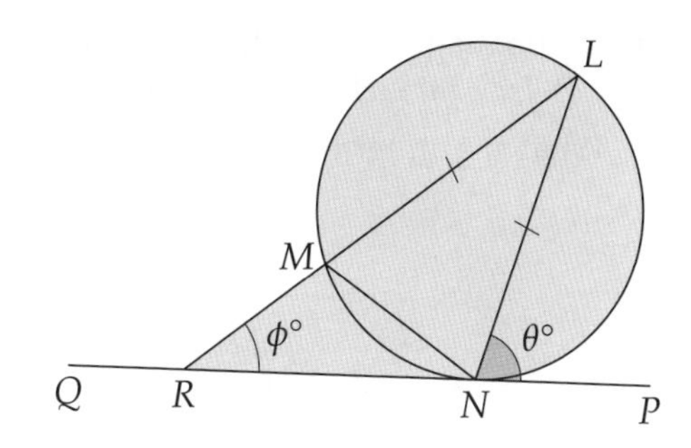

19 **9.** The diagram shows a quadrant of a circle of radius 2, and two touching semicircles. The larger semicircle has radius 1.

What is the radius of the smaller semicircle?

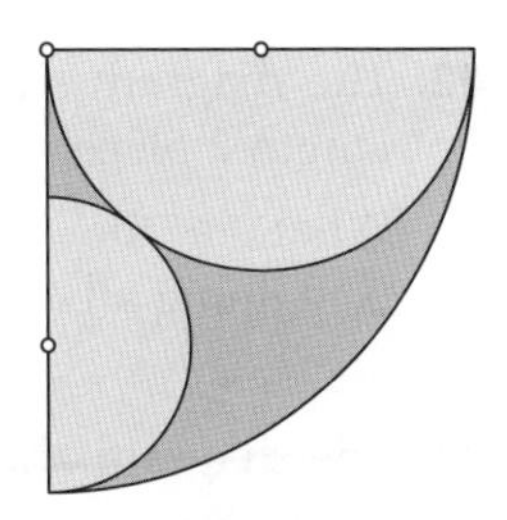

19 **10.** The largest circle that it is possible to draw inside triangle PQR touches the triangle at S, T and U, as shown alongside, and $\angle STU = 55°$.

What is the size of $\angle PQR$?

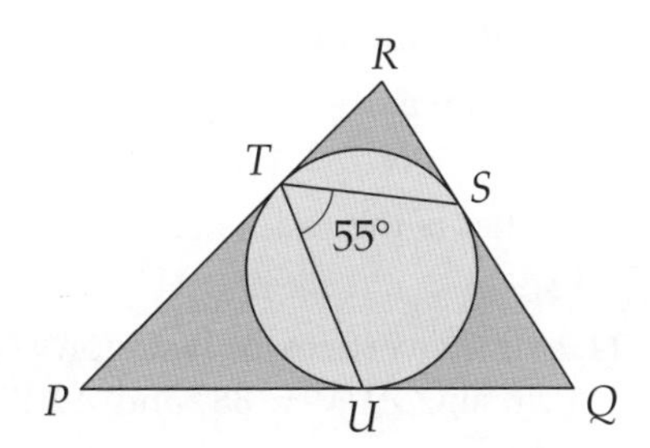

19 **11.** In the diagram, O is the centre of the circle, $\angle BOA = \alpha°$, $\angle DOC = \beta°$ and $\angle BXA = \gamma°$.

What is γ in terms of α and β?

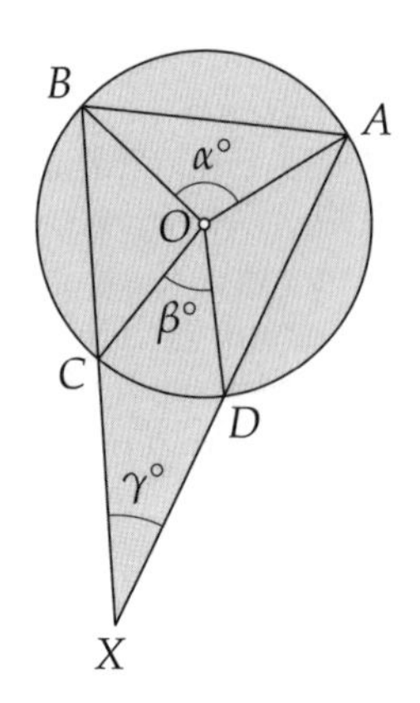

20 **12.** The diagram shows six squares with sides of length 2 placed edge-to-edge.

What is the radius of the smallest circle containing all six squares?

20 **13.** The diagram shows a trapezium $PQRS$ with SR parallel to PQ. All four sides of $PQRS$ are tangent to a circle.

The area of the trapezium is $600\,\text{cm}^2$ and $SP = QR = 25\,\text{cm}$.

What is the radius of the circle?

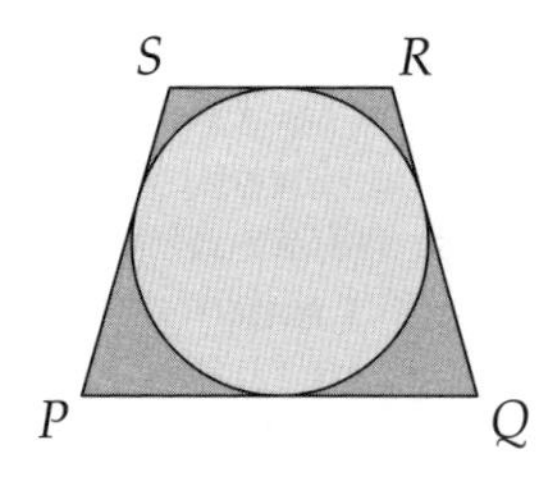

20 **14.** All six vertices of hexagon $UVWXYZ$ lie on the circumference of a circle; $\angle ZUV = 88°$ and $\angle XYZ = 158°$.

What is the size of $\angle VWX$?

20 **15.** In the diagram, AB, BC and XY are tangents to the circle with centre O, and $\angle ABC = 48°$.

What is the size of $\angle YOX$?

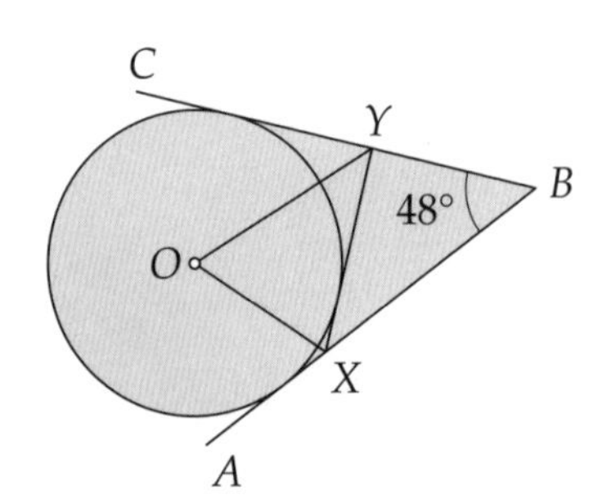

21 **16.** The shaded design shown in the diagram is made by drawing eight circular arcs, all with the same radius.

The centres of four arcs are the vertices of a square; the centres of the four touching arcs are the midpoints of the sides of the square. The diagonals of the square have length 1.

What is the total length of the border of the shaded design?

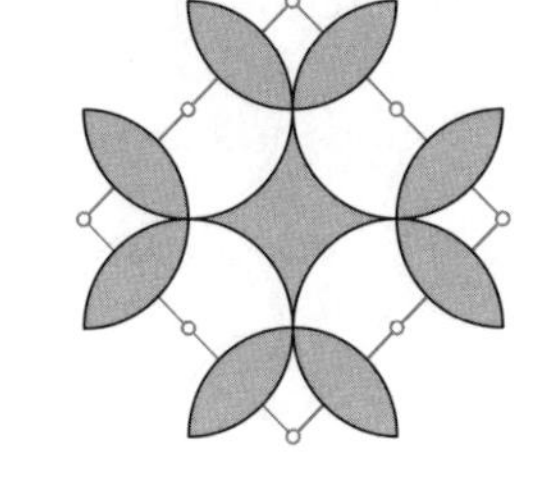

21 **17.** In the diagram, PQ and RS are tangents to the circle.

What is the value of x?

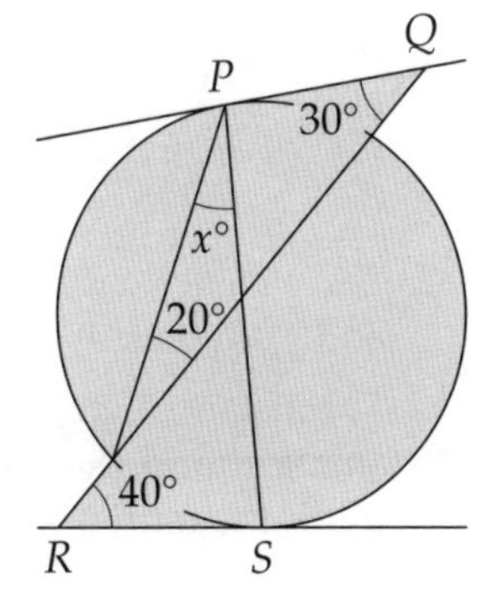

21 **18.** The diagram shows a semicircle enclosed by a triangle whose sides have lengths 1, 1 and $\sqrt{2}$.

What is the radius of the semicircle?

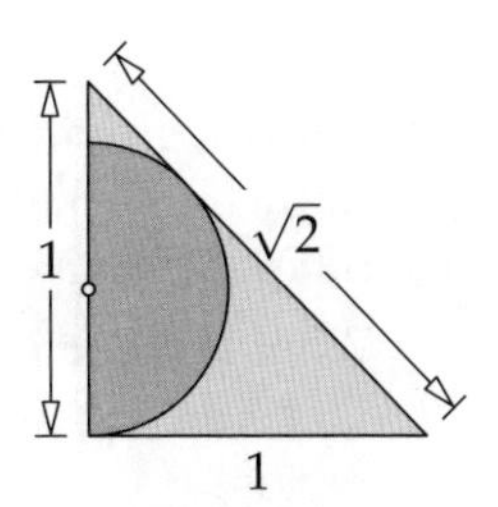

23 **19.** In the diagram, the circle and the two semicircles have radius 1.

What is the length of the perimeter of the square?

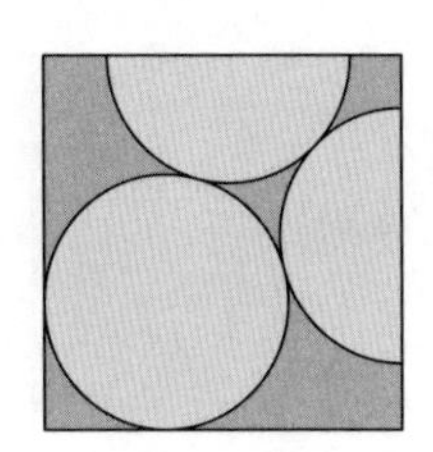

23 **20.** Circles with radii r and R (where $r < R$) touch each other and also touch two perpendicular lines as shown alongside.

What is the value of $\frac{R}{r}$?

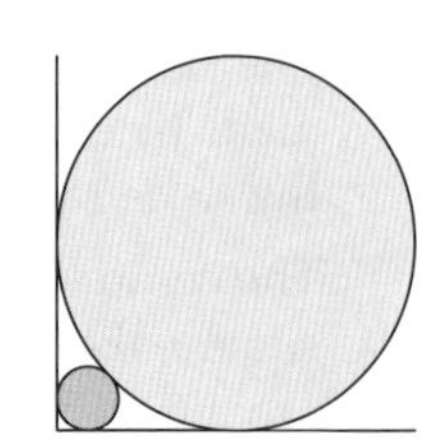

24 **21.** The diagram shows a square $PQRS$. The arc QS is a quarter-circle centre P. The point U is the midpoint of QR and the point T lies on RS. The line TU is a tangent to the arc QS.

What is the ratio $UR : RT$, numerically?

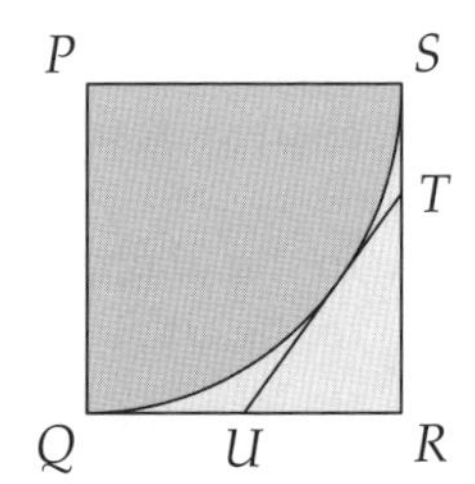

24 **22.** Three circles and the straight lines PQ and QR touch as shown alongside.

The distance between the centres of the smallest and the biggest circles is 16 times the radius of the smallest circle.

What is the size of $\angle PQR$?

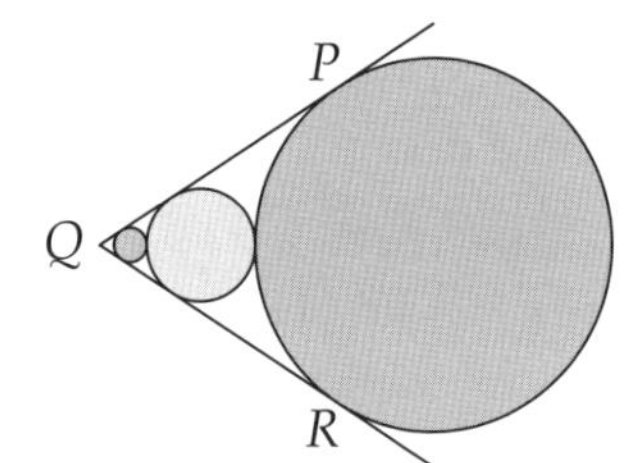

24 **23.** The diagram shows two circles of radius 105 that are tangent to each other and to a circle of radius 14.

What is the radius of the largest circle that can be placed in the shaded region?

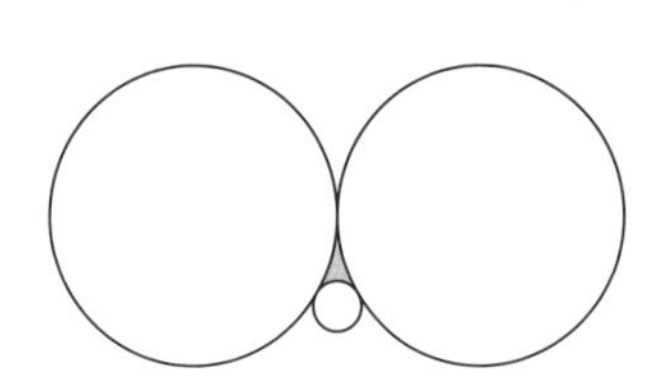

24 **24.** The diagram shows a right-angled isosceles triangle AOB in a quadrant of a circle of radius 1.

The largest possible circle in the minor segment cut off by the chord AB has radius r. The inscribed circle of the triangle AOB has radius R.

What is the value of $\frac{R}{r}$?

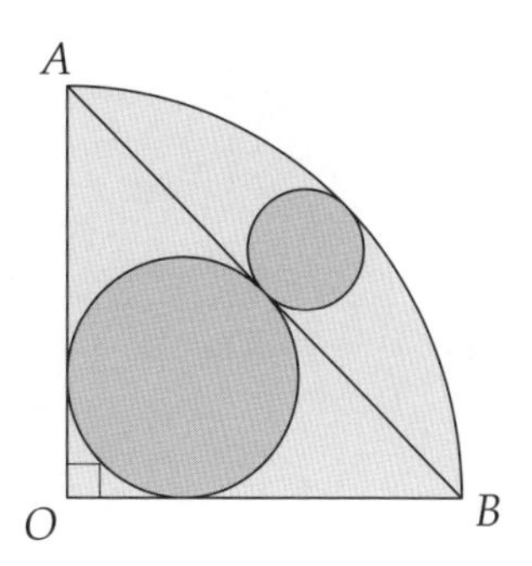

25 **25.** The diagram shows two parallel lines ℓ_1 and ℓ_2. Line ℓ_1 is a tangent to circles C_1 and C_2, line ℓ_2 is a tangent to circles C_2 and C_3, and the three circles touch as shown alongside.

Circles C_1 and C_2 have radius r and s respectively.

What is the radius of circle C_3 in terms of r and s?

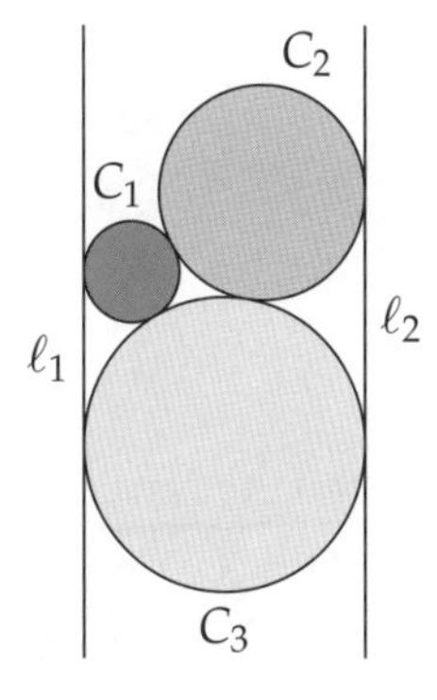

More counting

Exercise 22

16

1. Fnargs are either red or blue and have two, three or four heads.

   A group of six Fnargs consisting of one of each possible form is made to line up such that no immediate neighbours are the same colour nor have the same number of heads.

   How many ways are there of lining them up from left to right?

16

2. A hockey team consists of one goalkeeper, four defenders, four midfielders and two forwards. There are four substitutes: one goalkeeper, one defender, one midfielder and one forward.

   A substitute may only replace a player of the same category, such as midfielder for midfielder. A maximum of three substitutes may be used.

   There are still eleven players on the pitch at the end of the game.

   How many different teams could finish the game?

17

3. Aaron has to choose a three-digit code for his bicycle lock.

   The digits can be chosen from 1 to 9. To help him remember them, Aaron chooses three different digits in increasing order, such as 278.

   How many such codes can be chosen?

18 **4.** The year 1789 (when the French Revolution started) has exactly three adjacent digits (7, 8 and 9) that are consecutive integers in increasing order.

How many years between 1000 and 9999 have this property?

19 **5.** The 16 small squares shown in the diagram alongside each has sides of length 1.

How many pairs of vertices are there in the diagram whose distance apart is an integer?

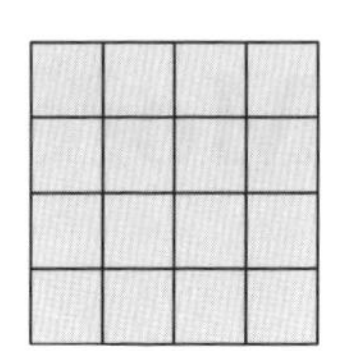

19 **6.** The digits 2, 3, 4, 5, 6, 7, 8 are to be placed, one per square, in the diagram shown so that the sum of the four digits in the row across equals 21 and the sum of the four digits in the column down also equals 21.

In how many different ways can this be done?

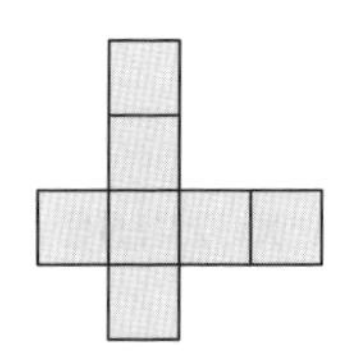

21 **7.** A bracelet is to be made by threading four identical red beads and four identical yellow beads onto a hoop.

How many different bracelets can be made?

21 **8.** A postman's sack contains five letters, one each for the five houses in Cayley Close. Mischievously, he posts one letter through each door without looking to see if it is the correct address.

In how many different ways could he do this so that exactly two of the five houses receive the correct letters?

22 **9.** Suppose that you have an unlimited supply of 50p, £1 and £2 coins.

In how many different ways can you make a sum of £100?

25 **10.** Challengeborough's underground train network consists of six lines p, q, r, s, t and u, as shown alongside.

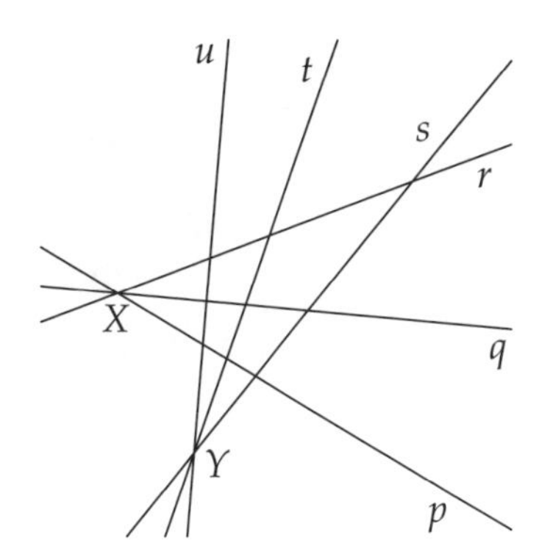

Wherever two lines meet there is a station that enables passengers to change lines. On each line, each train stops at every station.

Jessica wants to travel from station X to station Y.

She does not want to use any line more than once, nor return to station X after leaving it, nor leave station Y having reached it.

How many different routes, satisfying these conditions, can she choose?

25 **11.** All the digits of a positive integer are different, the first digit is not zero, and the sum of the digits is 36.

There are $N \times 7!$ such integers. What is the value of N?

25 **12.** Let N be a positive integer less than 10^{2002}. When the digit 1 is placed after the units digit of N, the number formed is three times the number formed when the digit 1 is placed in front of the first digit of N.

How many different values of N are there?

More in three dimensions

Exercise 23

16 **1.** A traffic cone is painted with red and white bands of paint as shown alongside.

The ratio of the 'slant lengths' of the bands is equal to 1 : 3 : 2, as indicated.

What, numerically, is the ratio of the area painted white to the area painted red?

[The area of the curved surface *of a cone of radius r and slant length ℓ is equal to $2\pi r\ell$.]*

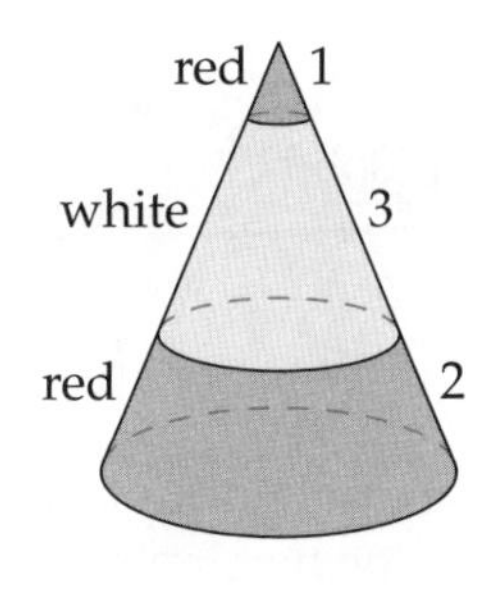

17 **2.** A solid cube is divided into two pieces by a single rectangular cut. As a result, the total surface area increases by a fraction f of the surface area of the original cube.

What is the greatest possible value of f?

18 **3.** Beatrix decorates the faces of a cube, whose edges have length 2.

For each face, she either leaves it blank, or draws a single straight line on it. Every line drawn joins the midpoints of two edges, either opposite or adjacent, as shown in the two diagrams alongside.

What is the length of the longest unbroken line that Beatrix can draw on the cube?

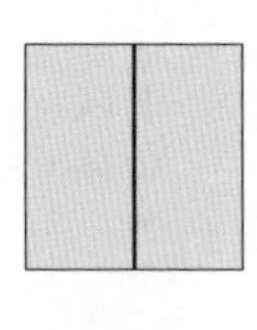

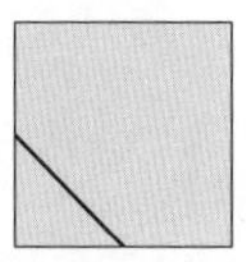

18 **4.** A solid cube with edges of length 2 cm is cut into two triangular prisms by a plane passing through four vertices, as shown alongside.

What is the total surface area of these two prisms?

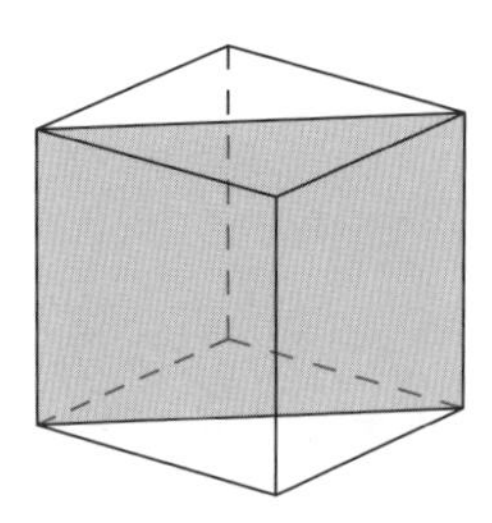

18 **5.** A cube exactly fits inside a sphere and another sphere exactly fits inside this cube.

What, numerically, is the ratio of the volume of the smaller sphere to the volume of the larger sphere?

18 **6.** A cylindrical hole of radius r and length $4r$ is bored symmetrically through a solid cylinder of radius $2r$ and length $4r$.

What is the total surface area of the resulting solid?

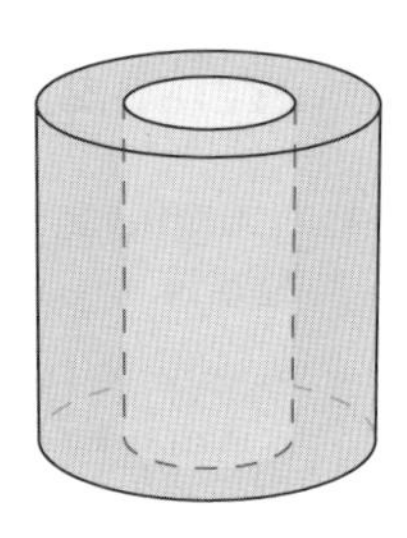

19 **7.** A sculpture consists of a row of 2 metre rods each placed with one end resting on horizontal ground and the other end resting against a vertical wall.

The diagram shows how the rods BT, CU, DV, ... appear from above.

The bases of the rods B, C, D, ... lie on a straight line on the ground at 45° to the wall.

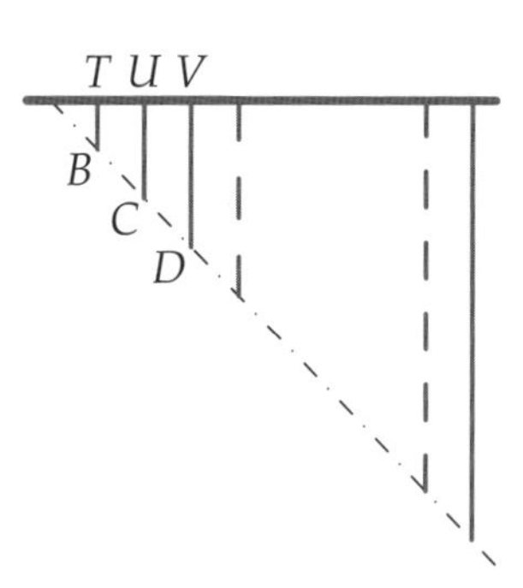

The top ends of the rods T, U, V, ... lie on part of a curve on the wall. What curve is it?

19 **8.** The point P is a vertex of a cuboid and Q, R and S are three points on the edges, as shown alongside.

The lengths of PQ, PR and PS are 2 cm, 2 cm and 1 cm respectively.

What is the area of triangle QRS?

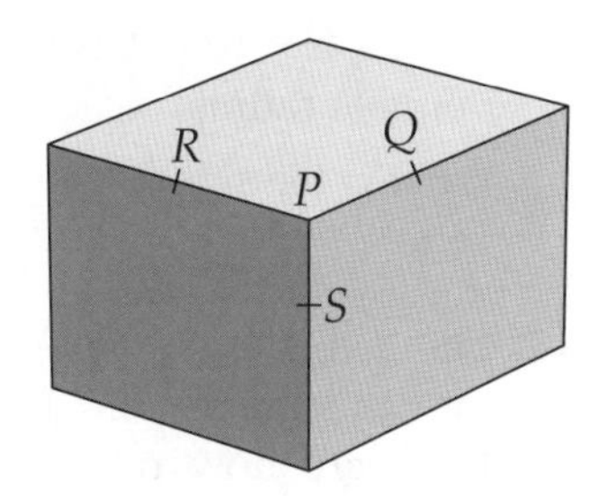

19 **9.** One end of an egg-timer is a hemisphere of radius r; the other end is a cone of radius r and height r. Both ends are attached to cylinders of radius r.

When the hemisphere is at the bottom, the sand in the egg-timer comes to a height $2r$ above the lowest point, as shown alongside.

What is the corresponding height of the sand when the egg-timer has been turned over and all the sand has been allowed to run through to the other end?

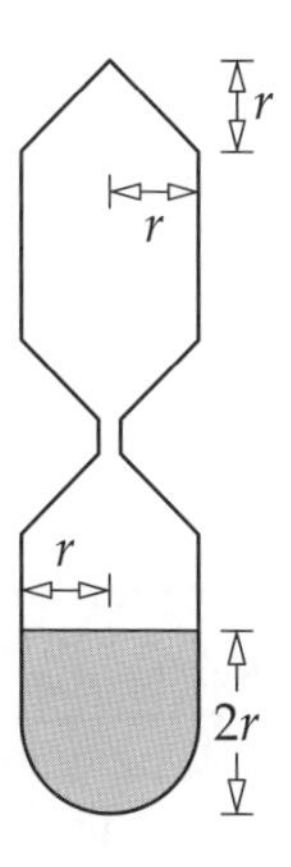

20 **10.** A cube is inscribed in a sphere of diameter 1 m.

What is the surface area of the cube?

21 **11.** A *frustum of a cone* is the solid obtained by slicing a right circular cone perpendicular to its axis and removing the small cone above the slice. This leaves a shape with two circular faces and a curved surface, as shown alongside.

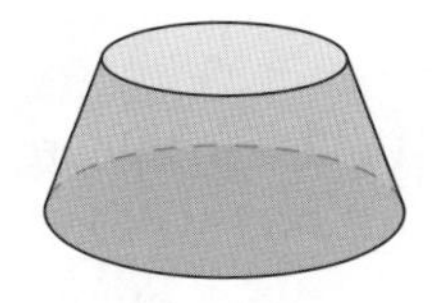

The original cone has base radius 6 cm and height 8 cm, and the curved surface area of the frustum is equal to sum of the areas of the two circles.

What is the height of the frustum?

[The area of the curved surface *of a cone of radius r and slant length ℓ is equal to $2\pi r\ell$.]*

23 **12.** A $22 \times 2 \times 10$ cuboid is contained within a sphere of the smallest possible radius.

What is the side-length of the largest cube that will fit inside the same sphere?

23 **13.** The net shown alongside is folded into an icosahedron. The unnumbered faces are now numbered so that at each vertex of the icosahedron all the numbers 1 to 5 appear.

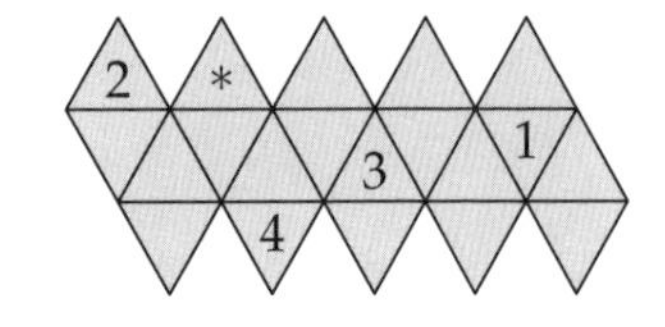

What number goes on the face with an asterisk?

23 **14.** The sum of the lengths of the 12 edges of a cuboid is x cm. The distance from one vertex of the cuboid to the furthest vertex is y cm.

What is the total surface area of the cuboid in terms of x and y, in cm^2?

23 **15.** The diagram shows a cube $XYZTABCD$.

The cube is cut into four pieces by cutting along the two planes $BCTX$ and $BDTY$.

What fraction of the volume of the cube is occupied by the piece containing vertex A?

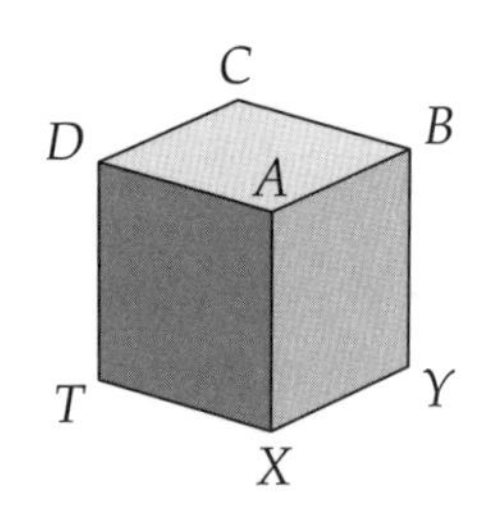

24 **16.** Three spheres of radius 1 are placed inside a hollow cylinder of height 2. The cylinder is just large enough to surround the spheres.

What, numerically, is the ratio of the internal volume of the cylinder to the volume occupied by the spheres?

24 **17.** A paperweight is made from a $2 \times 2 \times 2$ glass cube by first cutting off the eight tetrahedral corners that touch at the midpoints of the edges of the cube. The remaining inner core of the cube is discarded and replaced by a sphere. The eight corner pieces are now stuck onto the sphere so that they have the same positions relative to each other as they did originally, as shown alongside.

What is the diameter of the sphere?

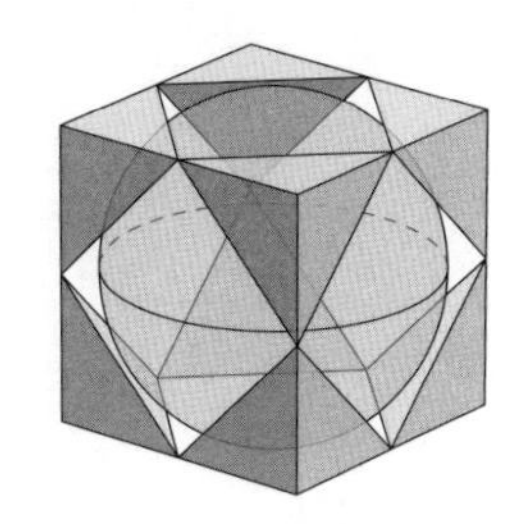

24 **18.** A solid red plastic $1 \times 1 \times 1$ cube is painted white on its outside.

The cube is cut by a plane passing through the midpoints of various edges, as shown alongside.

What is the *total* red area exposed by the cut?

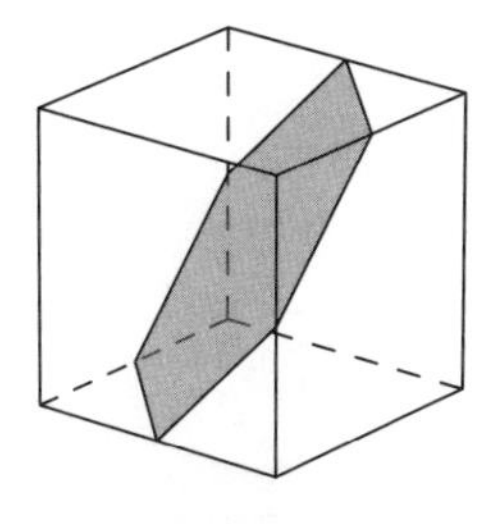

25 **19.** A solid sculpture consists of a $4 \times 4 \times 4$ cube with a $3 \times 3 \times 3$ cube sticking out, as shown alongside. Three vertices of the smaller cube lie on edges of the larger cube, the same distance along each.

What is the total volume of the sculpture?

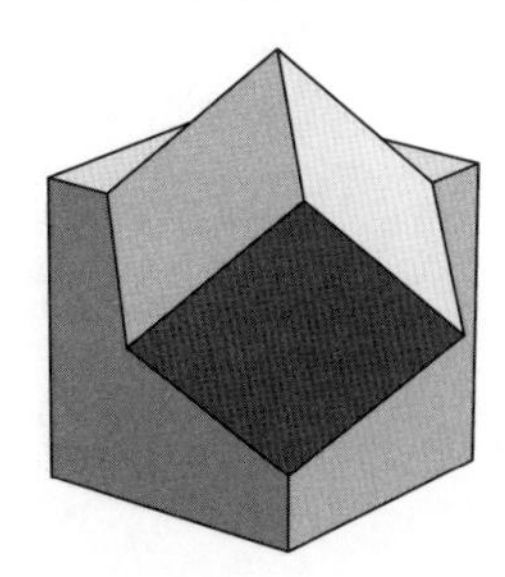

25 **20.** A right circular cone has apex angle 2α. A sphere is inscribed in the cone, touching the base and the curved surface, as shown alongside.

What fraction of the cone is occupied by the sphere?

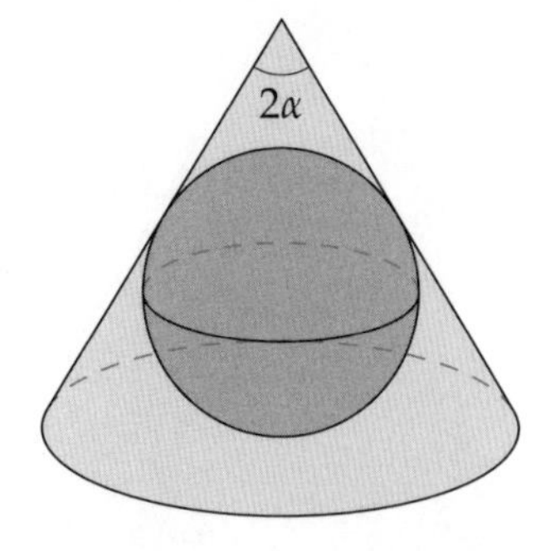

Miscellany 2

Exercise 24

16 **1.** When rounded to 3 significant figures, the number x is equal to 1000.

What is the largest range of possible values of x?

17 **2.** An oil tanker is 100 km due north of a cruise liner.

The tanker sails SE at a speed of 20 kilometres per hour and the liner sails NW at a speed of 10 kilometres per hour.

During the subsequent motion what is the shortest distance between the two ships?

17 **3.** Andy and his younger cousin Alice both have their birthdays on the same day. Remarkably, on their birthday in 2008, Andy was the same age as the sum of the digits of the year of his birth and the same was true of Alice.

How many years older than Alice is Andy?

17 **4.** The diagram shows a square $PQRS$ with sides of length 4 cm, and a square $PTUV$ with sides of length 2 cm.

What is the length of RV?

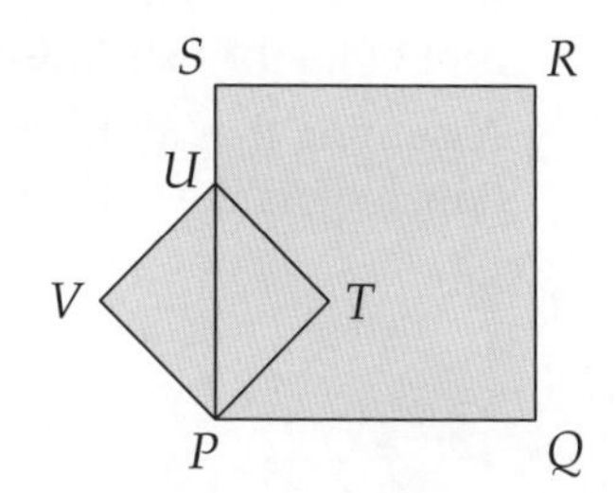

17 **5.** A newspaper reported the results of a survey as follows.

> On average, children in the UK get £3.10 pocket money a week.
> Scottish parents are the most generous, giving £5.35 a week.

Scottish children made up 10% of the survey.

What was the average pocket money per week in the rest of the UK?

18 **6.** The circumference of a circle with radius 1 is divided into four equal arcs. Two of the arcs are 'turned over' as shown alongside.

What is the area of the shaded region?

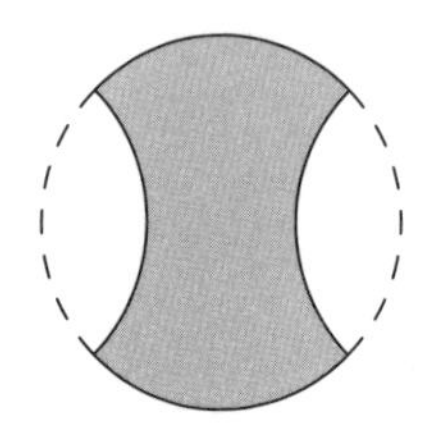

19 **7.** Let S be a set of five different positive integers, the largest of which is m. It is impossible to construct a quadrilateral with non-zero area with sides whose lengths are all distinct elements of S.

What is the smallest possible value of m?

20 **8.** Any positive number a is equal to $\lfloor a \rfloor + \{a\}$, where $\lfloor a \rfloor$ is the *integer part* of a and $\{a\}$ is the *fractional part* of a.

Suppose that x, y and z are positive, and satisfy the equations

$$\begin{aligned} x + \lfloor y \rfloor + \{z\} &= 4.2, \\ y + \lfloor z \rfloor + \{x\} &= 3.6 \\ \text{and} \quad z + \lfloor x \rfloor + \{y\} &= 2.0. \end{aligned}$$

What is the value of $\{y\}$?

20 **9.** It takes two weeks to clean the 3312 panes of glass in the $6000\,\mathrm{m}^2$ glass roof of the British Museum, a task performed once every two years.

Assuming that all the panes are equilateral triangles of the same size, how long is the side of each pane, to the nearest metre?

20 **10.**

$$1, 2, 2, 3, 3, 3, 4, 4, 4, 4, 5, \ldots$$

The sequence above consists of n copies of the integer n, with the terms being in increasing order.

What is the 1999th term of the sequence?

20 **11.** Denote the lengths of the three altitudes of a triangle by h_1, h_2 and h_3. Which of the following five s never occurs as the ratio $h_1 : h_2 : h_3$?

$$2:3:4 \qquad 2:3:5 \qquad 2:4:5 \qquad 3:4:5 \qquad 3:4:6$$

[In a triangle, an altitude *is the perpendicular from a vertex to the opposite side.]*

21 **12.** The fraction $\dfrac{2008}{1998}$ may be written in the form

$$a + \cfrac{1}{b + \cfrac{1}{c + \cfrac{1}{d}}},$$

where a, b, c and d are positive integers.

What is the value of d?

21 **13.** A toy pool table is 6 feet long and 3 feet wide. It has pockets at each of the four vertices P, Q, R and S. When a ball hits a side of the table, it bounces off the side at the same angle as it hit that side.

A ball, initially 1 foot to the left of pocket P, is hit from the side SP towards the side PQ. The ball lands in pocket S after two bounces, as shown alongside.

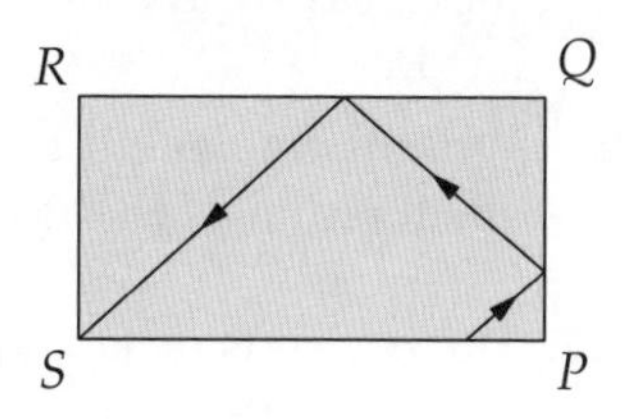

How many feet from P does the ball hit side PQ?

21 **14.** The diagram shows a right-angled isosceles triangle PQR in which $\angle PQR = 90°$ and $PQ = QR$.

The line through Q that divides the angle PQR in the $1:2$ meets PR at S.

What is the ratio $RS : SP$, numerically?

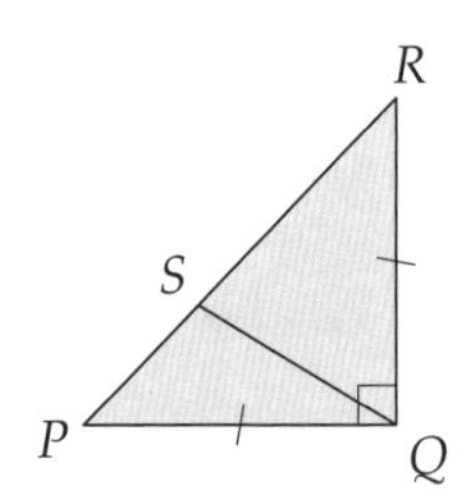

21 **15.** The expression $3 \boxplus 7 \to 4$ is a short way of writing the statement

> It is possible to fit a polygon with 3 sides and a polygon with 7 sides together (without overlap) to make a polygon with 4 sides.

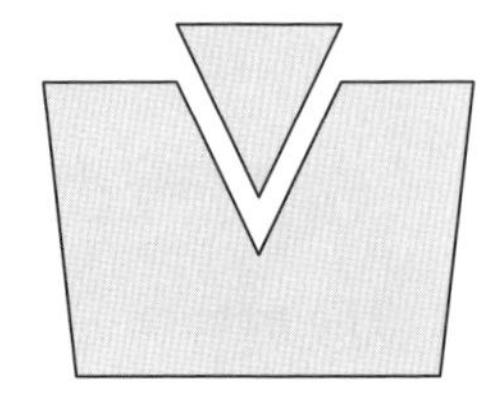

This statement is correct (as shown in the diagram).

Which one of the following represents a statement that is *not* correct?

$3 \boxplus 5 \to 4$ $\quad$ $3 \boxplus 6 \to 4$ $\quad$ $3 \boxplus 8 \to 4$ $\quad$ $4 \boxplus 6 \to 4$ $\quad$ $4 \boxplus 8 \to 4$

21 **16.** A square is divided into nine rectangles by four lines parallel to the sides, as shown alongside.

The areas of three of the small rectangles are indicated. The central small rectangle is a square.

What is the length of the perimeter of the small rectangle in the bottom left corner?

1		3
		6

22 **17.** Three friends make the following statements.

> Ben says "Exactly one of Dan and Cam is telling the truth."
> Dan says "Exactly one of Ben and Cam is telling the truth."
> Cam says "Neither Ben nor Dan is telling the truth."

Which of the three friends is lying?

22 **18.** A pentagon is made by attaching an equilateral triangle to a square with the same side-length.

Four such pentagons are placed inside a rectangle, as shown alongside.

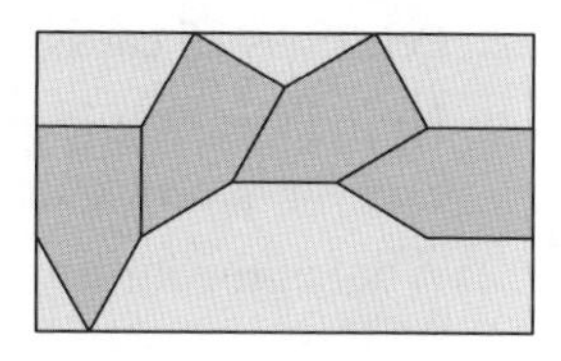

What, numerically, is the ratio of the width of the rectangle to its height?

22 **19.** In the trapezium shown alongside, XY is parallel to two sides and passes through the point of intersection of the diagonals.

What is the length of XY?

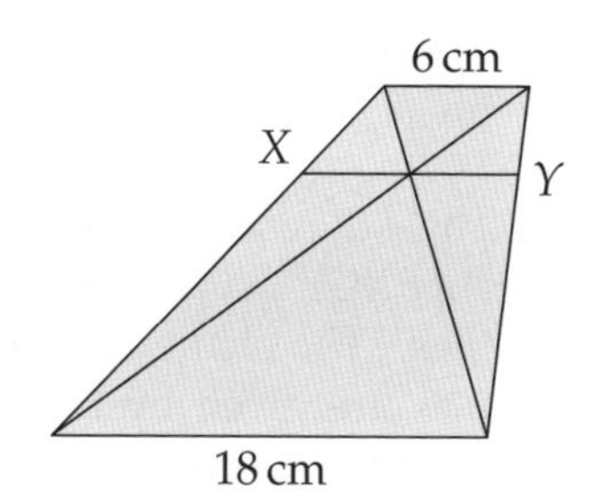

22 **20.** Suppose that the value of y is given by the fraction

$$y = \frac{x}{x + \dfrac{x}{x+y}}.$$

For which one of the following values of x is y not a real number?

$-6 \quad -3 \quad 1 \quad 3 \quad 6$

23 **21.** The diagram shows an equilateral triangle inscribed in a circle. Another equilateral triangle is drawn in one of the segments so that the final diagram has a line of symmetry.

What, numerically, is the ratio of the length of a side of the bigger triangle to the length of a side of the smaller triangle?

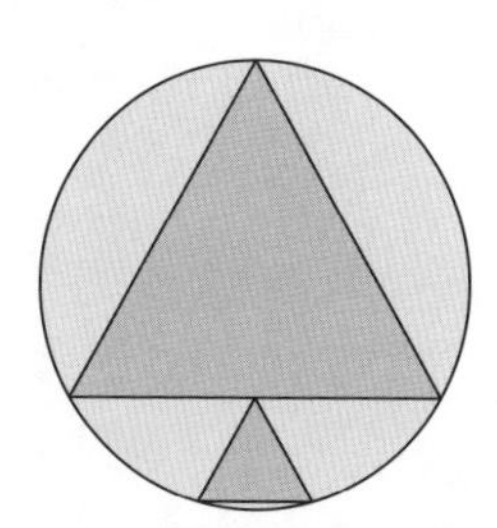

24 **22.** Peter has 25 cards, each printed with a different integer from 1 to 25.

He wishes to place N cards in a single row so that the integers on every adjacent pair of cards have a prime factor in common.

What is the largest value of N for which this is possible?

24 **23.** The function f is defined by $f(n+3) = \dfrac{f(n)-1}{f(n)+1}$ for all positive integers n.

Suppose that $f(2002)$ is non-zero.

What is the value of $f(2002) \times f(2008)$?

24 **24.** The diagram shows a hexagon $AZBXCY$ made from four congruent tiles. The shape and position of the tiles are given by triangle ABC and the three reflections of triangle ABC in the lines determined by its sides.

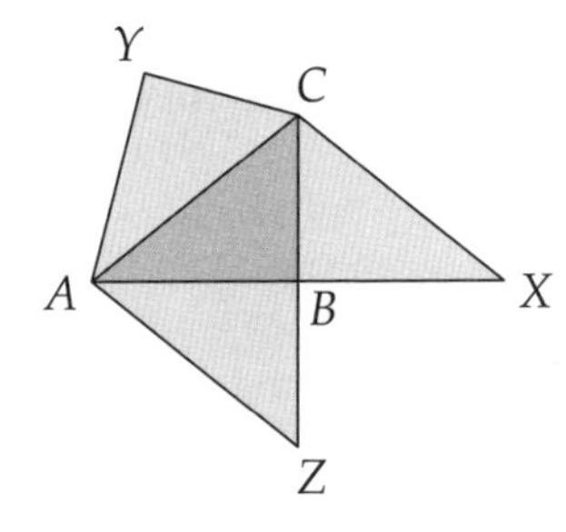

For example, ABZ is the image of ABC when reflected in the line determined by AB.

Another polygon is made from *five* tiles. The shape and position of these tiles are determined by a quadrilateral and the four non-overlapping reflections of that quadrilateral in the lines determined by its sides.

What is the smallest possible number of sides of the resulting polygon?

25 **25.** Figure 1 shows a tile that is a trapezium.

Several copies of the tile are placed together to form a symmetrical pattern, part of which is shown in Figure 2. The outer border of the complete pattern is a regular 'star polygon' (figure 3 shows an example of a regular 'star polygon').

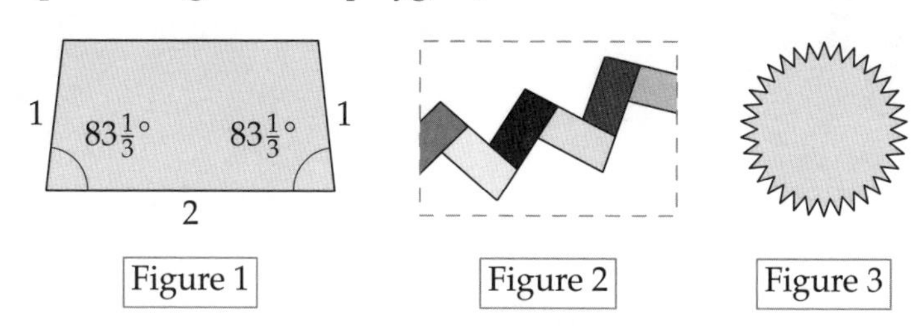

Figure 1 Figure 2 Figure 3

How many tiles are there in the complete pattern?

25 **26.** Every digit of the positive integer X is 1. In other words, X is of the form $1 \ldots 11$.

The integer Y is equal to $pX^2 + qX + r$, where p, q and r are fixed integer coefficients and $p > 0$. Every digit of Y is also 1, irrespective of the number of digits of X.

Which of the following is a possible value of q?

$-1 \quad 0 \quad 1 \quad 2 \quad 3$

25 **27.**

$$\frac{1}{2}+\frac{1}{4}+\frac{2}{8}+\frac{3}{16}+\frac{5}{32}+\frac{8}{64}+\frac{13}{128}+\frac{21}{256}+\frac{34}{512}+\cdots$$

Each term of the above series is a fraction with the next Fibonacci number as numerator and the next power of two as denominator. The series is convergent

What is the sum to infinity of the series?.

More areas

Exercise 25

16 **1.** The diagram shows a rectangle measuring 6×12 and a circle.

The two shorter sides of the rectangle are tangents to the circle.

The circle and rectangle have the same centre.

What is the area of the shaded region, which lies inside both the rectangle and the circle?

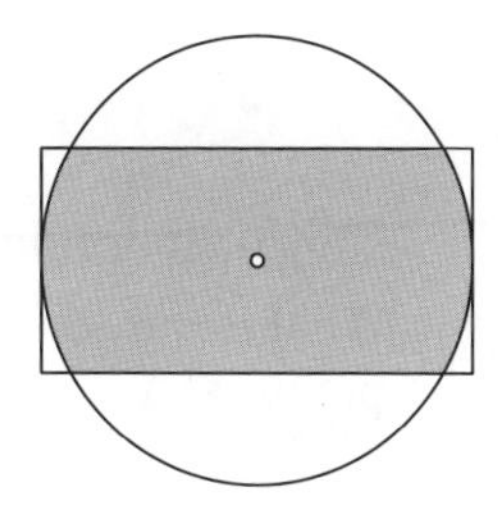

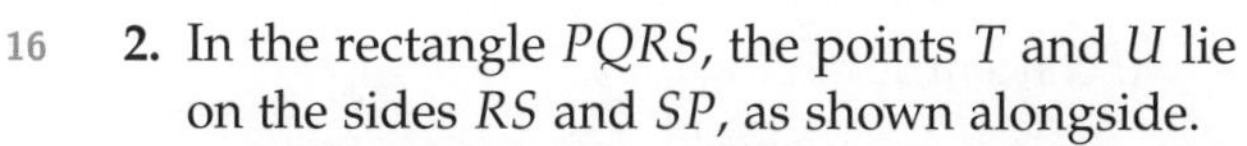

16 **2.** In the rectangle $PQRS$, the points T and U lie on the sides RS and SP, as shown alongside.

The area of triangle QRT is $\frac{1}{5}$ of the area of $PQRS$, and the area of triangle TSU is $\frac{1}{8}$ of the area of $PQRS$.

What fraction of the area of rectangle $PQRS$ is the area of triangle QTU?

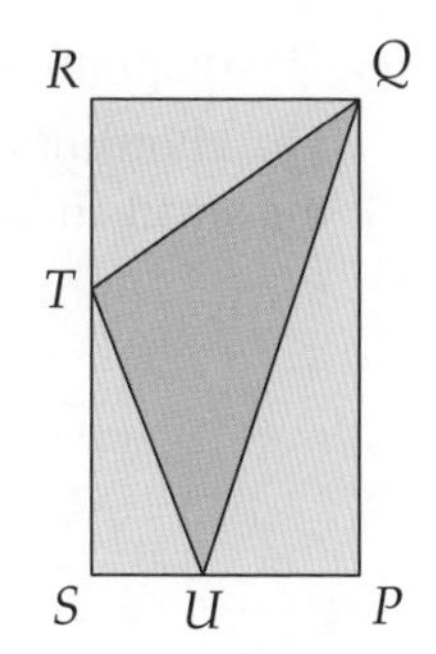

17 **3.** The two triangles shown below have equal areas and the four marked lengths are equal.

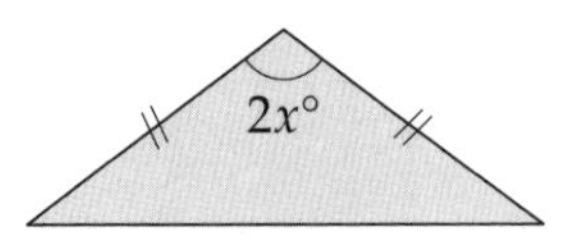

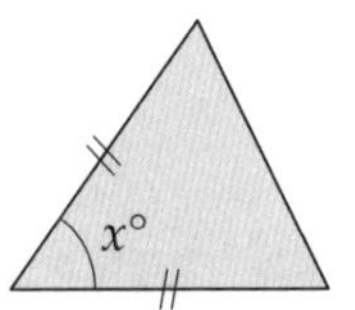

What is the value of x?

17 **4.** The diagram shows eight identical regular octagons placed edge-to-edge in a ring. A symmetrical star shape is formed by the internal edges. Each octagon has sides of length 1.

What is the area of the star?

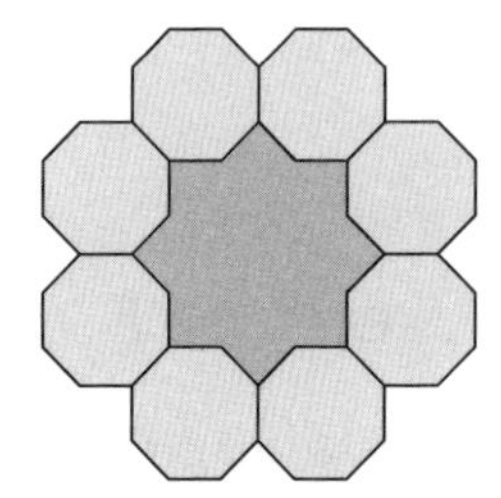

18 **5.** The shaded square of the dot lattice shown alongside has area 1.

What is the area of the circle through the points X, Y and Z?

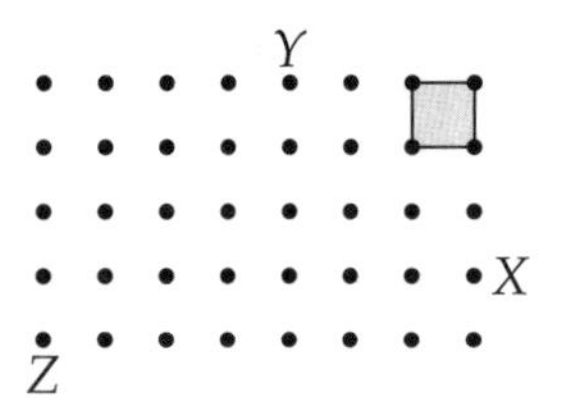

18 **6.** The diagram shows two concentric circles.

The chord of the large circle is a tangent to the small circle and has length $2p$.

What is the area of the shaded region?

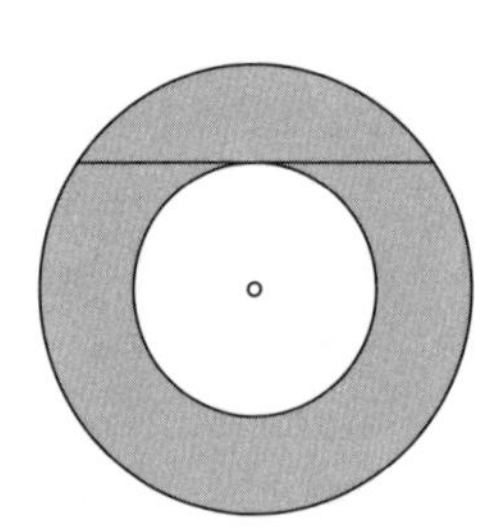

19 **7.** The diagram shows a small regular *octagram* (a 'star' with eight vertices) surrounded by eight squares (dark grey) and eight kites (light grey) to make a large regular octagram. Each square has area 1.

What is the area of one of the light grey kites?

19 **8.** Each diagram shows a shaded rhombus inside a square with sides of length 6.

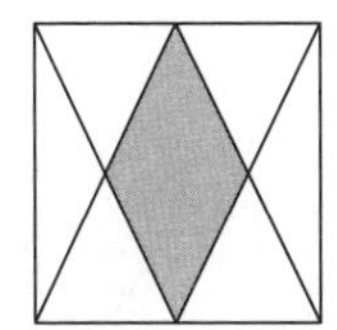

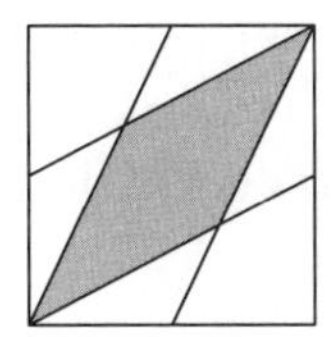

Each rhombus is formed by joining vertices of the square to midpoints of the sides of the square.

What is the difference between the shaded areas?

20 **9.** Michael was walking in Marrakesh when he saw a tiling formed by tessellating a square tile, as shown below.

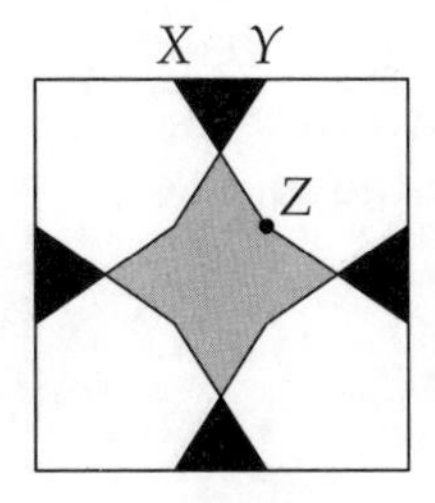

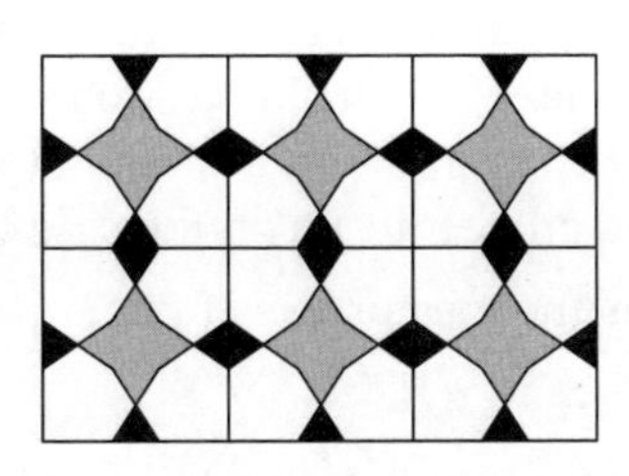

The tile has four lines of symmetry and the length of each side is 8 cm. The length XY is 2 cm. The point Z is such that XZ is a straight line and YZ is parallel to two sides of the square.

What is the area the central grey octagon?

20 **10.** A square ink pad has sides of length 1 cm. It is covered in black ink and carefully placed in the middle of a piece of white paper.

The pad is then rotated through $180°$ about one of its corners so that all of the pad remains in contact with the paper throughout the turn.

The pad is then removed from the paper.

What area of the paper is now black?

20 **11.** The diagram shows four semicircles symmetrically placed between two circles.

The inner circle has area 4 and each semicircle has area 18.

What is the area of the outer circle?

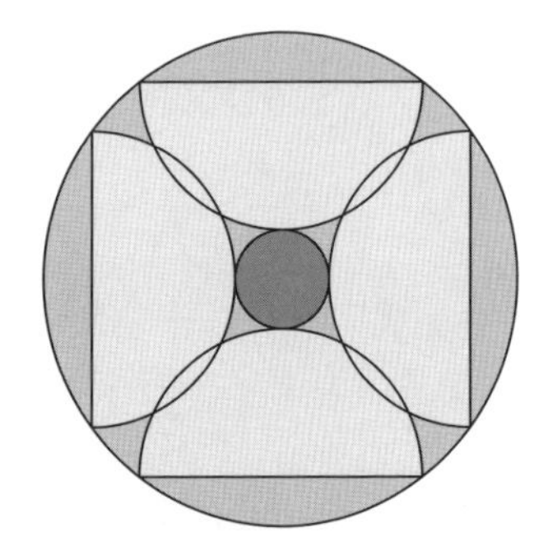

20 **12.** A triangle is cut from the corner of a rectangle. The resulting pentagon has sides of length 8, 10, 13, 15 and 20, though not necessarily in that order.

What is the area of the pentagon?

21 **13.** The diagram shows a regular hexagon, with sides of length 1, inside a square. Two vertices of the hexagon lie on a diagonal of the square and the other four lie on the sides.

What is the area of the square?

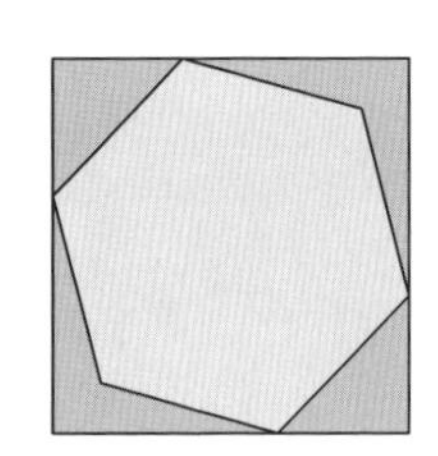

21 **14.** In the diagram, the outer equilateral triangle has area 1, and the points P, Q and R are a quarter of the way along the sides, as shown alongside.

What is the area of the equilateral triangle PQR?

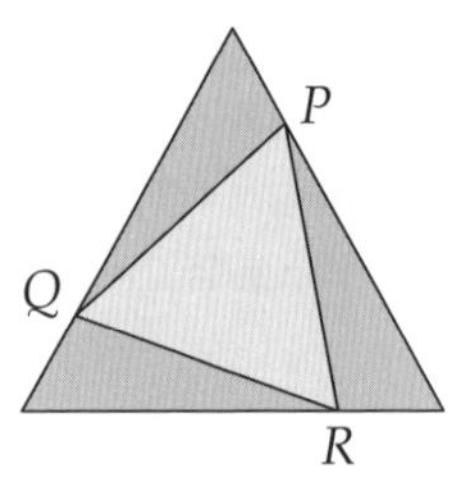

22 **15.** A semicircle of radius r is drawn with centre V and diameter UW.

The straight line UW is then extended to the point X, so that UW and WX are of equal length.

An arc YU of the circle with centre X and radius $4r$ is then drawn so that the line XY is a tangent to the semicircle at Z, as shown below.

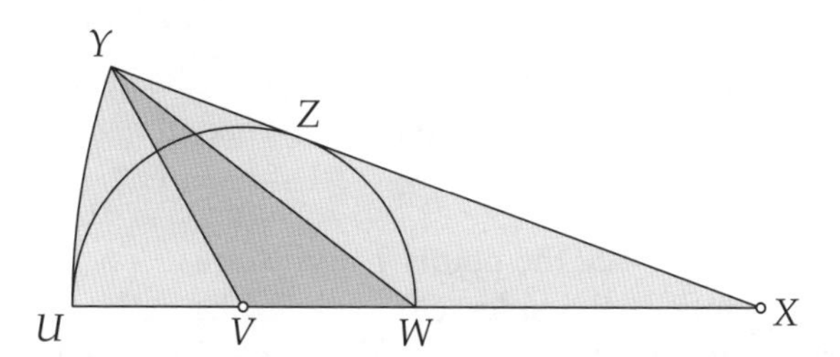

What is the area of triangle YVW in terms of r?

22 **16.** In parallelogram $EFGH$, the points M and N are the midpoints of sides GH and FG respectively.

The area of triangle ENM is $12\,\text{cm}^2$.

What is the area of the parallelogram $EFGH$?

22 **17.** In triangle PQR, the points S and T are the midpoints of RP and PQ respectively. The line QS is perpendicular to RT. Also, $QS = 12$ and $RT = 8$.

What is the area of triangle PQR?

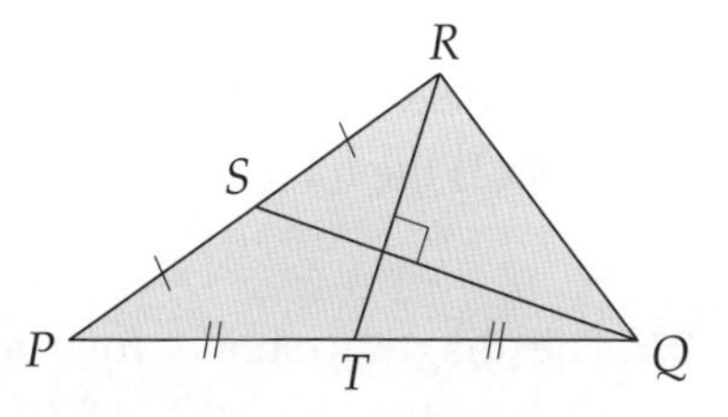

22 **18.** In the following diagrams, the area of each large semicircle is 2. The circles in the diagram on the right have the same radius.

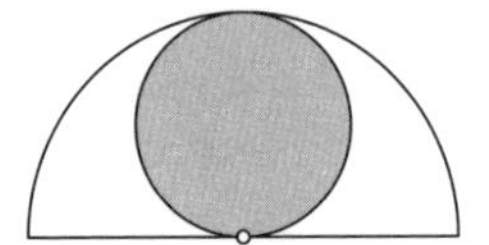

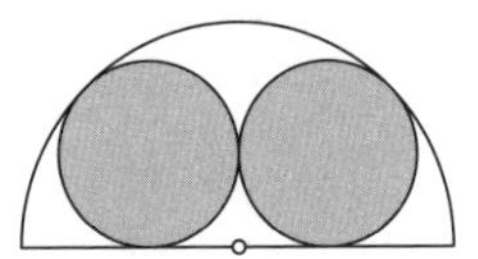

What is the difference between the area of the shaded region in the diagram on the left and the area of the shaded region in the diagram on the right?

23 **19.** In the square $PQRS$, the points T and U are the midpoints of the sides QR and RS, as shown alongside. The diagonal QS cuts PT and PU at W and V respectively.

What fraction of the area of the square $PQRS$ is the area of the pentagon $RUVWT$?

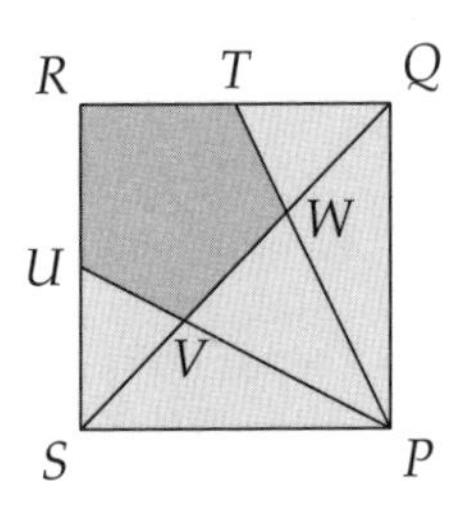

23 **20.** The diagram shows two different semicircles inside a square with sides of length 2. The common centre of the semicircles lies on a diagonal of the square.

What is the total shaded area?

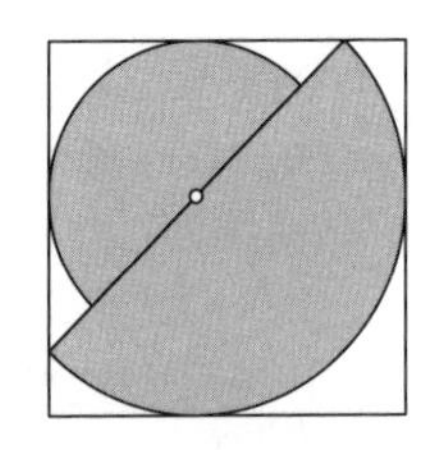

23 **21.** The diagram shows four touching circles, each of which also touches the sides of an equilateral triangle with sides of length 3.

What is the area of the shaded region?

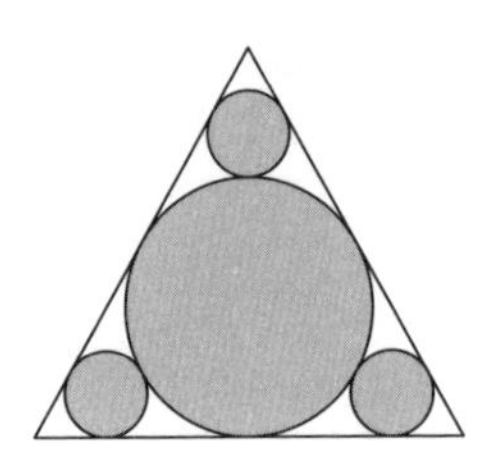

23 **22.** A square $XABC$ with sides of length 1 is drawn inside a circle with diameter XY of length 2. The point A lies on the circumference of the circle.

Another square $YDBE$ is drawn.

What is the area of square $YDBE$?

23 **23.** A circle is inscribed in an equilateral triangle. Small circles are then inscribed in each corner so that each of them touches two sides of the triangle and the large circle, as shown alongside.

What, numerically, is the ratio of the area of a small circle to that of the large circle?

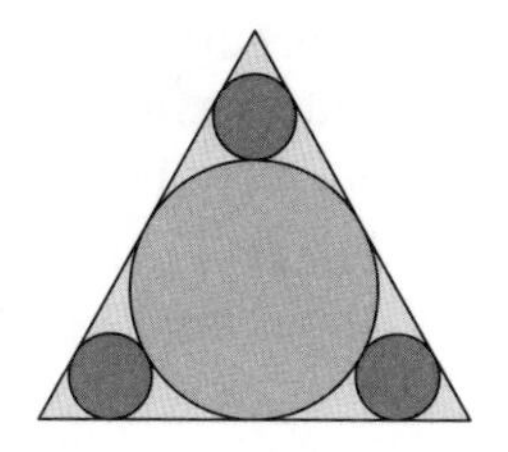

24 **24.** Figure 1 shows a shape that tiles the plane, as shown in Figure 2.

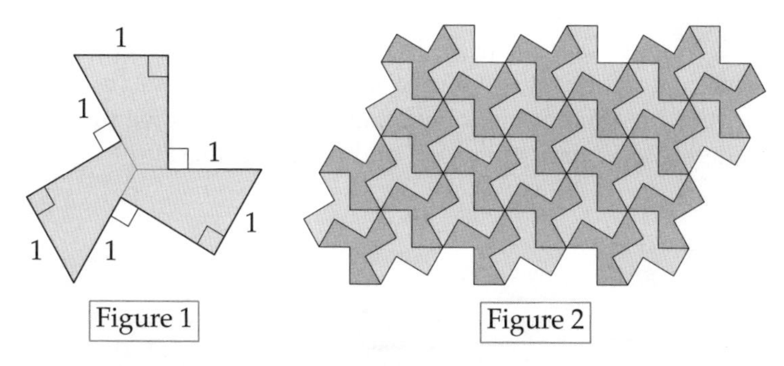

Figure 1 Figure 2

The tile has nine sides, six of which have length 1, and may be divided into three congruent quadrilaterals as shown in Figure 1.

What is the area of the tile?

24 **25.** A figure in the shape of a cross is made from five 1×1 squares, as shown alongside.

The cross is inscribed in a large square whose sides are parallel to the dashed square, formed by four of the vertices of the cross.

What is the area of the large outer square?

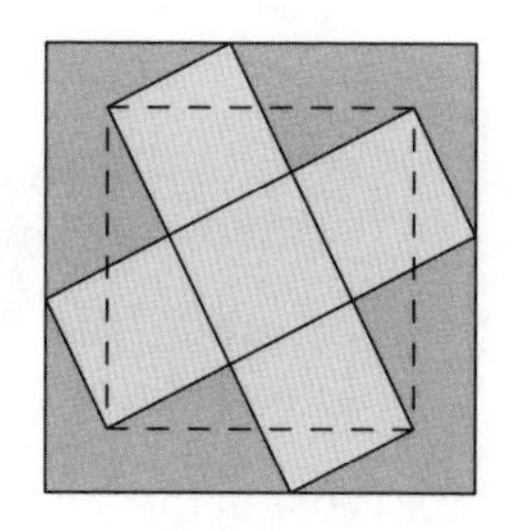

24 **26.** The curvy shape ABC in the diagram is called a *Reuleaux triangle* after the French engineer Franz Reuleaux (1829–1905).

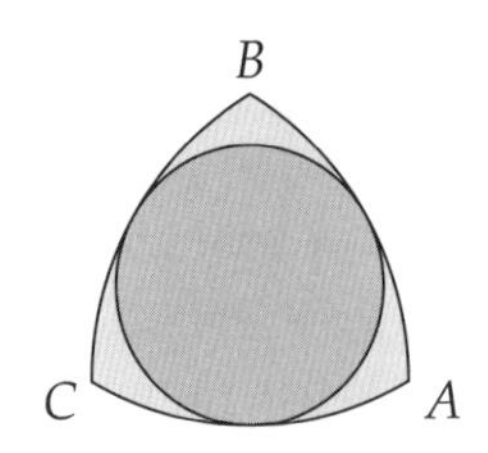

The perimeter of the shape consists of three equal arcs AB, BC and CA, each with the same radius and centred at the opposite vertex. In the Reuleaux triangle shown alongside, each arc has radius 3 cm.

What is the area of the inscribed circle?

25 **27.** The diagram shows a triangle shaded black, with a square drawn on each of its sides. Three new triangles (shaded grey) are then formed by drawing three straight lines that join vertices of the squares. A new square is now drawn on each of these three lines.

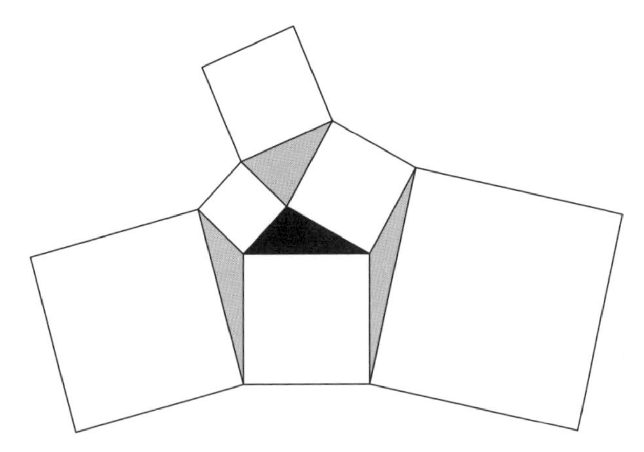

The sum of the areas of the original three squares is A_1, and the sum of the areas of the three new squares is A_2.

What is the value of $\frac{A_2}{A_1}$?

25 **28.** A company logo has a centrally-symmetric white cross with arms of width $\sqrt{2}$ on a shaded circle.

The shaded corner pieces have sides of length 1 as indicated.

What is the total area of the corners?

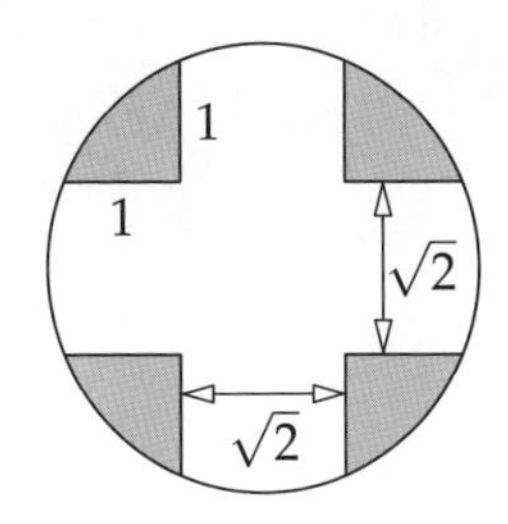

Powers and square roots

Exercise 26

16 **1.** For what value of k is $\sqrt{2016} + \sqrt{56}$ equal to 14^k?

17 **2.** Which of the following five expressions is equal to $\sqrt{9^{16x^2}}$ for all values of x?

3^{4x}	3^{4x^2}	3^{8x^2}	9^{4x}	9^{8x^2}

18 **3.** Which of the following five numbers is equal to

$$2^{2003} - 2^{2002} - 2^{2001} - 2^{2000}?$$

-2^{2002}	0	2^{-4000}	64	2^{2000}

18 **4.** When n is equal to 81, what is the value of $\dfrac{n^{20}}{3^n}$?

20 **5.** Positive integers m and n satisfy the equation $\sqrt{m} - \sqrt{11} = \sqrt{n}$. What is the maximum possible value of $\dfrac{m}{n}$?

21 **6.** Which of the following five numbers does not have a square root in the form $m + n\sqrt{2}$, where m and n are positive integers?

$17 + 12\sqrt{2}$ $\quad 22 + 12\sqrt{2}$ $\quad 38 + 12\sqrt{2}$ $\quad 54 + 12\sqrt{2}$
$73 + 12\sqrt{2}$

22 **7.** Let $f(x) = x + \sqrt{x^2+1} + \dfrac{1}{x - \sqrt{x^2+1}}$.

What is the value of $f(2015)$?

23 **8.** Two of the following six sets of inequalities have no real solutions. Which two?

$2x < 2^x < x^2$ $\quad x^2 < 2x < 2^x$ $\quad 2^x < x^2 < 2x$
$x^2 < 2^x < 2x$ $\quad 2^x < 2x < x^2$ $\quad 2x < x^2 < 2^x$

24 **9.** Which of the following five calculations gives the smallest answer?

$10 - 3\sqrt{11}$ $\quad 8 - 3\sqrt{7}$ $\quad 5 - 2\sqrt{6}$ $\quad 9 - 4\sqrt{5}$ $\quad 7 - 4\sqrt{3}$

24 **10.** The length of the hypotenuse of a particular right-angled triangle is

$$\sqrt{1+3+5+\cdots+25}.$$

The lengths of the other two sides are

$$\sqrt{1+3+5+\cdots+p} \quad \text{and} \quad \sqrt{1+3+5+\cdots+q},$$

where p and q are positive integers.
What is the value of $p+q$?

24 **11.** How many distinct pairs of positive integers (m, n) satisfy the equation

$$\sqrt{m} - \sqrt{17} = \sqrt{n}?$$

25 **12.** Which of the following is equal to $\dfrac{1}{\sqrt{2005+\sqrt{2005^2-1}}}$?

$\sqrt{1003}-\sqrt{1002}$	$\sqrt{1005}-\sqrt{1004}$	$\sqrt{1007}-\sqrt{1005}$
$\sqrt{2005}-\sqrt{2003}$	$\sqrt{2007}-\sqrt{2005}$	

25 **13.** Suppose that the positive integers p and q satisfy the equation

$$\sqrt{p+\tfrac{1}{2}\sqrt{q}}-\sqrt{p-\tfrac{1}{2}\sqrt{q}}=1.$$

Which of the following is a possible value of q?

5	6	7	8	9

More integers

Exercise 27

16 **1.** Damien wishes to find out if 457 is prime. In order to do this he checks whether 457 is divisible by various known primes.

What is the smallest number of potential prime divisors that Damien needs to check before he can be sure that 457 is prime?

17 **2.** I have a ten-volume collection of mathematical puzzles. Each volume contains the same number of puzzles and the puzzles are numbered consecutively throughout (for example, the number of the first puzzle in volume 2 is one more than that of the last puzzle in volume 1).

Whilst browsing one night, I was particularly intrigued by puzzle number 351 in volume 5 and puzzle number 689 in volume 8.

How many puzzles are there in each volume?

18 **3.** What is the largest integer k whose square k^2 is a factor of 10!?

[The notation $n!$ means the factorial *of n, which is $n \times (n-1) \times \cdots \times 2 \times 1$.*

For example, 6! means $6 \times 5 \times 4 \times 3 \times 2 \times 1$.]

18 **4.** The numbers

2	3	12	14	15	20	21

may be divided into two sets so that the product of the numbers in each set is the same.

What is this product?

19 **5.** How many primes p are there such that $199p + 1$ is a square?

19 **6.** Note that $2001 = 3 \times 23 \times 29$.

What is the number of the next year after 2001 that can be written as the product of three distinct primes?

20 **7.** The integer 396 is multiplied by a positive integer N to make a cube. What is the smallest possible such N?

20 **8.** A list of positive integers, not necessarily all different, has sum 100.

Written in terms of powers of primes, what is the maximum possible value of the product of the integers in the list?

21 **9.** What is the sum of the values of n for which both n and $\dfrac{n^2 - 9}{n - 1}$ are integers?

21 **10.** The value of just one of the following five numbers is prime. Which one?

$1000^2 + 111^2$ $\quad 555^2 + 666^2$ $\quad 2000^2 - 999^2$ $\quad 1001^2 + 1002^2$ $\quad 1001^2 + 1003^2$

22 **11.** Consider numbers of the form $10n + 1$, where n is a positive integer. We shall call such a number 'grime' if it cannot be expressed as the product of two smaller numbers, possibly equal, both of which are of the form $10k + 1$, where k is a positive integer.

How many 'grime numbers' are there in the sequence 11, 21, 31, 41, ..., 981, 991?

22 **12.** Which positive integer n satisfies the following equation?

$$\frac{3}{n^3} + \frac{4}{n^3} + \frac{5}{n^3} + \cdots + \frac{n^3-5}{n^3} + \frac{n^3-4}{n^3} + \frac{n^3-3}{n^3} = 60$$

22 **13.** Suppose that

$$S = (m+20) + (m+21) + (m+22) + \cdots + (m+100),$$

where m is a positive integer.

What is the smallest value of m for which S is a square?

22 **14.** For how many values of n are both n and $4^{\frac{n-1}{n+1}}$ integers?

23 **15.** From four different non-zero digits, it is possible to form 24 different positive four-digit integers containing each of these four digits.

What is the largest prime factor of the sum of the 24 integers?

3 **16.** *The robot *Lumber9* moves along the number line.

Lumber9 starts at 0, takes 1 pace forward (to 1), then 2 paces backward (to -1), then 3 paces forward, 4 paces backward, and so on, moving alternately forwards and backwards, one more pace each time.

At what number is *Lumber9* after 2011 paces?

23 **17.** The integer N has 4008 digits and is divisible by 7. Reading from left to right, each of the first 2003 digits of N is 2, the next digit is d, and each of the last 2004 digits is 8.

What are the possible values of d?

---

*This problem appeared, inadvertently, as question number 3 in the original Challenge paper; it is not that easy!

23 **18.** A tennis club has n left-handed players and $2n$ right-handed players. In total there are fewer than 20 players, each of whom is either left-handed or right-handed, but not both.

In last summer's tournament every player in the club played every other player exactly once. No matches were drawn, and the ratio of the number of matches won by left-handed players to the number of matches won by right-handed players was $3 : 4$.

What is the value of n?

23 **19.** The following statement is true only for certain values of the integer m.

> There are exactly four integer values of n for which $\dfrac{2n+m}{n-2}$ is an integer.

For how many values of m in the range $1 \leq m \leq 20$ is the statement true?

24 **20.** For how many positive integer values of k less than 50 is it impossible to find a value of n such that $n!$ ends in exactly k zeros?

[The notation $n!$ means the factorial *of n, which is $n \times (n-1) \times \cdots \times 2 \times 1$.*

For example, $6!$ means $6 \times 5 \times 4 \times 3 \times 2 \times 1$.]

25 **21.** Let n be the smallest integer for which $7n$ has 2016 digits.

What is the units digit of n?

25 **22.** The function f is such that $f(xy) = f(x) + f(y)$ for all positive integers x and y.

Suppose that $f(10) = 14$ and $f(40) = 20$.

What is the value of $f(500)$?

25 **23.** Four positive integers a, b, c and d are such that

$$\begin{aligned} abcd + abc + bcd + cda + dab \\ + ab + bc + cd + da + ac + bd \\ + a + b + c + d = 2009. \end{aligned}$$

What is the value of $a + b + c + d$?

25 **24.** How many pairs of positive integers (m, n) are solutions of the equation

$$\frac{1}{m} + \frac{2}{n} = \frac{3}{19}?$$

Part III

Remarks and answers

What is best in mathematics deserves not merely to be learnt as a task, but to be assimilated as a part of daily thought, and brought again and again before the mind with ever-renewed encouragement.

Bertrand Russell
The Study of Mathematics

The remarks are intended to help you to arrive at the answer, possibly using a different approach to any you may have in mind.

An answer is given for every problem in the book.

Exercise 1

1. ☛ *For any a and b:* $a^2 - b^2 = (a-b)(a+b)$ [difference of two squares].

Note that $(n-1)(n+1) = n^2 - 1$.

ANSWER: 1

2. ☛ *For any a and b:* $a^2 - b^2 = (a-b)(a+b)$ [difference of two squares].

Note that $(n-2)(n+2) = n^2 - 4$.

ANSWER: 9996

3. ☛ *Multiply and divide before adding and subtracting.*

ANSWER: $2 + 0 + 1 + 3$

4. Note that $2 \times n + n \times 8 = (2+8)n = 10n$.

ANSWER: 20 080

5. 2005 thousandths is equal to $2005 \times \frac{1}{1000}$.

ANSWER: 2007.005

6. ☛ *Multiply and divide before adding and subtracting.*

ANSWER: $2 + 4 \times 2$

7. ☛ *There are 100 pence in £1.*

The actual cost per pound weight is £255 $\div$ 1250.

ANSWER: 20p

8. The difference is equal to $(1\,000\,000 - 1000)$ million.

ANSWER: 999 000 000 000

9. $\frac{2}{81} = 2 \times \frac{1}{81}$.

ANSWER: 0.024 691

10. ANSWER: £1.02

11. The given expression is equal to $1^6 + 3^4 + 5^2 - (2^5 + 4^3 + 6^1)$.

ANSWER: 5

12. ☛ *For any positive a and b:* $\sqrt{ab} = \sqrt{a} \times \sqrt{b}$.

☛ *For any positive a and b:* $\sqrt{\frac{a}{b}} = \frac{\sqrt{a}}{\sqrt{b}}$.

$\frac{1}{2^6} + \frac{1}{6^2} = \frac{1}{4} \times \left(\frac{1}{16} + \frac{1}{9}\right)$.

ANSWER: $\frac{5}{24}$

13. ☛ *For any a and b:* $a^2 - b^2 = (a-b)(a+b)$ [difference of two squares].

Note that $(n-1)(n+1) = n^2 - 1$.

ANSWER: -1

14. $2 \boxtimes 6 = \sqrt{2 \times 6 + 4} = 4$.

ANSWER: 6

15. ☛ *For any positive a and any power p:* $(a^p)^2 = a^{2p}$.

A hundred thousand million is equal to 10^{11}.

ANSWER: 10^{22}

16. ☛ *For any positive a and any power p:* $\sqrt{a^{2p}} = a^p$.

$\sqrt{3^4} = 3^2$.

ANSWER: 5

17. ☛ *To find p% of something, multiply it by* $\frac{p}{100}$.

The total cost of the T-shirts is equal to $£400 \times \frac{117.5}{100}$.

ANSWER: 94

18. The second prize was equal to £4.00 $\times$ 18.

ANSWER: £22

19. Note that $2006 = 1 \times 2 \times 17 \times 59$.

ANSWER: $\times$

20. ☛ *The average of an odd number of consecutive odd integers is equal to the middle integer.*

ANSWER: 84

21. ☛ *For any a:* a^1 *is equal to* a.

☛ *For any non-zero a:* a^0 *is equal to 1.*

☛ *For any positive a:* $a^{\frac{1}{2}}$ *is equal to* $\sqrt{a}$.

☛ *For any positive a, and any power p:* a^{-p} *is equal to* $\dfrac{1}{a^p}$.

ANSWER: 2016^{-1}

22. ☛ *For positive a and b:* a *is less than* b *when* a^2 *is less than* b^2*, and not otherwise.*

The square of $4\sqrt{15}$, for example, is equal to 16×15.

ANSWER: $9\sqrt{3}$

23. ☛ *For any positive a:* a^{-1} *is equal to* $\dfrac{1}{a}$.

$2 \diamond 3 = 8 - 9$.

ANSWER: $\dfrac{3}{4}$

24. ☛ *For any a and b:* $a^2 - b^2 = (a - b)(a + b)$ [difference of two squares].

$61^2 - 39^2 = 22 \times 100$.

ANSWER: 11

25. ☛ *For positive a and b: a is less than b when a^2 is less than b^2, and not otherwise.*

The square of $19\sqrt{99}$, for example, is equal to $19^2 \times 99$.

ANSWER: $199\sqrt{9}$

26. ☛ *The median of an ordered list of numbers is equal to* either *the middle number (when there is one)* or *the average of the middle two numbers.*

☛ *For any positive a and b: if $a^2 < b^2$ then $a < b$.*

The square of $9\sqrt{2}$, for example, is equal to 81×2.

ANSWER: $5\sqrt{7}$

27. ☛ *For any positive a, and any powers p and q: $(a^p)^q$ is equal to a^{pq}.*

ANSWER: $9^{(9^9)}$

28. ☛ *For any a: $(a-1)\left(1+a+a^2+\cdots+a^{k-1}\right) = a^k - 1$.*

The given expression is equal to

$$1 + 2^1 + 2^2 + 2^3 + \cdots + 2^{10} + 2^{11}.$$

ANSWER: $2^{12} - 1$

Exercise 2

1. ☛ *A positive integer is a multiple of 2 when the rightmost digit is even, and not otherwise.*

☛ *A positive integer is a multiple of 3 when its digits add up to a multiple of 3, and not otherwise.*

☛ *A positive integer is a multiple of 4 when the integer formed by the rightmost two digits is a multiple of 4, and not otherwise.*

☛ *A positive integer is a multiple of 5 when the rightmost digit is either 0 or 5, and not otherwise.*

ANSWER: 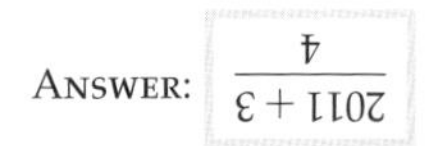

$$\frac{2011+3}{4}$$

2. ☛ *A positive integer is a multiple of 11 when the 'alternating sum' of its digits is a multiple of 11, and not otherwise. For example, 86 691 is a multiple of 11, because* $8-6+6-9+1=0$*, which is* 0×11.

For example, $2003 - 1505 = 498$, which is not a multiple of 11.

ANSWER: 1805

3. ☛ *When a positive integer is divided by 5, the remainder is the same as when the rightmost digit is divided by 5.*

☛ *For any positive integers a and b: the rightmost digit of* $a \times b$ *is equal to the rightmost digit of (the rightmost digit of a times the rightmost digit of b).*

ANSWER: 3

4. ☛ *For prime numbers p and q: an integer is divisible by* $p \times q$ *when it is both divisible by p and divisible by q, and not otherwise.*

☛ *A positive integer is a multiple of 3 when its digits add up to a multiple of 3, and not otherwise.*

☛ *A positive integer is a multiple of 5 when the rightmost digit is either 0 or 5, and not otherwise.*

ANSWER: 785

5. ☛ *A positive integer is a multiple of 11 when the 'alternating sum' of its digits is a multiple of 11, and not otherwise. For example, 86 691 is a multiple of 11, because* $8-6+6-9+1=0$, *which is* 0×11.

For example, 10^7 is not a multiple of 11, because the alternating sum is $1-0+0-0+0-0+0$.

ANSWER: $10^7 - 1$

6. ☛ *For prime numbers p and q: an integer is divisible by* $p \times q$ *when it is both divisible by p and divisible by q, and not otherwise.*

☛ *A positive integer is a multiple of 2 when the rightmost digit is even, and not otherwise.*

☛ *A positive integer is a multiple of 5 when the rightmost digit is either 0 or 5, and not otherwise.*

☛ *A positive integer is a multiple of 9 when its digits add up to a multiple of 9, and not otherwise.*

ANSWER: 2016

7. ☛ *A positive integer is a multiple of 3 when its digits add up to a multiple of 3, and not otherwise.*

☛ *The product of two odd integers is odd.*

123 456 789 is a multiple of 3, and each of 123 456 789 and 987 654 321 is odd.

ANSWER: 3

8. ☛ *For integers p and q: an integer is divisible by both p and q when it is divisible by the lowest common multiple of p and q, and not otherwise.*

A positive integer is a multiple of both 20 and 14 when it is a multiple of 140, and not otherwise.

ANSWER: Fourteen

9. ☛ *For prime numbers p and q: an integer is divisible by $p \times q$ when it is both divisible by p and divisible by q, and not otherwise.*

☛ *A positive integer is a multiple of 3 when its digits add up to a multiple of 3, and not otherwise.*

☛ *A positive integer is a multiple of 5 when the rightmost digit is either 0 or 5, and not otherwise.*

ANSWER: 5775

10. There are 286 integers between 1 and 2007 that are divisible by 7, and half of these are even; therefore 143 integers between 1 and 2007 are divisible by 2 and by 7.

ANSWER: 860

11. ☛ *For any integers a, b and n: $a + b$ is a multiple of n when each of a and b is a multiple of n.*

All the digits of $10^{2014} - 1$ are 9.

ANSWER: $10^{2014} + 8$

12. ☛ *When a positive integer is divided by 9, the remainder is the same as when the sum of its digits is divided by 9.*

ANSWER: 2

13. ☛ *For prime numbers p and q: an integer is divisible by $p \times q$ when it is both divisible by p and divisible by q, and not otherwise.*

☛ *A positive integer is a multiple of 2 when the rightmost digit is even, and not otherwise.*

☛ *A positive integer is a multiple of 3 when its digits add up to a multiple of 3, and not otherwise.*

ANSWER: Seven

14. An integer that has remainder 1 when divided by 3 and remainder 2 when divided by 4 is of the form $12k - 2$, for some integer k.

ANSWER: Eight

15. ☛ *For any a and b:* $a^2 - b^2 = (a-b)(a+b)$ [difference of two squares].

☛ *One of three consecutive integers is a multiple of* 3.

ANSWER: $n^3 - n$

16. For example, the square 3^2 has remainder 3 when divided by 6.

ANSWER: 2

Exercise 3

1. ☛ *There are 24 hours in 1 day.*

100 hours is equal to 4 days and 4 hours.

ANSWER: Thursday

2. ☛ *There are 1000 mm in 1 m.*

☛ *There are 100 cm in 1 m.*

ANSWER: 2.083 m

3. ANSWER: 1976 or 1977

4. ☛ *There are 365 days in 1 year (366 days in a leap year).*

☛ *There are 7 days in 1 week.*

ANSWER: 53

5. ☛ *There are 365 days in 1 year (366 days in a leap year).*

☛ *There are 7 days in 1 week.*

ANSWER: 53

6. On average, Steve travelled 15 miles using 1 litre of petrol.
So he travelled 15×4.5 miles using 4.5 litres.

ANSWER: 70

7. ☛ *A year with 365 days advances the days of the week for the following year by one, and a leap year advances them by two.*

☛ *There are 365 days in 1 year (366 days in a leap year).*

☛ *There are 7 days in 1 week.*

ANSWER: Monday

8. ☛ *There are 60 minutes in 1 hour.*

17 hours and 21 minutes is equal to 1041 minutes.

ANSWER: 40

9. ☛ *There are 10 mm in 1 cm.*

ANSWER: 4

10. 29 feet 3 inches is equal to 351 inches.

ANSWER: 8 feet 8 inches

11. A furlong is equal to 220×36 inches; a furlong is also equal to $10 \times 44 \times 54$ barleycorns.

ANSWER: 3

12. ☛ *There are 1000 cm³ in 1 litre.*

The volume of water was equal to $652.7 \times 23\,450 \times 100 \times 100\,\text{cm}^3$.

ANSWER: 150

13. ☛ *There are 60 seconds in 1 minute.*

☛ *There are 60 minutes in 1 hour.*

☛ *There are 24 hours in 1 day.*

There are $60 \times 60 \times 24$ seconds in a day.

ANSWER: 10^5

14. ☛ *A year with 365 days advances the days of the week for the following year by one, and a leap year advances them by two.*

☛ *There are 7 days in 1 week.*

ANSWER: Thursday

15. ANSWER: 31 December

16. ☛ *There are 7 days in 1 week.*

☛ *There are 24 hours in 1 day.*

☛ *There are 60 minutes 1 hour.*

☛ *There are 60 seconds 1 minute.*

ANSWER: $10!$

Exercise 4

1. ☛ *To find p% of something, multiply it by* $\frac{p}{100}$.

ANSWER: 6%

2. The given expression is equal to $\dfrac{2007 + 7002}{9}$.

ANSWER: 1001

3. ☛ *To find p% of something, multiply it by* $\frac{p}{100}$.

ANSWER: 1.68 m

4. ☛ *To find p% of something, multiply it by* $\frac{p}{100}$.

The normal price of the book is £5.00.

ANSWER: £4.50

5. Altogether, the fraction of the original pail of water that Jack and Jill spilt is equal to $\frac{2}{3} + \frac{1}{3} \times \frac{2}{5}$.

ANSWER: $\frac{1}{5}$

6. ☛ *The percentage change in something is equal to* $\dfrac{\textit{change}}{\textit{original}} \times 100$.

The cost of 1 litre of petrol increased from £0.80 to £1.25.

ANSWER: 56

7. ☛ *The average of n numbers is equal to their sum divided by n.*

The five numbers are 1, 16, 27, 16 and 5.

ANSWER: 13

8. The amount remaining is equal to $\frac{3}{4} \times \frac{4}{5}$ of my money.

ANSWER: £25

9. ANSWER: Buy two, get one free!

10. ☛ *The percentage change in something is equal to* $\frac{\textit{change}}{\textit{original}} \times 100$.

The price increased by 73.3 − 15.2 pence.

ANSWER: 400

11. ☛ *The percentage change in something is equal to* $\frac{\textit{change}}{\textit{original}} \times 100$.

The cost increased by 500 − 40 pence.

ANSWER: 1150

12. ☛ *The value of* $x \div \frac{a}{b}$ *is equal to* $x \times \frac{b}{a}$.

☛ *The value of* $\frac{a}{b} \div x$ *is equal to* $\frac{a}{b \times x}$.

ANSWER: $\frac{1}{\left(\frac{\left(\frac{2}{3}\right)}{4}\right)}$

13. ☛ *To find p% of something, multiply it by* $\frac{p}{100}$.

Mary's height on her fifteenth birthday is equal to her height on her fifth birthday multiplied by 1.3 × 1.2.

ANSWER: 56

14. ☛ *The percentage change in something is equal to* $\frac{\textit{change}}{\textit{original}} \times 100$.

The entries increased by 92 690 − 87 400.

ANSWER: 6

15. Matt black paint reflects 3% of light.

ANSWER: 99.7

16. ☛ *To find p% of something, multiply it by* $\frac{p}{100}$.

The new area is equal to the original area multiplied by 0.75.

ANSWER: 10

17. ☛ *To find p% of something, multiply it by* $\frac{p}{100}$.

Let the advertised selling price be £s, and let the cost price of the dress be £c.

Then $0.8 \times s$ is equal to $1.04 \times c$.

ANSWER: 30

18. The given expression is equal to $\frac{3}{2} \times \frac{4}{3} \times \cdots \times \frac{2006}{2005}$.

ANSWER: 1003

19. ☛ *To find p% of something, multiply it by* $\frac{p}{100}$.

Before the pay rise, Mary, for example, earned £23 100 ÷ 1.1.

ANSWER: £1000

20. For example, $\frac{3}{4}$ can be expressed as $\frac{1}{2} + \frac{1}{4}$.

ANSWER: $\frac{3}{7}$

21. ☛ *The value of* $x \div \frac{a}{b}$ *is equal to* $x \times \frac{b}{a}$.

The expression is equal to $\frac{0.1}{0.\dot{1}}$, and $0.\dot{1}$ is equal to $\frac{1}{9}$.

ANSWER: 0.9

22. $\frac{A}{B} = \frac{167}{835}$ because $\frac{167}{835} = \frac{1}{5}$.

ANSWER: 68

23. ☛ *To find p% of something, multiply it by* $\dfrac{p}{100}$.

Let the price of a wild goose yesterday be t Tugriks; then the price of a white elephant yesterday was $99t$ Tugriks.

The price of a wild goose today is $t \times 1.1$ Tugriks, and the price of a white elephant today is $99t \times 0.9$ Tugriks.

ANSWER: 81

24. ☛ *To find p% of something, multiply it by* $\dfrac{p}{100}$.

☛ *The area of a trapezium with height h and parallel sides of length a and b is equal to* $\frac{1}{2}h(a+b)$.

The new height is equal to $h \times 1.1$; the new values of a and b are $a \times 0.9$ and $b \times 0.9$.

ANSWER: The area decreases by 1%.

Exercise 5

1. ☛ *The interior angle of an equilateral triangle is 60°.*

   ☛ *The interior angle of a square is 90°.*

   ☛ *The interior angle of a regular pentagon is 108°.*

   ☛ *The angles at a point add up to 360°.*

   ANSWER: 102

2. ☛ *The angles on a straight line add up to 180°.*

   ☛ *The interior angle of an equilateral triangle is 60°.*

   ANSWER: 240°

3. ☛ *Corresponding angles on parallel lines are equal.*

   ☛ *The interior angle of a square is 90°.*

   ☛ *The angles at a point add up to 360°.*

   Consider the angles at the vertex V of one of the squares in the diagram alongside.

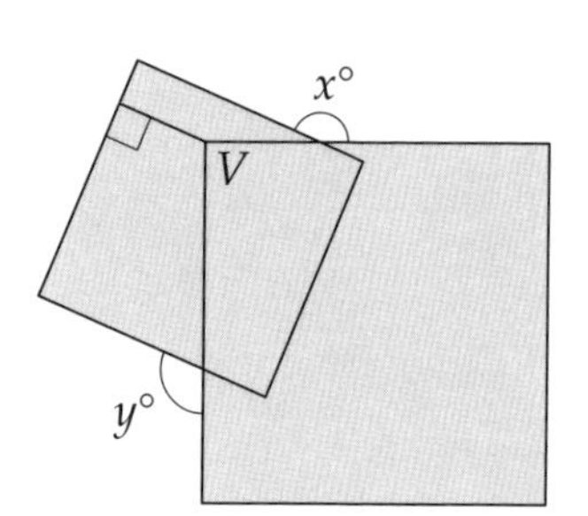

   ANSWER: 270

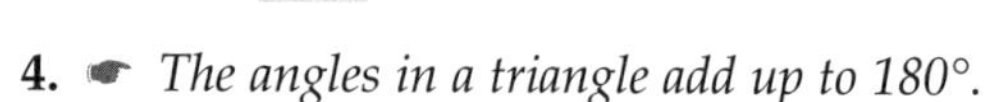

4. ☛ *The angles in a triangle add up to 180°.*

   ANSWER: 80°

5. ☛ *The exterior angle of a regular hexagon is 60°.*

☛ *The interior angle of a square is 90°.*

☛ *An exterior angle of a triangle is equal to the sum of the interior opposite angles.*

☛ *The base angles of an isosceles triangle are equal.*

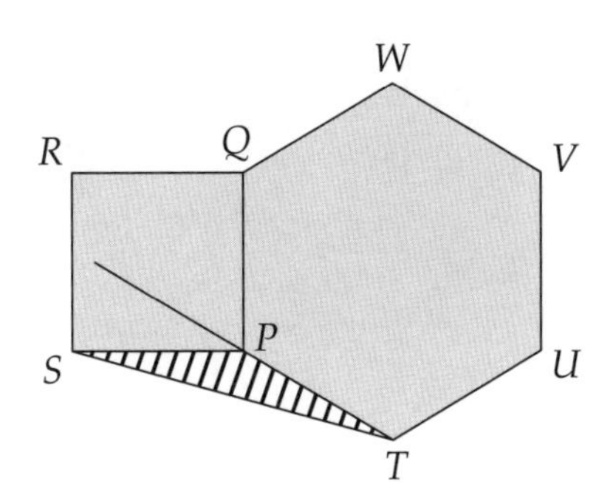

Consider angles at P in the square and the hatched isosceles triangle in the diagram above.

ANSWER: 15°

6. ☛ *The interior angle of a rectangle is 90°.*

☛ *The angles in a triangle add up to 180°.*

☛ *The exterior angle of a regular hexagon is 60°.*

☛ *The angles on a straight line add up to 180°.*

☛ *The angles in a quadrilateral add up to 360°.*

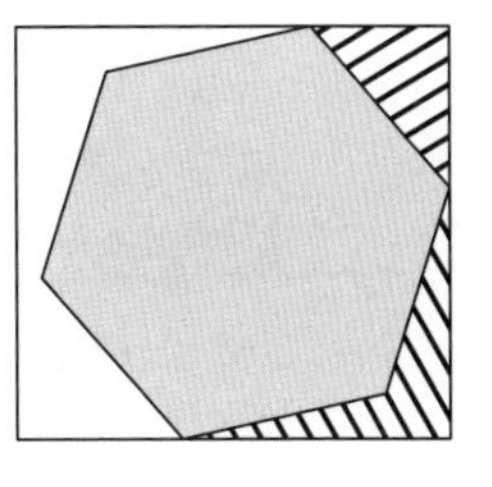

Consider the triangle and quadrilateral shown hatched in the diagram above.

ANSWER: 120°

7. ☛ *The angles on a straight line add up to 180°.*

☛ *The exterior angles of a polygon add up to 360°.*

Let each exterior angle be equal to $x°$; then $x = \frac{1}{4}(180 - x)$.

ANSWER: Ten

8. ☛ *An exterior angle of a triangle is equal to the sum of the interior opposite angles.*

☛ *Vertically opposite angles are equal.*

☛ *The base angles of an isosceles triangle are equal.*

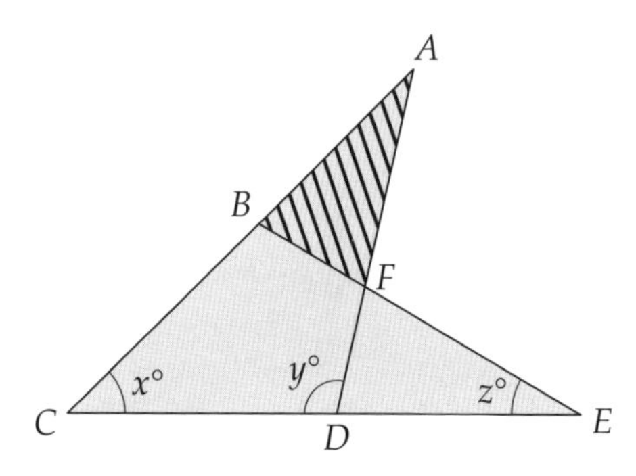

Consider the hatched isosceles triangle shown in the diagram above.

ANSWER: $\frac{y-x}{2}$

9. ☛ *The two tangents from a point outside a circle to the circle are equal in length.*

☛ *The base angles of an isosceles triangle are equal.*

☛ *The angles on a straight line add up to 180°.*

Consider the angles at S.

ANSWER: $\frac{1}{2}(\alpha + \beta)$

10. ☛ *The interior angle of an equilateral triangle is 60°.*

☛ *The interior angle of a regular octagon is 135°.*

☛ *The base angles of an isosceles triangle are equal.*

☛ *The angles in a triangle add up to 180°.*

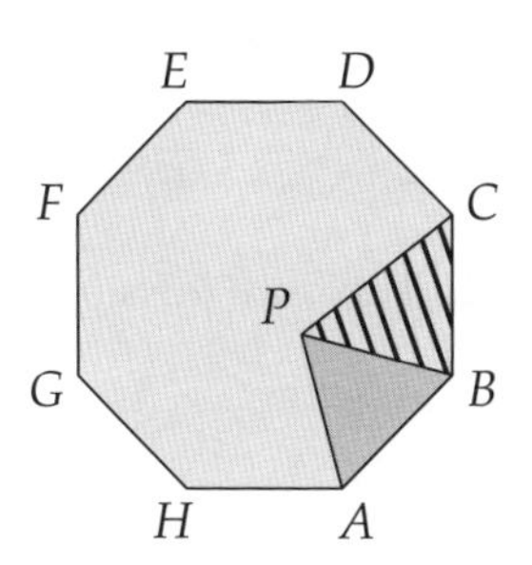

Consider the isosceles triangle shown hatched in the diagram above.

ANSWER: $112\frac{1}{2}°$

11. ☛ *The angles on a straight line add up to 180°.*

When you travel once once around *PQRST*, as indicated by the arrows in the diagram alongside, you turn through 720°.

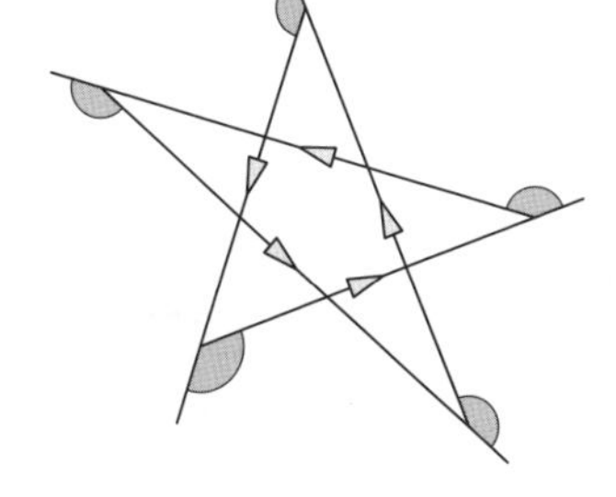

ANSWER: 180°

12. ☛ *Corresponding angles on parallel lines are equal.*

☛ *The exterior angles of a polygon add up to 360°.*

Consider the hatched hexagon in the diagram alongside.

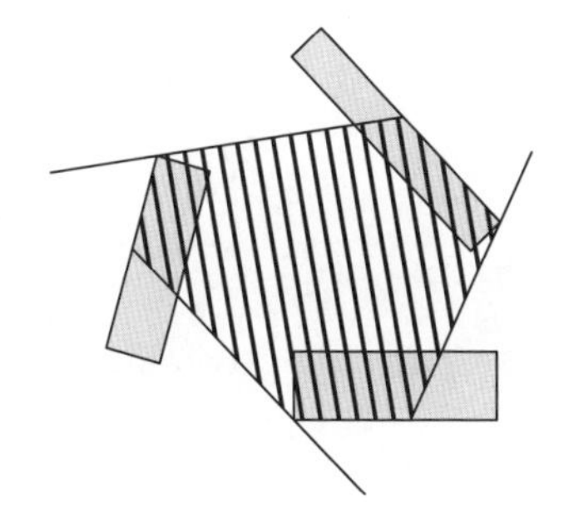

ANSWER: 180°

Exercise 6

1. ANSWER: Once

2. The only possibilities for 1 ACROSS are the two-digit cubes 27 and 64.

   ANSWER: 4

3. ANSWER: 5

4. ☛ *For any positive a and any powers p and q:* $(a^p)^q = a^{p \times q}$.

   Since $3^4 = 81$ the units digit of 3^{4k} is equal to 1 for any positive integer k.

   ANSWER: 7

5. Rearranging, we get '$8Q0S$' = '$P0R2$' + 2008.

   ANSWER: 16

6. The only three-digit squares with the required digits are 256, 324 and 625.

   ANSWER: 2

7. For the largest possible sum, the digits are 9, 8, 7, 6, 5 and 4,

   ANSWER: 255

8. ANSWER: 22

9. The only possibilities for 1 ACROSS are the two-digit cubes 27 and 64.

   ANSWER: 3

10. The two-digit integers with consecutive and increasing digits have the form '$d(d+1)$', where the digit d is from 1 to 8.

    ANSWER: 22

11. N has the form '$d99\ldots99$'.

    ANSWER: 6

12. Consider the digits in the four hatched squares in the diagram on the left below. They are 1 and 3 in some order, and 2 and 6 in some order.

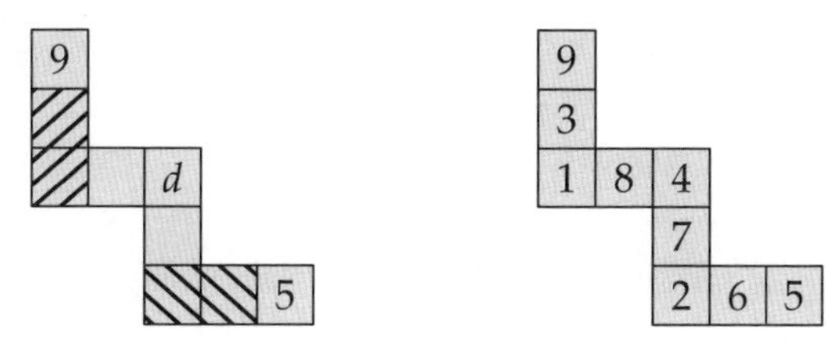

However, 7 and 8 cannot appear in the same row or column of three squares.

The diagram on the right above shows that the required result may be achieved.

ANSWER: 4

13. Consider the six cells adjacent to the digit d, shown hatched in the diagram alongside.

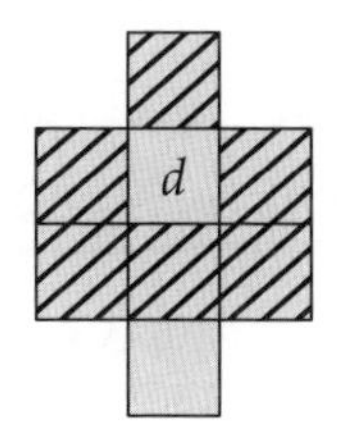

ANSWER: 8

14. Let the two-digit integer N be equal to 'ab', that is, $10a + b$; then the sum of N and the integer formed by reversing the digits of N is equal to $11(a + b)$.

ANSWER: Eight

15. ☛ *For any power p:* $1^p = 1$.

☛ *For any positive a and any powers p and q:* $(a^p)^q = a^{p \times q}$.

Since $3^4 = 81$, $7^4 = 2401$ and $9^2 = 81$, the units digits of 3^{4k}, 7^{4k} and 9^{2k} are equal to 1 for any positive integer k.

ANSWER: 6

16. ☛ *For any positive a and any powers p and q:* $(a^p)^q = a^{p \times q}$.

☛ *For any positive a and any powers p and q:* $a^p \times a^q = a^{p+q}$.

☛ *For any positive a and b and any power p:* $a^p \times b^p = (a \times b)^p$.

Sam calculates $10^8 \times 2^7$.

ANSWER: Eleven

17. ☛ *A positive integer is a multiple of 9 when its digits add up to a multiple of 9, and not otherwise.*

Let the three numbers be '*abc*', '*def*' and '*ghi*'; then

$$\begin{aligned} 'abc' + 'def' + 'ghi' &= 100(a+d+g) + 10(b+e+h) + c + f + i \\ &= 99(a+d+g) + 9(b+e+h) + 45, \end{aligned}$$

since $a+b+c+d+e+f+g+h+i$ is equal to $1+2+3+4+5+6+7+8+9$.

Hence the answer to the addition is a multiple of 9.

It is possible to check that each of the four given numbers which *is* a multiple of 9 is indeed the sum of three positive three-digit integers that between them use all the digits from 1 to 9. For example, $1503 = 236 + 548 + 719$.

ANSWER: 1500

Exercise 7

1. Let the smallest integer be k; then the other integers are $k+2$, $k+4$, $k+6$ and $k+8$.

   ANSWER: 8

2. If $x = s$ is a solution of the equation $6x = \dfrac{150}{x}$, then so is $x = -s$.

   ANSWER: 0

3. Subtracting the given equations, we obtain $7(x-y) = 7$.

   ANSWER: 1

4. ☛ *The average of an odd number of consecutive integers is equal to the middle one.*

   ANSWER: 20

5. Suppose that Milly has eaten $2x$ g; then $100 - x = 3(100 - 2x)$.

   ANSWER: $\frac{4}{5}$

6. Suppose that Anakin Skywalker has s coins and Obi-Wan Kenobi has k coins; then

$$\begin{aligned} k+1 &= 2(s-1) \\ \text{and} \quad k-1 &= s+1. \end{aligned}$$

   ANSWER: Twelve

7. The integer n is equal to $\dfrac{17+23+2n}{3}$.

   ANSWER: 40

8. Subtract one of the given equations from the other.

   ANSWER: 20

9. Consider the objects on the left of each pair of scales. Those on the left of the third pair are the same as those on the left of the first pair plus half of those on the left of the second pair.

ANSWER: Ten

10. Let n be the number of lengths of the pool that Rebecca intended to complete; then $\frac{1}{5}n + 6 = \frac{1}{4}n$.

ANSWER: 120

11. Subtracting the second equation from the first, we obtain $z = -\frac{1}{2}$.

ANSWER: $\frac{1}{2}$

12. ☛ *For any a and b:* $a^2 - b^2 = (a-b)(a+b)$ [difference of two squares].

ANSWER: $x^2 - (y+z)^2$

13. Let the smaller number be x and let the larger be y; then $y - x = \frac{1}{4}(x+y)$.

ANSWER: $3:5$

14. Let the smaller number be y and let the larger be x; then

$$\begin{aligned} x - y &= 9 \\ \text{and} \quad x + y &= 99. \end{aligned}$$

ANSWER: $6:5$

15. Let the scores be p, n, g and f, naming them in the obvious way; then

$$\begin{aligned} p + n + g + f &= 64, \\ p + n &= 32, \\ p + f &= 26 \\ \text{and} \quad n + f &= 36. \end{aligned}$$

ANSWER: 17

16. ☛ *The sum of the integers from 1 up to n is equal to* $\frac{1}{2}n(n+1)$.

Milly's total is equal to half of the sum of the integers from 1 to 20.

ANSWER: 14

17. ☛ *Pythagoras' Theorem.*

Let the sides of the rectangle have lengths a cm and b cm; then $ab = 120$ and $a + b = 23$.

ANSWER: 17 cm

18. They each had the same amount of money, say £m; then $m + 5 = 5(m - 5)$.

ANSWER: £15

19. ☛ *For any a and b:* $m - a$ *and* $b - m$ *are equal, where m is the average of a and b.*

The numbers in the squares are 10, $10 + d$, $10 + 2d$, $10 + 3d$, $10 + 4d$ and $10 + 5d$, for some number d.

ANSWER: 19

20. Let the smallest integer be n; then $4n + 2(n+4) = 3(n+2) + 2006$.

ANSWER: 668

21. ☛ *For any a and b:* $a^2 - b^2 = (a-b)(a+b)$ [difference of two squares].

The given expression is equal to $(x+y)(y-x)$.

ANSWER: $y^2 - x^2$

22. Let the number of cherries that each of them has be k, ℓ and m, naming them in the obvious way; then $k = 3\ell$, $k = 2m$ and $m = \ell + 7$.

ANSWER: 77

23. Multiplying each term in the given equation by xy, we obtain

$$x^2y - y = xy^2 - x,$$

so that

$$0 = (xy + 1)(y - x).$$

ANSWER: -1

24. ☛ *For any positive a:* $a^{\frac{1}{2}} = \sqrt{a}$.

☛ *For any positive a and any power p:* $a^{-p} = \dfrac{1}{a^p}$.

☛ *For any positive a and b:* $\sqrt{\dfrac{a}{b}} = \dfrac{\sqrt{a}}{\sqrt{b}}$.

ANSWER: $\sqrt{2}$

25. From the given equation $y = 2x$.

ANSWER: 7

26. Since $x = a$ is a solution we have $a^2 + a^2 + b = 0$, so that

$$b = -2a^2. \qquad (*)$$

Since $x = b$ is a solution we have $b^2 + ab + b = 0$, so that $4a^4 - 2a^3 - 2a^2 = 0$ from equation (*).
Hence $2a^2(2a^2 - a - 1) = 0$. But $a \neq 0$ and $a \neq -\frac{1}{2}$ because a and b are different, using equation (*).

ANSWER: One

27. Let Rachel have n pennies; then Heather has n^2 pennies, and $n^2 + n$ is a multiple of 100. But $n^2 + n = n(n+1)$ and $100 = 4 \times 25$.

ANSWER: 600

Exercise 8

1. A square of area $4\,\text{cm}^2$ has a perimeter of length $8\,\text{cm}$.

   ANSWER: Two

2. ☛ *In a network, when the number of vertices with an odd number of edges is at most two the network is traversable, otherwise the network is not traversable.*

   ANSWER:

3. The centre of the circle travels once around a square with sides of length 3.

   ANSWER: 12

4. At the end of the second day Peri has reached $(2,3)$.

   ANSWER: (13,21)

5. ANSWER: 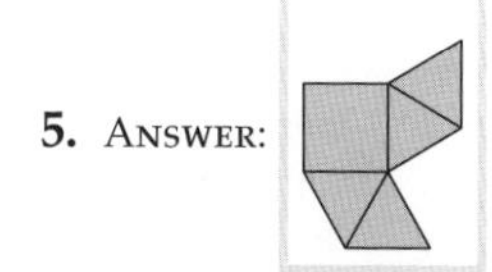

6. As a fraction of the integer part, the decimal part of 4.45, for example, is equal to $\dfrac{0.45}{4}$, that is, 0.9 eighths.

   ANSWER: 2.25

7. The smallest amount that cannot be paid exactly using four or fewer standard British coins is 38p.

   ANSWER: 24p

8. ☛ *For any a and any powers p and q:* $(a^p)^q = a^{p \times q}$.

☛ *For any positive a and positive integers p and q:* $a^{\frac{p}{q}} = (\sqrt[q]{a})^p$.

Four of the given expressions are equal to 2^8.

ANSWER: $32^{\frac{9}{5}}$

9. The numbers in the circles are alternately even and odd.

Only 6 and 8 can be placed next to 5.

ANSWER: 10

10. ☛ *The sum of the lengths of two sides of a triangle is greater than the length of the third side* [triangle inequality].

The smallest possible length of the third side is 2 cm; the greatest is 8 cm.

ANSWER: Seven

11. ☛ *Two rectangles are similar when the ratio length : width is the same for each, and not otherwise.*

For example, 240 : 120 is the same as 110 : 55.

ANSWER: 320 × 200

12. ☛ *The ratio of the areas of similar shapes is equal to the square of the ratio of corresponding lengths.*

The ratio of the volumes of ropes of the same length is equal to the square of the ratio of the diameters.

ANSWER: 4 kg

13. When placed on the shelf each volume is 'turned round', so the names inside appear in the order Ba–A, Ca–Be, Ei–Ce, Fe–Ek, Fi–Fee, Fum–Fo.

ANSWER: Bernoulli

14. The arrangement described determines a division of an equilateral triangle into smaller equilateral triangles. Hence 3 × (the number of small equilateral triangles in one tile) is a square, which rules out the first two tiles.

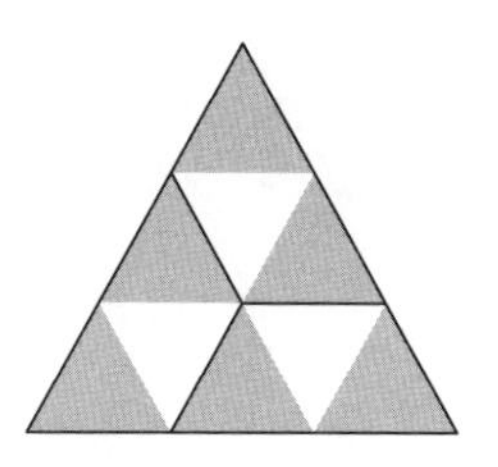

The diagram alongside shows that it is possible to place together three identical copies of the third tile, for example, to make an equilateral triangle.

ANSWER: Two

15. ☛ *The angles on a straight line add up to 180°.*

☛ *The angles in a triangle add up to 180°.*

☛ *Two triangles are congruent when two angles and a side of one are equal to two angles and the corresponding side of the other* [AAS test for congruency].

☛ *Pythagoras' Theorem.*

The two triangles shown hatched in the diagram alongside are congruent.

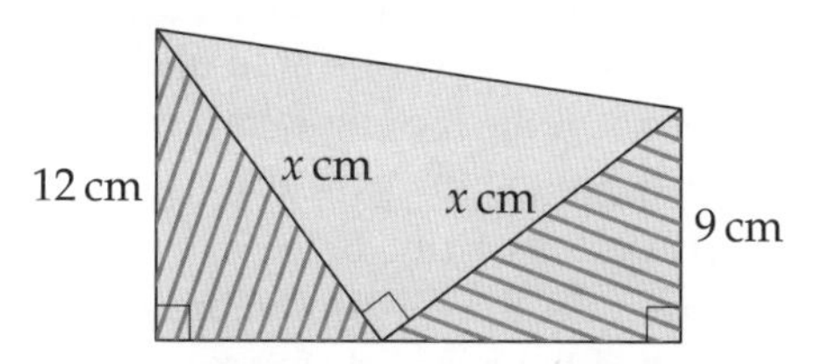

ANSWER: 15

16. The total of the marks of the twelve students was 12 × 6.5; the total of the marks of the other eight students was between 8 × 0 and 8 × 10 (inclusive).

ANSWER: The average for the whole group lies between 3.9 and 7.9 (inclusive).

17. ☛ *The diagonals of a square bisect the angles at the vertices.*

☛ *The angles in a triangle add up to 180°.*

☛ *Sides opposite equal angles of a triangle are equal.*

☛ *Pythagoras' Theorem.*

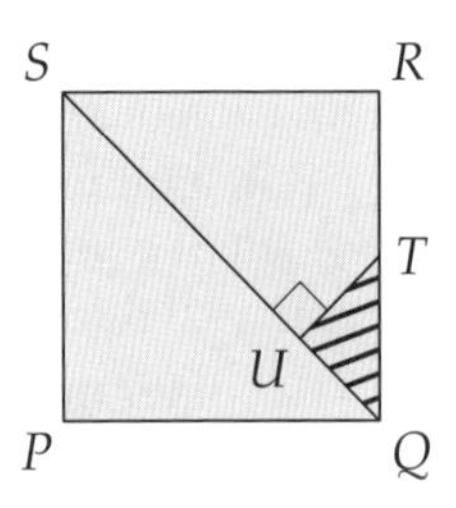

Consider the hatched triangle in the diagram above. The lengths of the sides are in the ratio $1 : 1 : \sqrt{2}$.

ANSWER: 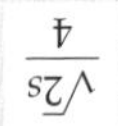

18. The only way to cut the original square is as shown in the diagram alongside (or a rotation of this).

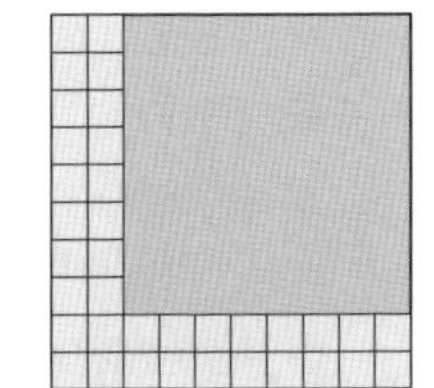

ANSWER: 10 cm

19. The fold forms one side of the resulting polygon. In addition, each vertex of the rectangle can contribute at most two sides to the resulting polygon. So the greatest number of sides is 9.

All values from 5 to 9 are possible. For example, the diagram alongside shows how to fold the rectangle to create a polygon with 9 sides.

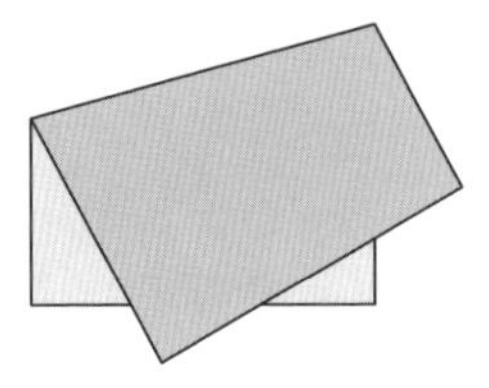

ANSWER: 10

20. P moves once around a square with sides of length 16 cm.

ANSWER: 64 cm

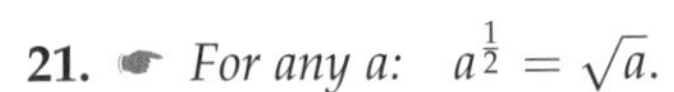

21. ☛ *For any a:* $a^{\frac{1}{2}} = \sqrt{a}$.

☛ *For any a and powers p and q:* $a^p \times a^q = a^{p+q}$.

ANSWER: $\frac{5}{2}$

22. Consider the rectangle formed by combining two of the triangles, as shown in the diagram alongside.

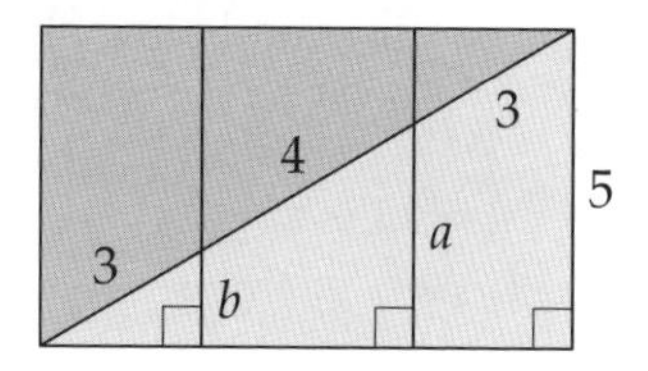

ANSWER: 5

23. The numbers on the first few squares that the painted face lands on are 3, 7 and 11.

ANSWER: 80

24. The side lengths of the smaller triangles are 1 cm, 2 cm or 3 cm.

Consider in turn the ways in which a 4 cm triangle may be cut. For example:

(i) cutting into 2 cm triangles (only) gives the diagram on the left below; and

(ii) cutting into 3 cm and 1 cm triangles (at least one of each) gives the diagram on the right.

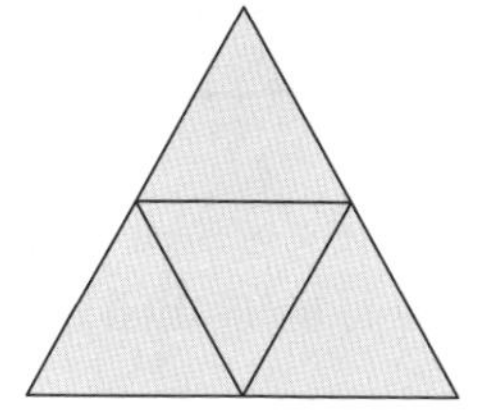

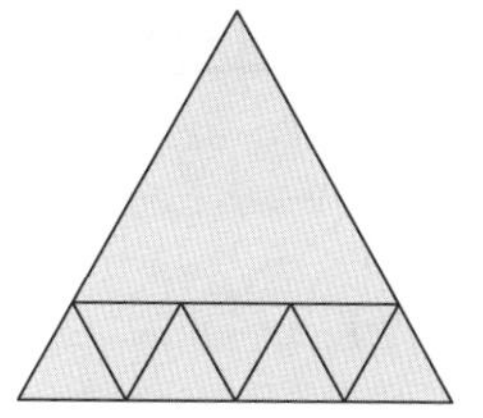

ANSWER: 12

25. ☛ *The angles in a quadrilateral add up to 360°.*

☛ *Each exterior angle of a regular polygon with n sides is equal to* $\frac{360^\circ}{n}$.

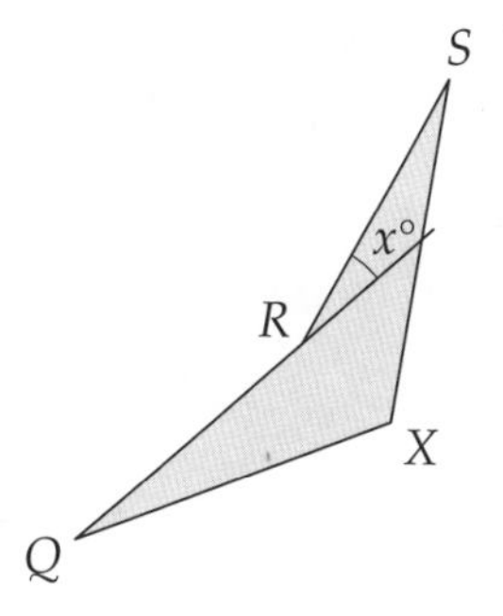

Let each exterior angle of the polygon be equal to $x°$. From the angles in $QXSR$ (enlarged in the diagram alongside) we have $2x + (x + 180) + 140 = 360$.

ANSWER: 27

26. The diagram below shows the five lines.

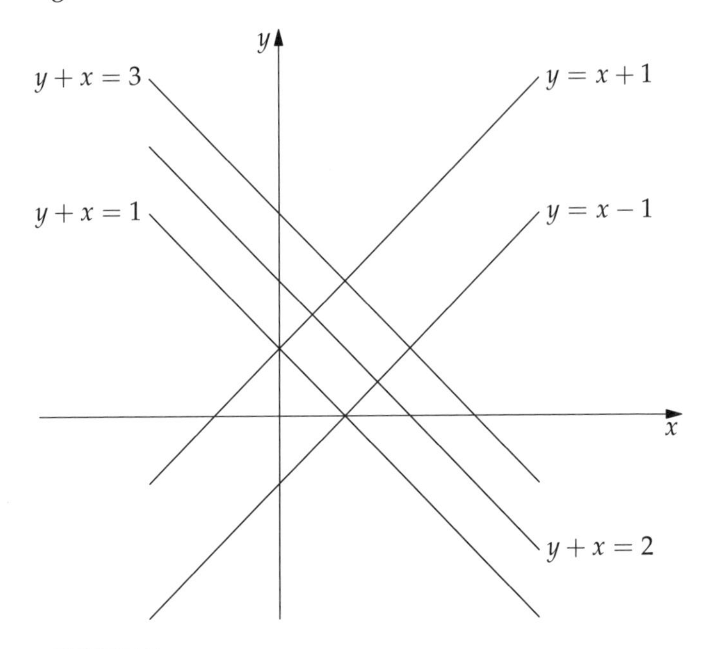

ANSWER: $y + x = 2$

27. Let the height of each equilateral triangle be h; then $h - XY + h = 1$.

ANSWER: $\sqrt{3} - 1$

28. The sequence is 13, 40, 20, 10, 5, 16, 8, 4, 2, 1, . . . ; the block 4, 2, 1 now repeats.

ANSWER: 1

Exercise 9

1. For example, 5 may be written $2 + 3$.

ANSWER: 11

2. The primes are $2, 3, 5, 7, \ldots$.

ANSWER: Eight

3. Note that $1001 = 7 \times 11 \times 13$.

ANSWER: 343

4. Since the sum is odd, one of the primes is equal to 2.

ANSWER: 53

5. The only primes in the teens are 13, 17 and 19.

ANSWER: 37 years old

6. Note that 2047 factorises as 23×89.

ANSWER: $2^{11} - 1$

7. Note that $210 = 2 \times 3 \times 5 \times 7$; the next prime above 7 is 11.

ANSWER: Four

8. ☛ *For any positive a and any powers p and q:* $(a^p)^q = a^{p \times q}$.

☛ *For any a and b:* $a^2 - b^2 = (a - b)(a + b)$ [difference of two squares].

Note that

$$\begin{aligned} 4^n - 1 &= (2^2)^n - 1 \\ &= 2^{2n} - 1 \\ &= (2^n)^2 - 1. \end{aligned}$$

ANSWER: One

9. One of the two primes is 2, so the sum is the highest of a 'prime pair'; all three primes are odd, so the smallest possible sum is $3+5+7$.

ANSWER: 19

10. Consider the prime factorisation of each of the given numbers. For example, $120 = 2^3 \times 3 \times 5$ is ruled out because the required number is the product of six primes.

ANSWER: 12 100

Exercise 10

1. Some regions share a side with three others, so that at least four colours are required.

ANSWER: Four

2. Each diagonal of the hexagon divides it into two quadrilaterals; two triangles sharing a side also form a quadrilateral.

ANSWER: Twelve

3. The routes through the unlabelled corner cells are determined, as shown in the diagram alongside.

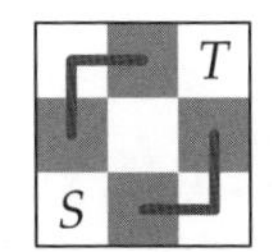

A route leaves cell S in one of two ways, either 'up' or to the right; the rest of the route is then determined.

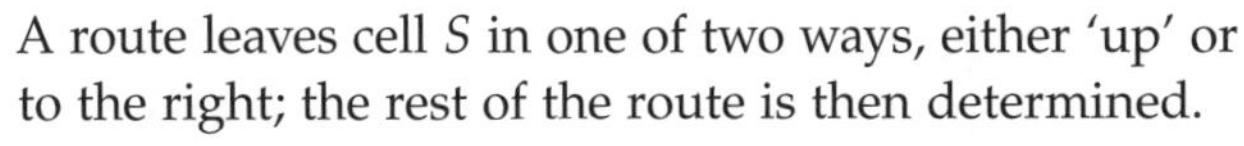

ANSWER: Two

4. Eight marbles— two marbles of each of the colours—may be taken without fulfilling the requirement.

ANSWER: Nine

5. The only possible axis of symmetry is shown in the diagram alongside.

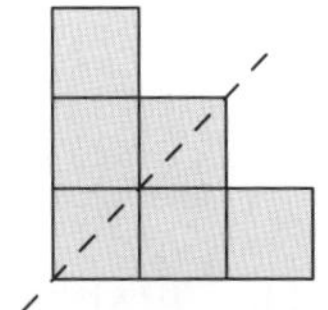

ANSWER: Fifteen

6. ☛ *The sum of the lengths of two sides of a triangle is greater than the length of the third side* [triangle inequality].

The largest possible perimeter has length 12, achieved by the triangle with side lengths 3, 4 and 5.

ANSWER: Three

7. The diagram alongside shows the number of ways of travelling along the belts to reach each of three of the points in the network.

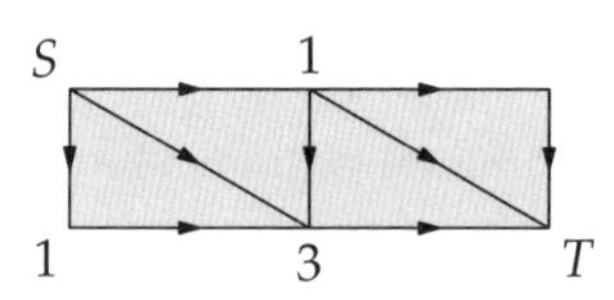

Answer: Five

8. The hatched squares in the diagram alongside may be occupied by either one or two 1×2 rectangles. In the latter case, there is only one way of dividing the rest of the shape.

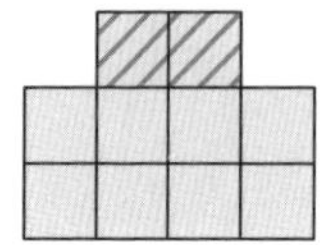

Answer: Six

9. ☛ *Suppose there are m ways of making one choice and, whichever first choice is made, n ways of making a second choice, then there are $m \times n$ ways of making both choices in succession* [multiplication principle].

There are 24 arrangements of the five letters in the word ANGLE with A as the first letter. Of these, ANLGE is the last in alphabetical order.

Answer: 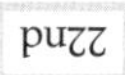

10. The empty cells in the 2×2 block at the bottom left are 3, 4 in some order. Once these cells are filled, the rest of the numbers in the grid are determined.

Answer: 

11. Consider a cut and rearranged large square, as shown for the given example in the diagram alongside

There are $2n^2$ small squares altogether, of which $2n$ are not shaded.

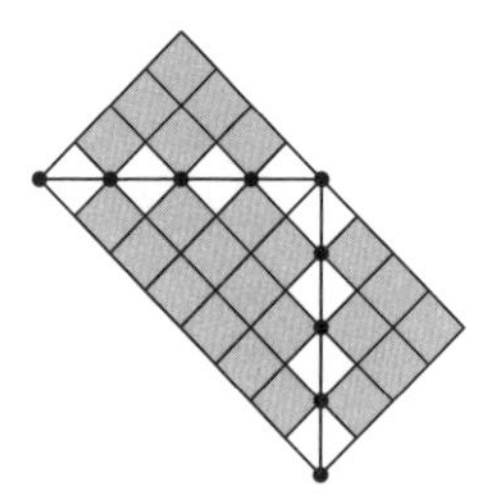

Answer: 84

12. The two crosshatched squares in the diagram alongside cannot be used together, because they fold into the same place. Only two of the three hatched squares in the diagram alongside can be used.

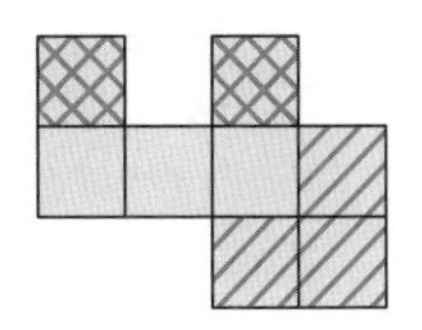

ANSWER: Six

13. The number of points of intersection is equal to

$$\tfrac{1}{2}\big((2+3+4+5)^2-(2^2+3^2+4^2+5^2)\big).$$

ANSWER: 71

14. When four different straight lines intersect in two points, then some three of them do. This can only happen when two of them are parallel, as shown in the diagram alongside, and it is not possible to add a fourth different line to this arrangement without creating more points of intersection.

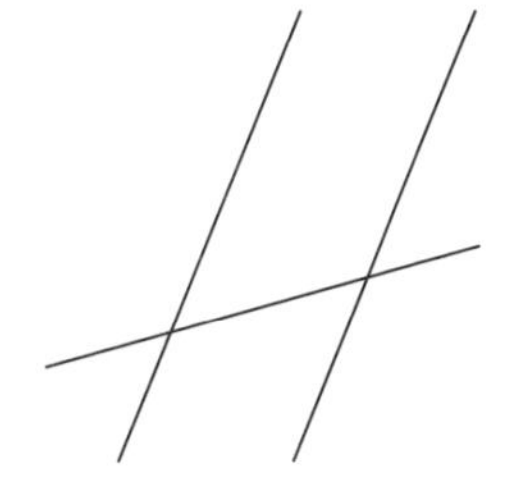

1, 3, 4 and 5 points of intersection are all possible.

ANSWER: 2

15. The lowest tower has height $4\,\text{cm}+4\,\text{cm}+4\,\text{cm}$, and the highest $10\,\text{cm}+10\,\text{cm}+10\,\text{cm}$. Every height is an even number of centimetres. Every even height from 12 cm to 26 cm is possible.

ANSWER: Nine

16. ☛ *Suppose there are m ways of making one choice and, whichever first choice is made, n ways of making a second choice, then there are* $m \times n$ *ways of making both choices in succession* [multiplication principle].

Consider choosing row by row which letters to circle. There are five letters to choose from in the first row, four in the second, and so on.

ANSWER: 120

17. ☛ *Suppose there are m ways of making one choice and, whichever first choice is made, n ways of making a second choice, then there are $m \times n$ ways of making both choices in succession* [multiplication principle].

Sammy has three choices for the flavour of thc first sweet. Then he has two choices for the each other sweet.

ANSWER: 48

18. Consider the number of ways of combining each of the ways of expressing 3 with either two 1s or 2. Then add $1 + 4$, $4 + 1$ and 5.

ANSWER: Sixteen

19. The diagram alongside shows the number of ways of reaching some of the cells in the maze.

→	1		
1	2		
2	2		
2	4	4	→

ANSWER: Eight

20. ☛ *Suppose there are m ways of making one choice and, whichever first choice is made, n ways of making a second choice, then there are $m \times n$ ways of making both choices in succession* [multiplication principle].

The central disc may be any of the three colours; then there is a choice of two colours for the disc connected to the central one. The two hatched discs in the diagram alongside are either the same colour or different colours.

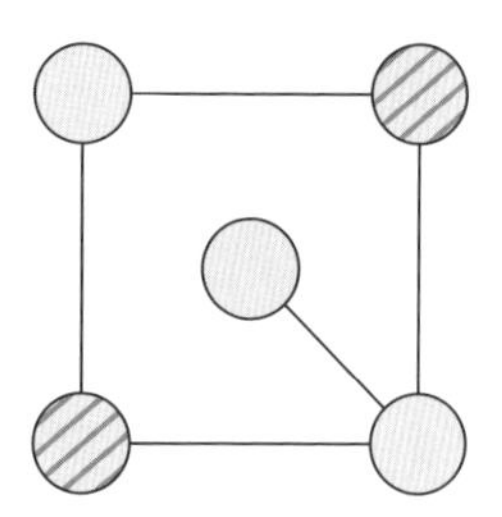

ANSWER: 36

21. The crosshatched square in the diagram alongside is never shaded black, because it meets every other small square along a side or at a corner. Also, if the hatched square in the diagram is shaded black, then the only other square that may also be shaded black is the top one.

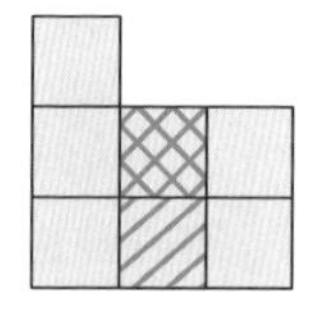

ANSWER: Ten

22. The three possible shapes of hexagon are shown in the diagrams below. Each of them appears in the grid in more than one position.

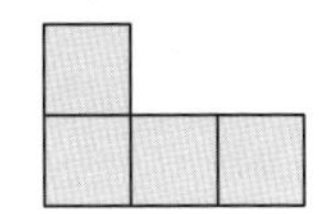

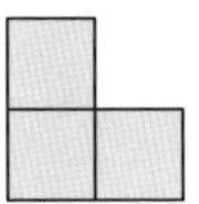

ANSWER: Sixteen

Exercise 11

1. ☛ *Triangles with the same base and equal heights have equal areas.*

   ANSWER: All four triangles have the same area.

2. ☛ *The area of a rhombus is equal to half of the product of the lengths of the diagonals.*

   ANSWER: $3\,\text{cm}^2$

3. Half of the area between the two squares is shaded.

   ANSWER: $\frac{4}{9}$

4. Divide up the rectangle as shown in the diagram alongside; the required fraction is equal to $\frac{1}{3}$ + half of $\frac{1}{6}$.

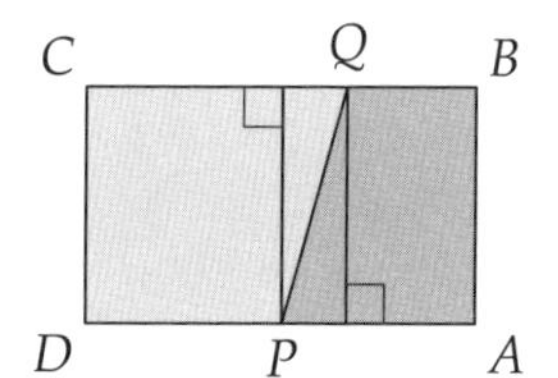

   ANSWER: $\frac{5}{12}$

5. The length of the perimeter of a $4\,\text{cm} \times 2\,\text{cm}$ rectangle is equal to $12\,\text{cm}$.

   ANSWER: $9\,\text{cm}^2$

6. ☛ *When two angles of one triangle are equal to two angles of a second triangle the triangles are similar* [AA test for similar triangles].

   ☛ *The ratio of the areas of similar shapes is equal to the square of the ratio of corresponding lengths.*

   The 3 by 4 triangle and the hatched triangle in the diagram alongside are similar (AA).

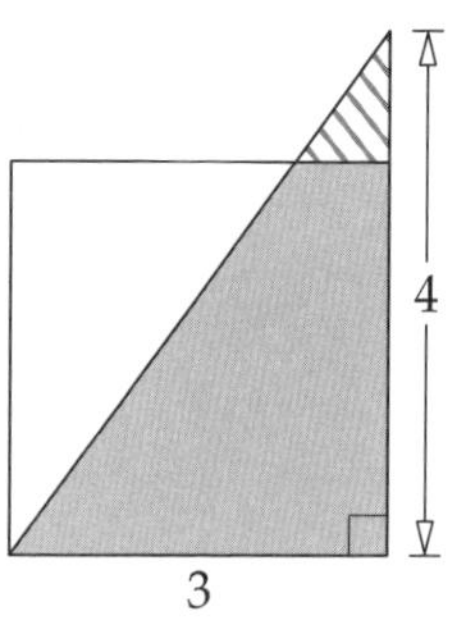

   ANSWER: 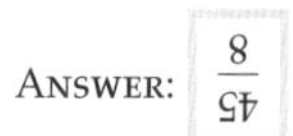

7. Each of the three regular hexagons may be divided into three rhombuses, as shown in the diagram alongside.

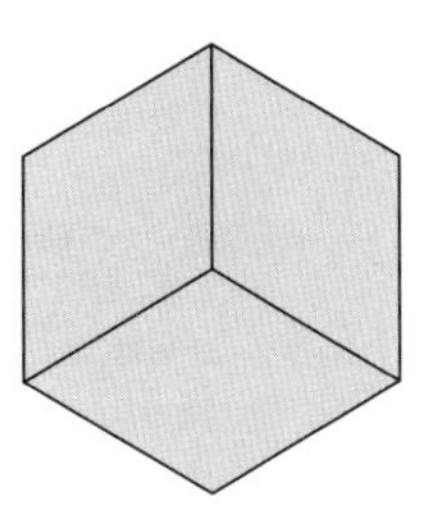

In each of the three given hexagons, half of each rhombus is shaded.

ANSWER: X is equal to Y and to Z.

8. ☛ *The area of a triangle is equal to $\frac{1}{2} \times$ base $\times$ height.*

The area of each triangle is equal to $2h^2$, and the area of the square is equal to $16h^2$.

ANSWER: $2\sqrt{2}h$

9. Consider the regular hexagon when it has been divided into three congruent rhombuses, as shown in the diagram alongside.

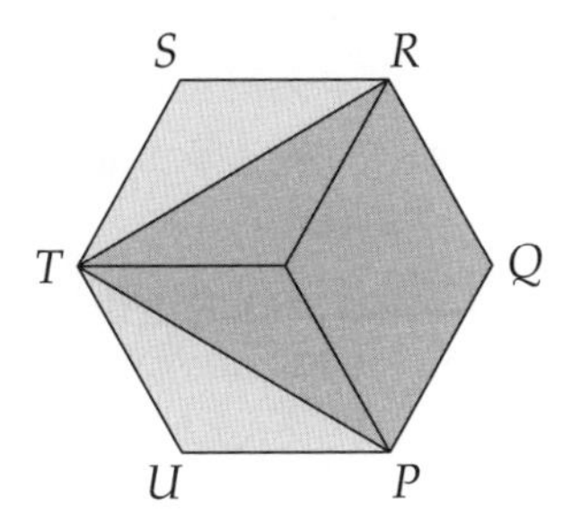

ANSWER: 40

10. ☛ *The area of a triangle is equal to $\frac{1}{2} \times$ base $\times$ height.*

☛ *Pythagoras' Theorem.*

Let one of the sides of length 5 be the base of the triangle. The area of the triangle is a maximum when the height is greatest, which is when the height equals 5 (see the diagram alongside), and the triangle is right-angled.

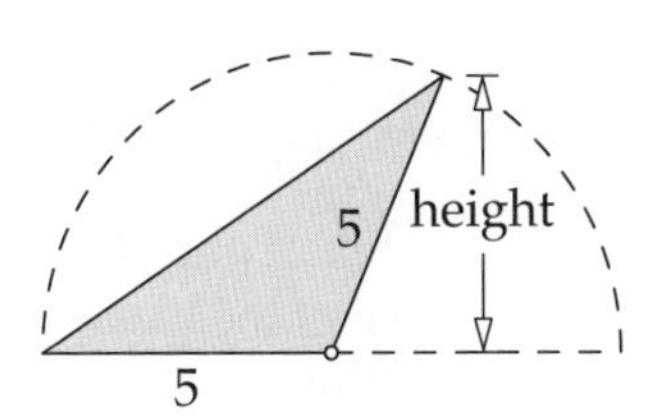

ANSWER: 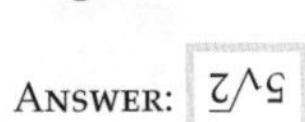

11. ☛ *The ratio of the areas of similar shapes is equal to the square of the ratio of corresponding lengths.*

ANSWER: 2500

12. ☛ *Triangles with the same base and equal heights have equal areas.*

The area of triangle PQV is equal to the area of triangle PQS (see the diagram alongside).

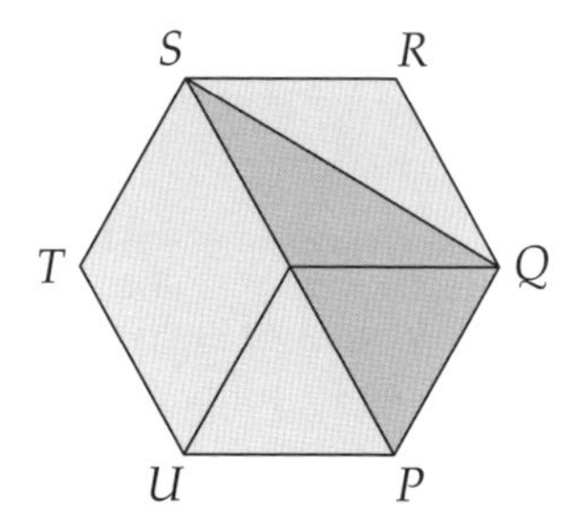

ANSWER: $\frac{1}{3}$

13. ☛ *When two angles of one triangle are equal to two angles of a second triangle the triangles are similar* [AA test for similar triangles].

☛ *The area of a rhombus is equal to half of the product of the lengths of the diagonals.*

The two hatched triangles in the diagram alongside are similar (AA).

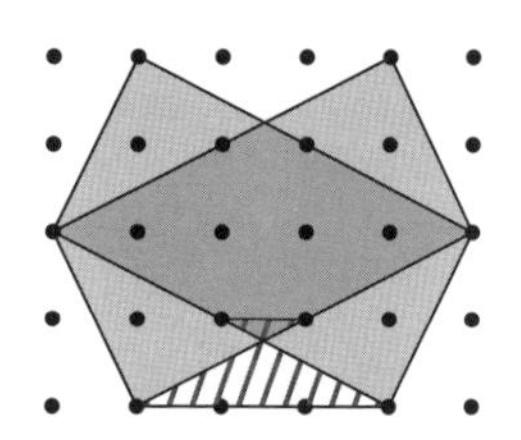

ANSWER: $\frac{25}{4}$

14. The area of each rectangle is equal to $\frac{1}{4}$.

ANSWER: $\frac{2}{3}$

15. The area of the shaded triangle is equal to the area of the hatched square in the diagram alongside.

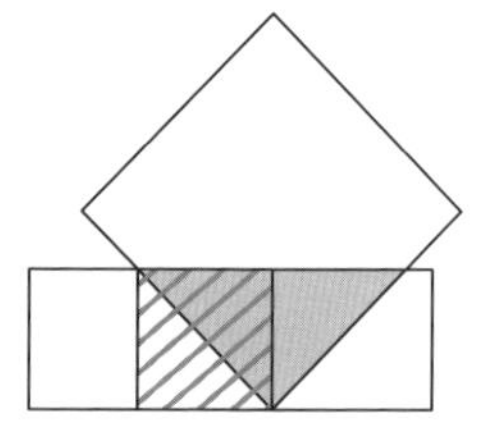

ANSWER: 1

16. The overlapping region of the cards in the new position is a square with sides of length 2 cm (see the diagram alongside).

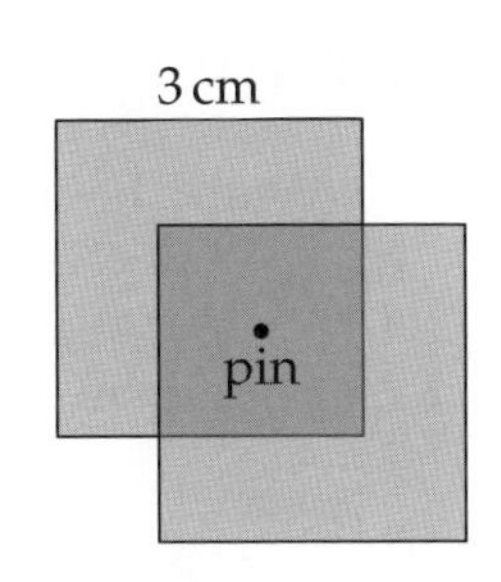

ANSWER: $4\,\text{cm}^2$

17. ☛ *The area of a triangle is equal to $\frac{1}{2}$ × base × height.*

☛ *Pythagoras' Theorem.*

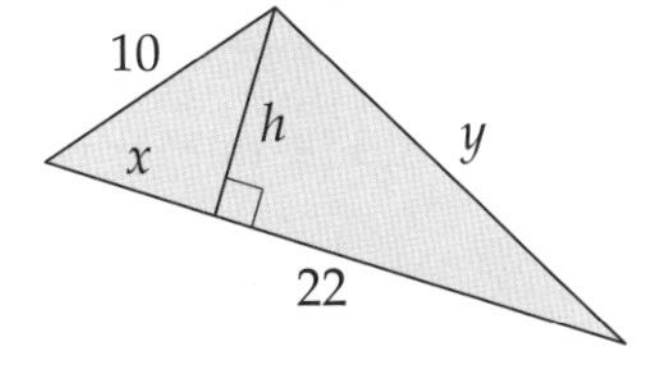

The height h of the triangle, shown in the diagram alongside, is equal to 8, and therefore x is equal to 6.

ANSWER: $8\sqrt{5}$

18. ☛ *When two angles of one triangle are equal to two angles of a second triangle the triangles are similar* [AA test for similar triangles].

☛ *The area of a triangle is equal to $\frac{1}{2}$ × base × height.*

Triangles QTP, RTQ and PQR are similar (AA). It follows that T divides the diagonal PR in the ratio 1 : 4.

ANSWER: 1 : 10

19. ☛ *When two angles of one triangle are equal to two angles of a second triangle the triangles are similar* [AA test for similar triangles].

☛ *The area of a triangle is equal to $\frac{1}{2}$ × base × height.*

See the diagram alongside. Triangles STV and QTP are similar (AA). It follows that T divides the diagonal QS in the ratio 2 : 1.

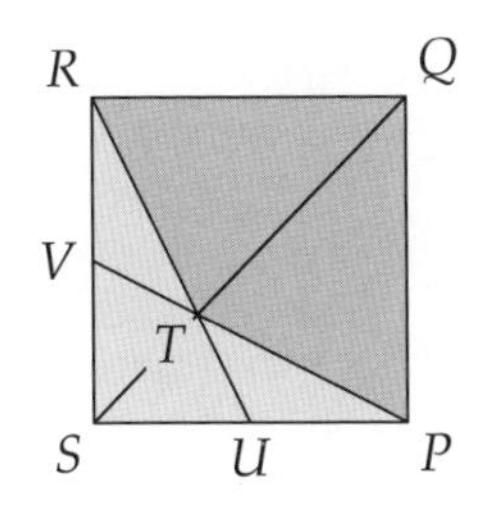

ANSWER: $\frac{2}{3}$

Exercise 12

1. Note that $1+2+9=12$.

   ANSWER: 6

2. p, q and r are 1, 2 and 3 in some order.

   ANSWER: 43

3. ☛ *The average of an odd number of consecutive integers is equal to the middle one.*

   The middle integer is 401.

   ANSWER: 400

4. ANSWER: £16.04

5. The only possible ways of making 21 points are either $1 \times 5 + 8 \times 2$ or $3 \times 5 + 3 \times 2$.

   ANSWER: Eleven

6. Let Gill be g years old today; then $15g + 4 = (g+4)^2$.

   ANSWER: 56

7. Rachel swam for 63 days, and the ratio of the lengths of the pools is $5:4$.

   ANSWER: 28

8. Let the number of two-pence coins in the bag be t; then $2t + 5(50-t) = 181$.

   ANSWER: Four

9. Note that, for example,

$$\begin{aligned} 1 &= 1^2 + 0^2 + 0^2 + 0^2, \\ 5 &= 1^2 + 2^2 + 0^2 + 0^2 \\ \text{and} \quad 10 &= 1^2 + 3^2 + 0^2 + 0^2. \end{aligned}$$

ANSWER: Fifteen

10. Each item that Susanna buys costs a whole number of pounds less 1 pence. She cannot buy more than 66 items.

ANSWER: 24

11. Terms in the first sequence increase by 7, and terms in the second by 9. The lowest common multiple of 7 and 9 is 7×9.

ANSWER: 2068

12. The apprentice planted 50 rows. For each row that the apprentice planted, the gardener planted the next row above, with one rose fewer.

ANSWER: 51

13. The first large sheet of paper has page numbers 1, 2 19 and 20. After that, the sum of the four page numbers on a sheet does not change, because two numbers increase by 2 and two decrease by 2 as you go from one sheet to the next.

ANSWER: 37

14. Any positive integer from 1 to 50 is a factor of 50!. But 51, for example, is also factor of 50! because $51 = 3 \times 17$.

ANSWER: 53

15. ☛ *A positive integer is a multiple of 5 when the rightmost digit is either 0 or 5, and not otherwise.*

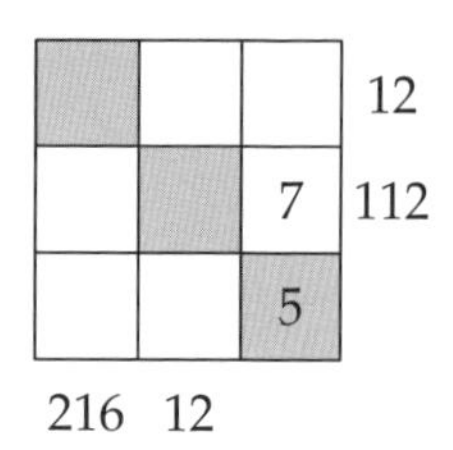

None of the given products is a multiple of 5, and only one is a multiple of 7; this determines the positions of 5 and 7, as shown in the diagram alongside.

ANSWER: 30

16. The median is equal to 10 and there are five numbers, so that the middle number in the list is 10. The mode is equal to 11, so that the list contains at least two copies of the number 11. The mean is equal to 9, so that the sum of the numbers is equal to 45.

ANSWER: 4

17. When a and b are positive integers, $a + b = a \div b$, for example, is never true. This is because $a + b$ is strictly greater than a whereas $a \div b$ is at most equal to a.

ANSWER: $a - b = a \div b$

18. Note that $2016 = 2^5 \times 3^2 \times 7$.

ANSWER: 168^2 or 28 224

19. Since $\sqrt{n}$ is between 15 and 16, n is between 225 and 256.

ANSWER: Four

20. No multiple of 3 from 2002 to 2022 has the required form; no multiple of 5 from 2005 to 2020 has the required form; and no number between 2000 and 2025 is a power of 2.

ANSWER: 2025

21. ☛ *For any positive a and any powers p and q:* $a^p \times a^q = a^{p+q}$.

Note that $1280 = 2^8 \times 5$ and that $5 = 2^2 + 1$.

ANSWER: 18

22. Suppose that Noel originally bought n cards; then $\dfrac{1560}{n} - 1 = \dfrac{1560}{n+1}$.
Note that $1560 = 39 \times 40$.

ANSWER: 12

23. Let the grid be $a \times b$, so that $ab = 1000$. For each of the possible values of a and b, the corresponding number $2a + 2b - 4$ of corner and edge pieces may be determined. For example, when $a = 25$ and $b = 40$ there are 126 corner and edge pieces.

ANSWER: 316

24. ☛ *For any different primes p and q: the number of positive divisors of $p^{\alpha} \times q^{\beta}$ is equal to $(\alpha + 1)(\beta + 1)$.*

Note that $\dfrac{n}{100 - n} = -1 + \dfrac{100}{100 - n}$. Therefore $\dfrac{n}{100 - n}$ is an integer precisely when $100 - n$ is a (positive or negative) divisor of 100.

ANSWER: Eighteen

25. ☛ *For any positive a and any powers p and q: $a^p \times a^q = a^{p+q}$.*

☛ *For any positive a and any powers p and q: $(a^p)^q = a^{p \times q}$.*

A square factor of 2003^{2003} has the form 2003^{2k} for some positive integer k.

ANSWER: 1002

26. ☛ *For any prime p: the number of positive divisors of p^{α} is equal to $\alpha + 1$.*

Note that, since x is not zero, the given equation may be rewritten $n = \dfrac{16}{x} - x$. Therefore n is an integer precisely when x is a (positive or negative) divisor of 16.

However, since $\dfrac{16}{a} - a = \dfrac{16}{b} - b$ when $ab = -16$, the divisors a and b give the same value of n.

ANSWER: 5

Exercise 13

1. ☛ *There are 60 minutes in 1 hour.*

☛ *There are 60 seconds in 1 minute.*

On average, each man took $27 \times 60 \times 60$ seconds for 32 000 seats.

ANSWER: Three

2. ☛ *There are roughly half a million minutes in 1 year.*

20 million years is roughly $2 \times 10^7 \times 5 \times 10^5$ minutes.

ANSWER: 6×10^{13}

3. ☛ *Time is equal to distance ÷ speed.*

☛ *There are 60 minutes in 1 hour.*

Dean's speeds are in the ratio 2 : 3 and the distance is the same up the mountain road and down it, so his times are in the ratio 3 : 2.

ANSWER: 40

4. ☛ *There are 60 minutes in 1 hour.*

☛ *There are 24 hours in 1 day.*

☛ *There are about $365\frac{1}{4}$ days in 1 year.*

☛ *There are 12 months in 1 year.*

The tortoise would have run 2.7 miles in 1 year

ANSWER: 40

5. ☛ *Distance is equal to speed × time.*

☛ *Time is equal to distance ÷ speed.*

☛ *There are 60 minutes in 1 hour.*

The journey took $300 \div 90$ hours.

ANSWER: 20

6. ☛ *Time is equal to distance ÷ speed.*

☛ *Speed is equal to distance ÷ time.*

Let the distance from Newcastle to South Shields be d miles; then the time taken for the outward journey is $\frac{d}{30}$ hours.

ANSWER: $34\frac{2}{7}$ mph

7. ☛ *There are 60 minutes in 1 hour.*

In one hour they mow $\frac{1}{3} + \frac{1}{4} + \frac{1}{6}$ of the lawn.

ANSWER: 80

8. ☛ *There are 60 minutes in 1 hour.*

☛ *Distance is equal to speed × time.*

☛ *Time is equal to distance ÷ speed.*

Angus walks for 20 minutes and runs for 20 minutes, so the course is 3 miles long.

ANSWER: 45

9. ☛ *Time is equal to distance ÷ speed.*

Rosie's time for the second race was $1.2 \div 0.8$ times her time for the first race.

ANSWER: 50

10. ☛ *Distance is equal to speed × time.*

The speed increases from, say, $10v$ to $11v$. Since the distance remains the same, the time reduces from $11x$ to $10x$.

ANSWER: $11x$

11. ☛ *Time is equal to distance ÷ speed.*

Let the total distance that the jogger travels be equal to $3d$ m; then $\frac{2d}{V} + \frac{d}{U} = T$.

ANSWER: $\frac{3UV}{2U+V}$

Exercise 14

1. ☛ *The ratio of the areas of similar shapes is equal to the square of the ratio of corresponding lengths.*

   Any two circles are similar, and these two have radii in the ratio 1 : 2.

   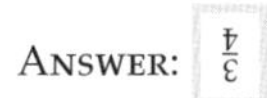

2. This problem is essentially the same as question 1 above.

   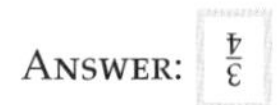

3. The radii are in the ratio 3 : 4, so that the numbers of revolutions are in the ratio 4 : 3.

   ANSWER: 90 000

4. ☛ *The length of the circumference of a circle of radius r is equal to* $2\pi r$.

   The radius is equal to $\frac{4}{80}$ miles, which is about $\frac{4}{80} \times \frac{8}{5}$ kilometres.

   ANSWER: 500 m

5. ☛ *The ratio of the areas of similar shapes is equal to the square of the ratio of corresponding lengths.*

   Any two circles are similar, and the ratio of the radius of the larger circle to that of each of the seven smaller circles is 1 : 3.

   ANSWER: 2 : 7

6. ☛ *There are 24 hours in 1 day.*

   ☛ *The length of the circumference of a circle of diameter D is equal to* πD.

   The balloon travelled $\pi \times 12\,750$ km in $13\frac{1}{2} \times 24$ hours.

   ANSWER: 120 km/h

7. ☛ *The area of a triangle is equal to* $\frac{1}{2} \times$ *base* $\times$ *height.*

☛ *The area of a circle of radius* r *and whose circumference has length* C *is equal to* $\frac{1}{2} \times C \times r$.

Let the radius of the circle be r and the length of the circumference be C; then $\frac{1}{2}PQ \times r = \frac{1}{2} \times C \times r$.

ANSWER: 1 : 1

8. ☛ *The ratio of the areas of similar shapes is equal to the square of the ratio of corresponding lengths.*

Any two circles are similar, and these two have radii in the ratio 1 : 2.

ANSWER: 5 : 7

9. ☛ *The length of the circumference of a circle of radius* r *is equal to* $2\pi r$.

The largest quarter-circle has radius 5.

ANSWER: 6π

10. ☛ *The ratio of the areas of similar shapes is equal to the square of the ratio of corresponding lengths.*

☛ *The ratio of the area of a sector of a circle with angle* $\theta°$ *to the area of the whole circle is equal to* $\theta : 360$.

The sector of the inner circle, with angle $x°$, is similar to that of the outer circle. Their radii are in the ratio 1 : 4, so that $\frac{x}{360} \times \frac{15}{16} = \frac{1}{6}$.

ANSWER: 64

11. The ratio of the diameters is 1 : 3, so the ratio of the lengths of the circumferences is 1 : 3. Therefore the disc turns three times anticlockwise about its centre, but its centre turns once clockwise about the centre of the ring.

ANSWER: Two

12. ☛ *The angle in a semicircle is 90°* [Thales' Theorem].

☛ *Pythagoras' Theorem.*

Angle BCA is 90°, so that $BC^2 + CA^2 = AB^2$.

ANSWER: 16

13. ☛ *The volume of a circular cylinder of radius r and height h is equal to* $\pi r^2 h$.

Assume that the tree is really a cylinder. The inner core of the tree makes up 81% of its volume, that is, 90% of its diameter.

ANSWER: 2 cm

Exercise 15

1. It is not possible to remove five (or more) unit cubes, because the surface area of the resulting shape is at most 3×6, not 24 as required.

   The diagram alongside shows one way to remove four unit cubes.

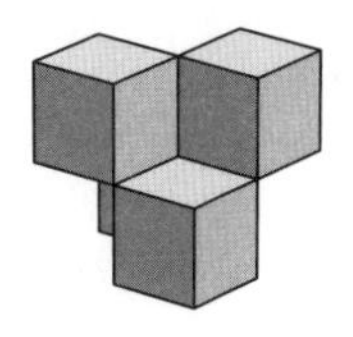

   ANSWER: Four

2. The base of the pyramid has n vertices, each of which is joined to the 'top' vertex to form an edge, so altogether the pyramid has $2n$ edges and $n + 1$ faces.

   ANSWER: $n - 1$

3. Because no cubes of the same colour meet face-to-face, the colours in the $3 \times 3 \times 3$ block will alternate, as shown in the diagram alongside.

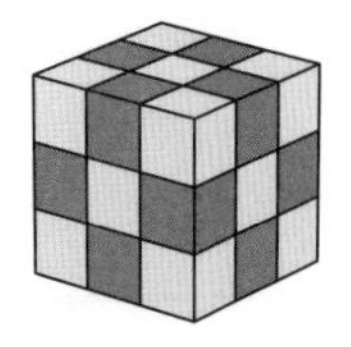

   ANSWER: One

4. ☛ *Pythagoras' Theorem.*

   Suppose that the cube is $s \times s \times s$; then $PQ = \sqrt{2}s$ and triangle PQR is right-angled at P.

   ANSWER: $\frac{1}{3}\sqrt{6}$

5. ☛ *The length of the circumference of a circle of radius r is equal to $2\pi r$.*

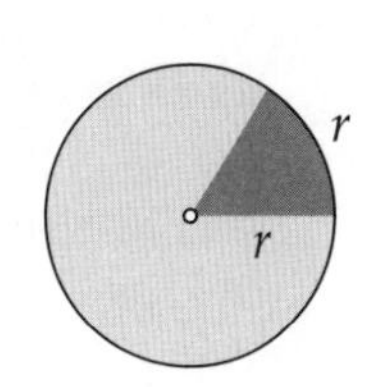

   Let the radius of the piece of cardboard be r; then each hat forms a sector of a circle with arc length r, as shown in the diagram alongside.

   ANSWER: 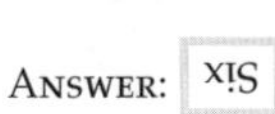

6. There is a $1 \times 1 \times 1$ cube at each vertex of the original cube. Each of these $1 \times 1 \times 1$ cubes contributes 3 to the surface area of the resulting solid.

In addition, there are two $1 \times 1 \times 1$ cubes along each edge of the original cube. Each of these $1 \times 1 \times 1$ cubes contributes 4 to the surface area.

ANSWER: 120

7. ☛ *The area of a circle of radius r is equal to πr^2.*

☛ *The area of the curved surface of a cylinder of radius r and height h is equal to $2\pi rh$.*

☛ *The sum of the integers from 1 up to n is equal to $\frac{1}{2}n(n+1)$.*

Seen from a long way above, the sculpture looks like a circle with diameter 24 cm.

The sum of the areas of the curved surfaces is equal to

$$4\pi(1 + 2 + \cdots + 12)\,\text{cm}^2.$$

ANSWER: $456\pi\,\text{cm}^2$

8. ☛ *Pythagoras' Theorem.*

ANSWER: $(3 + \sqrt{3})\,\text{m}$

9. Apart from the six edges of the hexagon, there is at least one more edge at each of the six vertices of the hexagon, so that the smallest possible number of edges is at least twelve.

The polyhedron in the diagram alongside shows that it is possible for the polyhedron to have twelve edges.

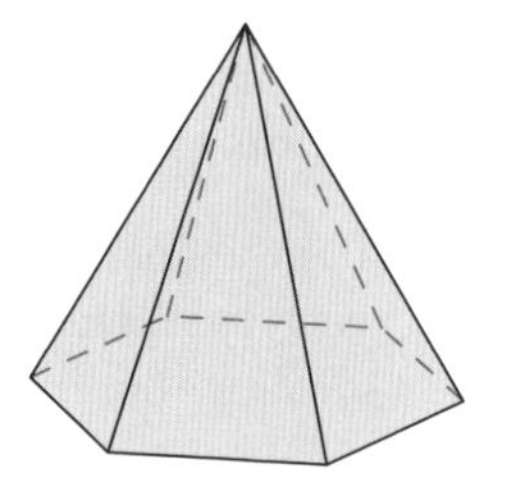

ANSWER: 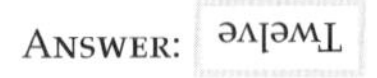

10. When folded, all five nets form the same cube, shown in the diagram alongside.

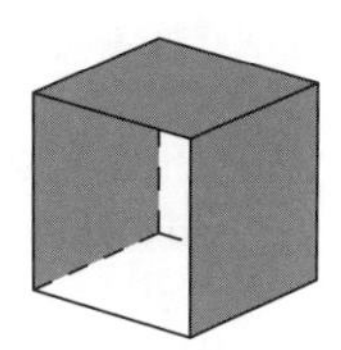

ANSWER: Four

11. Let O be the centre of the cube; then $OL = LM = MO$, so that triangle LMO is equilateral.

Repeating for other midpoints of sides, we see that LMN is part of a regular hexagon (see the diagram alongside).

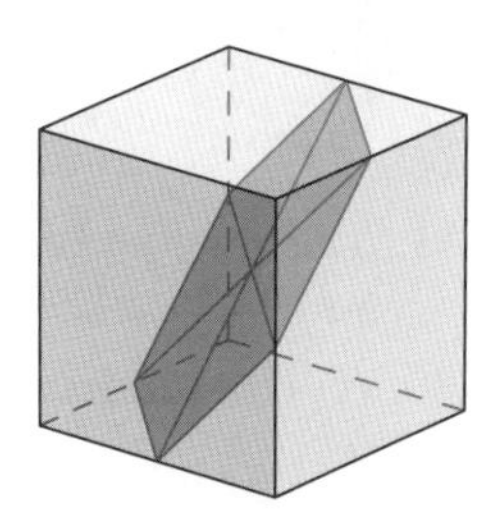

ANSWER: 120°

12. Each edge of a cross-section appears on a different face of the triangular prism, which only has five faces.

The diagram alongside shows one way to obtain a cross-section that is a trapezium, for example.

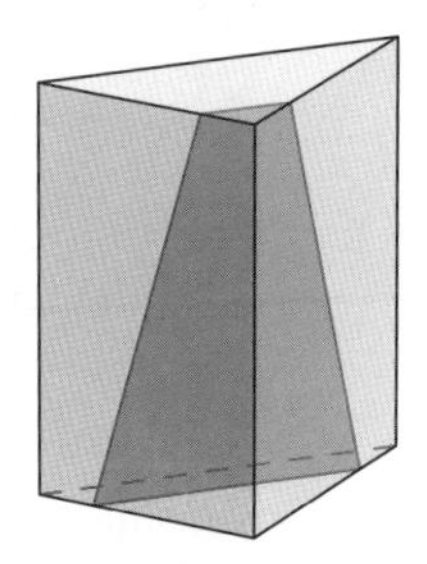

ANSWER: hexagon

13. ☛ *The ratio of the volumes of similar shapes is equal to the cube of the ratio of corresponding lengths.*

Suppose that the large vase has height 32 cm, so that the two vases are similar.

In the final position, a volume of water with depth 8 cm has been removed from the small vase. This is equivalent to removing a depth of 2 cm from the large vase.

ANSWER: 14 cm

Exercise 16

1. The headteacher may deduce that the greatest possible number of girls who are not right-handed is eight.

ANSWER: That the smallest possible number of girls who are right-handed is six.

2. ANSWER: Sandra

3. The number of children in the village is both a multiple of three and a multiple of seven.
Of the children in the village: $\frac{1}{3} - \frac{1}{7}$ can swim but not ride a bicycle; $\frac{2}{3} - \frac{1}{7}$ can ride a bicycle but bot swim; $\frac{1}{7}$ can both swim and ride a bicycle. Hence $\frac{1}{7}$ can neither swim nor ride a bicycle.

ANSWER: Three

4. Pierre cannot have been telling the truth, because then Ratna was also telling the truth, which contradicts what Pierre said.

ANSWER: Two

5. ☛ *A statement of the form "if P then Q" is false when P is true and Q is false, and not otherwise.*

For example, when $n = 3$, then $n^2 + 2 = 11$ is prime.

ANSWER: 5

6. ☛ *A statement of the form "if P then Q" is false when P is true and Q is false, and not otherwise.*

For example, when $n = 1$, then n is not prime.

ANSWER: 5

7. The Knave of Hearts can only have made the statement on Monday (telling the truth) or Friday (telling a lie).

ANSWER: Friday

8. ☛ *A statement of the form "if P then Q" is false when P is true and Q is false, and not otherwise.*

For example, when $n = 6$, then neither n nor $n - 2$ is prime.

ANSWER: 27

9. For example, if one of Alice, Beth or Diane is the mother then (at least) two statements are true.

ANSWER: Ella

10. ☛ *A statement of the form "if P then Q" is false when P is true and Q is false, and not otherwise.*

For example, when $n = 19$, then n is *not* composite.

ANSWER: 91

11. 30% of pupils do not like pears. Therefore at least 75% – 30%, that is, 45%, like both pears and oranges, and at least 80% – 55% like pears, oranges and bananas.

ANSWER: 10

12. If $a < 0$ and $b < 0$ then $\frac{1}{a} < \frac{1}{b}$ and $a < b$ cannot both be true.

However, when $a = -2$ and $b = -1$ four of the statements true.

ANSWER: Four

13. One of dArtagnan and Athos is lying, or both are. Exactly one of Porthos and Aramis is lying.

ANSWER: Two or three

14. Suppose that none of the Knaves ate any tarts; then both the first and fourth statements are true.

Suppose that exactly one of the Knaves ate some tarts; then both the third and fourth statements are true.

ANSWER: More than one of the three Knaves ate some tarts.

Exercise 17

1. As indicated by the graphs in the diagram alongside, $\sin x = \cos x$ when $x = 45°$, and $\sin 50° > \cos 50°$.

   But $\tan 50° = \dfrac{\sin 50°}{\cos 50°}$ and $\sin 50° < 1$.

   ANSWER: $\dfrac{1}{\cos 50°}$

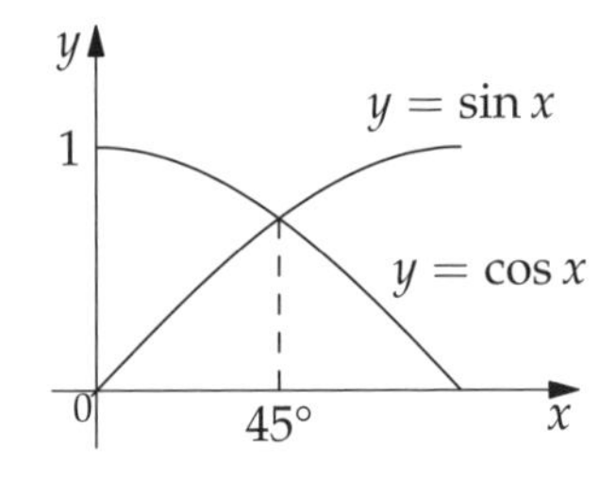

2. ☛ *The base angles of an isosceles triangle are equal.*

   Consider the figure formed by adding a rotated copy of the trapezium, as shown in the diagram below. In the copy, draw the other diagonal of the trapezium.

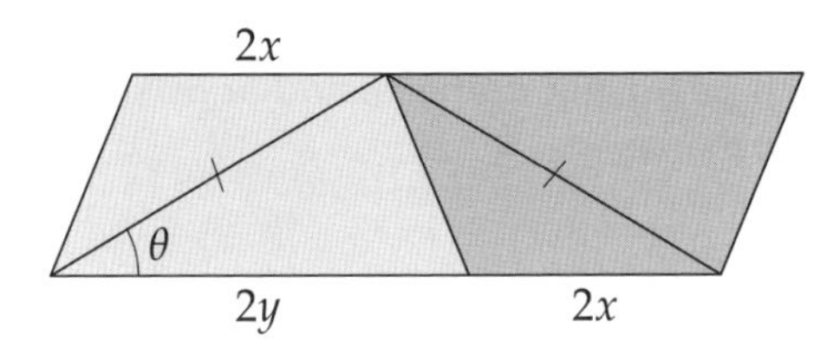

   ANSWER: $\dfrac{x+y}{\cos\theta}$

3. ☛ *A tangent to a circle is perpendicular to the radius through the point of contact.*

Consider the diagram below, which shows the circle through the points of contact and joins its centre to the centres of the five touching circles and to the five points of contact. In addition, the centres of each pair of touching circles are joined.

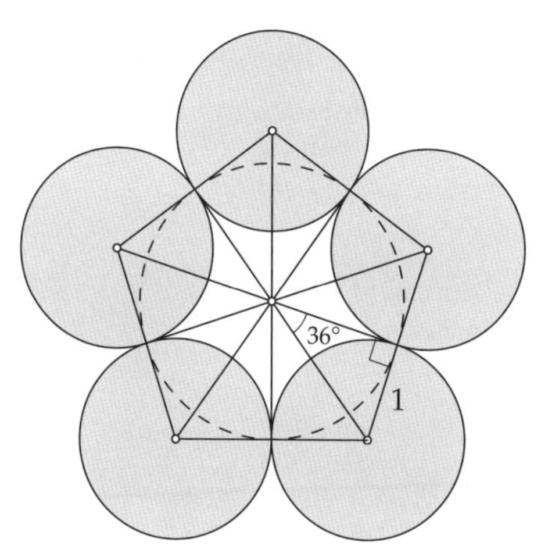

ANSWER: $\tan 54^\circ$

4. ☛ *An exterior angle of a triangle is equal to the sum of the interior opposite angles.*

☛ *The base angles of an isosceles triangle are equal.*

☛ *The sides opposite equal angles of a triangle are equal.*

☛ *The median through the vertex angle of an isosceles triangle meets the opposite side at right angles.*

Let $AB = CA = 4$ (see the diagram alongside).

Triangle BCD is isosceles, since $\angle CDB$ is equal to $\theta + \angle DCA$, which is equal to $\angle DBC$. Now insert the median CF of triangle BCD, as shown.

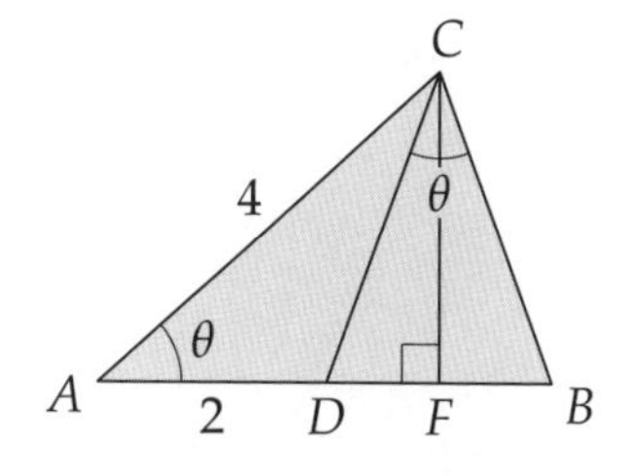

ANSWER: $\frac{3}{4}$

5. ☛ *The angles in a triangle add up to 180°.*

Because α and β add up to $90°$ it follows that $\cos\beta = \sin\alpha$ and $\sin\beta = \cos\alpha$. But α and β are different, so that $\cos\alpha$ is different to $\sin\alpha$.

ANSWER: Three

6. ☛ *The sides opposite equal angles of a triangle are equal.*

☛ *The median through the vertex angle of an isosceles triangle meets the opposite side at right angles.*

The diagram alongside shows two hatched isosceles triangles.

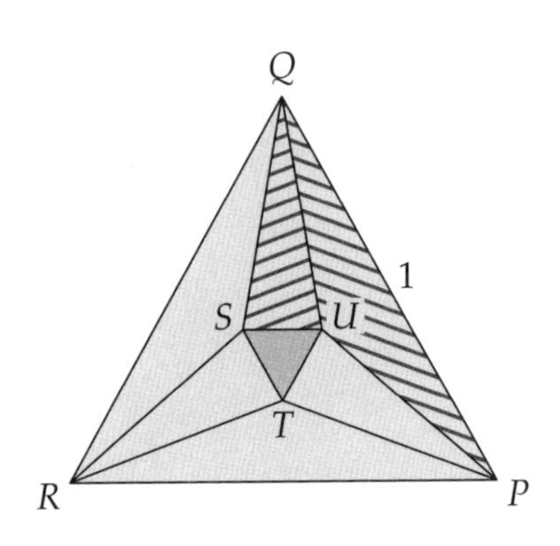

ANSWER: $\dfrac{\cos 20°}{\cos 80°}$

7. ☛ *The base angles of an isosceles triangle are equal.*

☛ *The median through the vertex angle of an isosceles triangle meets the opposite side at right angles.*

The hatched triangle in the diagram alongside is isosceles.

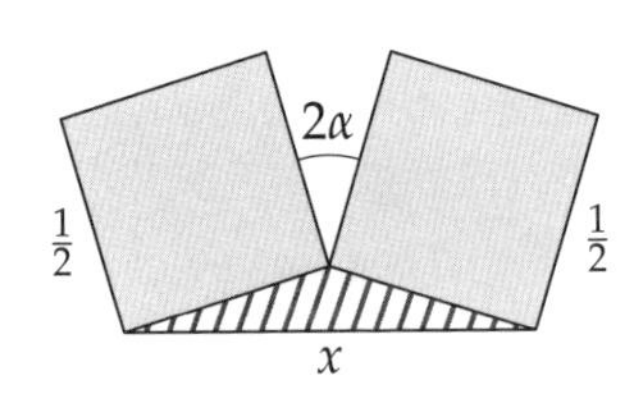

ANSWER: $\cos\alpha$

8. ☛ *For any angle* θ*:* $\sin 2\theta = 2\sin\theta\cos\theta$.

☛ *For any angle* θ*:* $\sin^2\theta + \cos^2\theta = 1$.

Whenever $\cos\theta = \frac{1}{2}$,

$$\sin 2\theta = \sin\theta \quad \text{and}$$
$$\sin\theta \neq \tfrac{1}{2}.$$

ANSWER: $\frac{1}{2}$

9. ☛ *The median through the vertex angle of an isosceles triangle meets the opposite side at right angles.*

☛ *The median through the vertex angle of an isosceles triangle bisects that angle.*

Let the radius of each disc be r; then the hatched triangle in the diagram alongside has sides of length $1+r$, $1+r$ and $2r$, and the radius of the outer circle is $1+2r$.

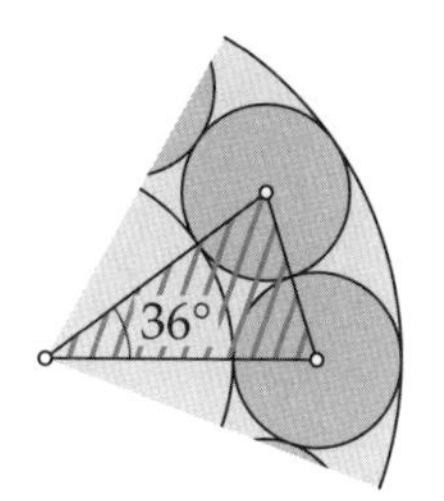

ANSWER: $\dfrac{1+\sin 18°}{1-\sin 18°}$

10. ☛ *The angles in a triangle add up to 180°.*

☛ *Vertically opposite angles are equal.*

☛ *The angles on a straight line add up to 180°.*

All the angles at F are right angles. Hence $\tan\alpha° = \dfrac{FD}{EF}$; and, for example, $\tan 50° = \dfrac{EF}{FC}$.

ANSWER: $\dfrac{\tan 10° \tan 20°}{\tan 50°}$

11. ☛ *For any a and b:* $a^3 + b^3 = (a+b)(a^2 - ab + b^2)$.

☛ *For any angle θ:* $\sin^2\theta + \cos^2\theta = 1$.

ANSWER: $(\sin x + \cos x)(1 - \sin x \cos x)$

12. ☛ *Vertically opposite angles are equal.*

☛ *With the standard notation for a triangle:* $c^2 = a^2 + b^2 - 2ab\cos C$ [cosine rule].

ANSWER: $9\sqrt{2}$

Exercise 18

1. The graph with equation $y = \dfrac{1}{x}$, for example, only passes through one vertex of the square, namely the point $(1, 1)$.

ANSWER: Three

2. A reflection in the line with equation $y = -x$ has the effect of mapping y to $-x$ and x to $-y$.

ANSWER: $3y = x + 4$

3. ☛ *The area of a quadrilateral with perpendicular diagonals is equal to half the product of the diagonals.*

At the points A and C the ellipse cuts the y-axis, so that $x = 0$. Hence $y^2 - 4y = 12$, and therefore either $y = -2$ or $y = 6$.

ANSWER: 28

4. ☛ *Pythagoras' Theorem.*

☛ *The area of a trapezium with height h and parallel sides of length a and b is equal to $\frac{1}{2}h(a + b)$.*

The shaded quadrilateral in the diagram alongside is the trapezium in the question (here k is less than zero).

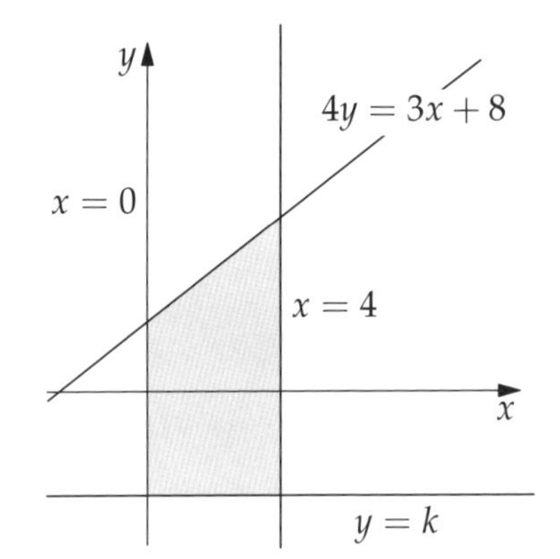

ANSWER: -1

5. Each of the four sections of the given curve, such as that shown dashed in the diagram alongside, may be reflected in the x-axis.

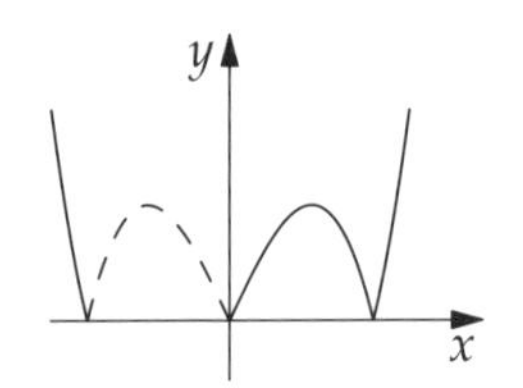

ANSWER: Sixteen

6. Because replacing y by $-y$ leads to the same equation, the curve with equation $y^2 = x(2-x)$ is symmetrical about the x-axis. Also, $y^2 \geq 0$, so that $0 \leq x \leq 2$.

ANSWER: 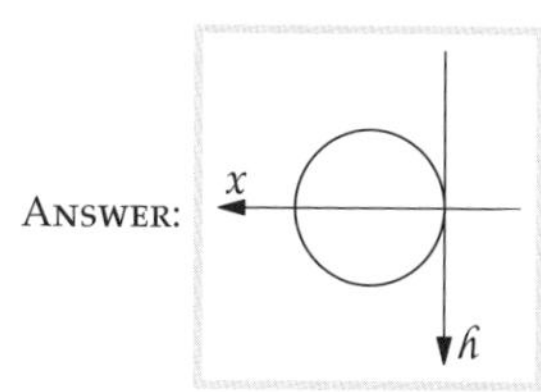

7. The closest that the line $y = x - 4$, for example, gets to the origin is at the point $(2, -2)$. The curve $y = x^4 - 4$ crosses the x-axis at $(\sqrt{2}, 0)$ and $(-\sqrt{2}, 0)$.

ANSWER: $y = x^4 - 4$

8. A rotation through 180° about the origin has the effect of mapping x to $-x$ and y to $-y$.

ANSWER: $y = -x^2 - 6x - 11$

9. The given 'curve' is symmetrical about the x-axis, so that replacing y by $-y$ in the equation leads to the same equation; in addition, some values of x are excluded by the 'curve'.

ANSWER: $|y| = \sin x$

10. Note that $x|x|$ is equal to x^2 when $x \geq 0$ and $-x^2$ when $x < 0$.

ANSWER: 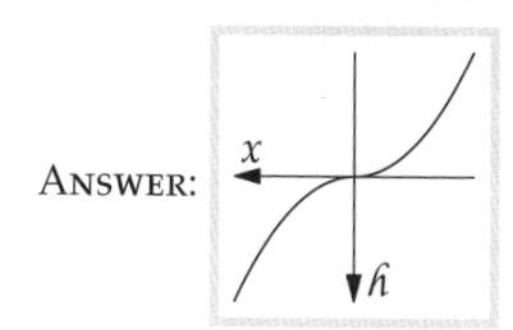

11. We have $\dfrac{1}{y} = m\sqrt{x} + c$, for some m and c.

ANSWER: $y^2 = \dfrac{1}{x + 2\sqrt{x} + 1}$

12. Replacing x by $-x$ in the equation leads to the same equation, so that the graph is symmetrical about the y-axis; in addition, the curve passes through the origin.

ANSWER:

13. ☛ *The perpendicular bisector of a chord passes through the centre of a circle.*

The perpendicular bisectors of PS and QR do not meet.

ANSWER: Fiona can draw a square and an equilateral triangle.

14. Whenever the point (x, y) lies in the region, so do the points $(x, -y)$, $(-x, y)$ and $(-x, -y)$, so that the required area is equal to four times the area of the polygon in the first quadrant formed by all points satisfying the inequality $|x-2| + |y-2| \leq 4$. The diagram alongside shows this region.

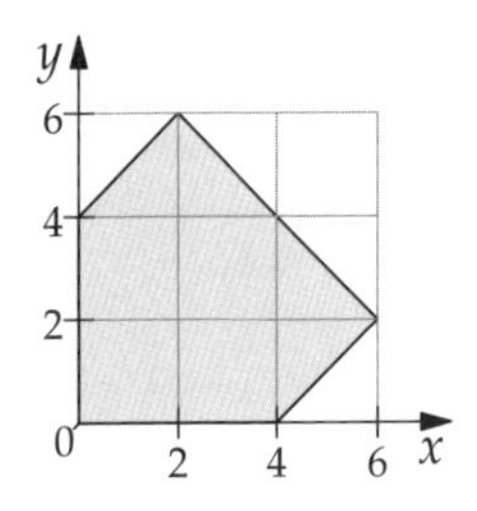

ANSWER: 96

15. Because the line with equation $y = x$ is an axis of symmetry of the curve, replacing x by y and y by x leads to the same equation. In other words, the equations $x = \dfrac{py+q}{ry+s}$ and $y = \dfrac{px+q}{rx+s}$ are the same equation. It follows that $rxy - q$ is the same (for any x and y) in both cases.

ANSWER: $p + s = 0$

Exercise 19

1. ☛ *The number of different ways of placing n different objects in order is equal to $n!$.*

Consider the four particular cards that are dealt; they may be placed in order (ignoring the face value) in 4! different ways.

ANSWER: $\frac{1}{24}$

2. Notice that every student speaks a common language with exactly four other students.

ANSWER: $\frac{4}{5}$

3. ☛ *There are 52 weeks in 1 year.*

We have

$$\frac{1}{T} = 52 \times \frac{6}{49} \times \frac{5}{48} \times \frac{4}{47} \times \frac{3}{46} \times \frac{2}{45} \times \frac{1}{44}$$

ANSWER: one quarter of a million

4. ☛ *Suppose that the probability of event A is a, and the probability of event B is b whatever the outcome of A, then the probability of both events A and B happening is equal to $a \times b$.*

Let the number of boys in the class be b; then $\frac{10}{10+b} \times \frac{9}{9+b} = \frac{15}{100}$.

ANSWER: Fifteen

5. ☛ *The angle in a semicircle is 90°* [Thales' Theorem].

When $\angle RPQ$ is acute, the point P lies *outside* the hatched semicircle shown in the diagram alongside.

ANSWER: $1 - \frac{\pi}{8}$

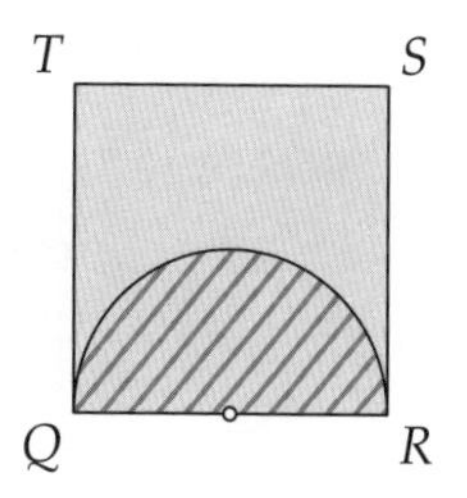

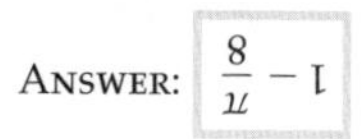

6. ☛ *Suppose that the probability of event A is a, and the probability of event B is b whatever the outcome of A, then the probability of both events A and B happening is equal to $a \times b$.*

☛ *Suppose that the probability of event A is a, the probability of event B is b, and the events cannot happen together, then the probability of either one event or the other happening is equal to $a + b$.*

For a successful outcome, the marbles are either red then blue, or blue then blue.

The probability that the marbles are red then blue is equal to

$$\frac{n}{m+n} \times \frac{m}{m+n+k}.$$

ANSWER: $\frac{m}{m+n}$

7. ☛ *A point equidistant from two sides of a triangle lies on the angle bisector through the common vertex.*

☛ *A triangle with angles of 30°, 60° and 90° is half an equilateral triangle.*

☛ *Two triangles are congruent when two angles and a side of one are equal to two angles and the corresponding side of the other* [AAS test for congruency].

The point P being nearer to AB than to CA is equivalent to P lying inside the hatched triangle in the diagram alongside.

The hatched triangle is congruent to the other two small right-angled triangles in the diagram (AAS).

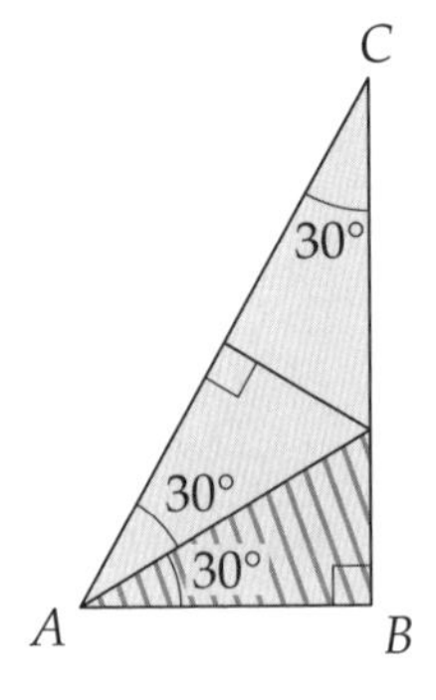

ANSWER: $\frac{1}{3}$

8. ☛ *Suppose that the probability of event A is a, and the probability of event B is b whatever the outcome of A, then the probability of both events A and B happening is equal to $a \times b$.*

☛ *Suppose that the probability of event A is a, the probability of event B is b, and the events cannot happen together, then the probability of either one event or the other happening is equal to $a + b$.*

Tom goes on to win the competition provided:

✲ either he hits the target on the first attempt and Geri misses;

✲ or they both miss or both hit on the first attempt, and then Tom goes on to win.

Let the probability that Tom goes on to win the competition be w; then

$$w = \tfrac{4}{5} \times \tfrac{1}{3} + \left(\tfrac{4}{5} \times \tfrac{2}{3} + \tfrac{1}{5} \times \tfrac{1}{3}\right) \times w.$$

ANSWER: $\frac{2}{3}$

Exercise 20

1. ☛ *For any a and b:* $a^2 - b^2 = (a-b)(a+b)$ [difference of two squares].

   ☛ *For any positive a and any powers p and q:* $(a^p)^q = a^{p \times q}$.

   Note that $x^4 - y^4 = (x^2)^2 - (y^2)^2$.

   ANSWER: 2

2. Consider the result of adding the three given equations.

   ANSWER: 250

3. 15 peaches, 9 oranges and 6 melons cost £9.54, whereas 8 peaches, 16 oranges and 6 melons cost £8.98. Hence 7 peaches cost $(954 - 898)$ pence more than 7 oranges.

   ANSWER: Eight pence

4. The given equation is true for all a, b and c, so set $a = 2$, $b = -1$ and $c = -1$, for example.

   ANSWER: 3

5. Suppose that the ratio is 2 : 1 in n years time, and that at that time Jan's age is a years; then $3 \times (a-n) = 2a - n$ and $4 \times (a - n - 3) = 2a - n - 3$.

   ANSWER: Nine

6. ☛ *For any a and b:* $a^2 - b^2 = (a-b)(a+b)$ [difference of two squares].

   ☛ *For any positive a and any powers p and q:* $(a^p)^q = a^{p \times q}$.

   Note that, for example, $x^4 - 1 = (x^2 - 1)(x^2 + 1)$.

   ANSWER: $x^8 - 1$

7. Note that $f(f(x)) = -\dfrac{1}{x}$.

   ANSWER: $-\dfrac{1}{x}$

8. Note that $x^2y + xy^2 = xy(x + y)$, and multiplying each term in the first equation by $2xy$, we obtain $2(x + y) = xy$.

ANSWER: 008

9. ☛ *Corresponding angles on parallel lines are equal.*

☛ *The exterior angle of a square is 90°.*

☛ *When two angles of one triangle are equal to two angles of a second triangle the triangles are similar* [AA test for similar triangles].

Let the length of the sides of the smallest square be x cm. Now the triangles PXQ and QYR shown in the diagram alongside are similar (AA), so that $\dfrac{8}{x} = \dfrac{42 + x}{8 + x}$.

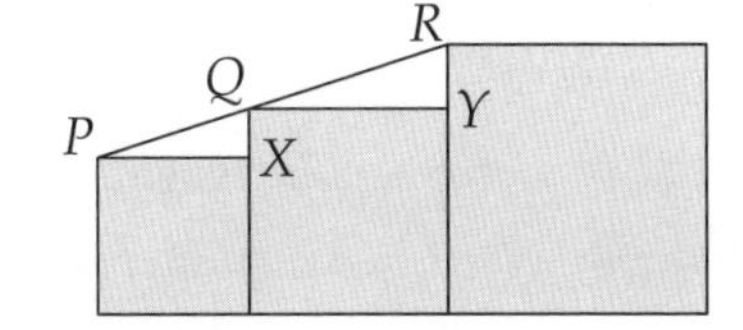

ANSWER: 2 cm and 32 cm

10. ☛ *Distance is equal to speed × time.*

☛ *There are 60 minutes in 1 hour.*

Note that $y \times 2 + x \times 4 = 51$ and $y \times \dfrac{17}{6} + x \times \dfrac{17}{6} = 51$.

ANSWER: $10\frac{1}{2}$

11. ☛ *Time is equal to distance ÷ speed.*

Let the speed of the train be s mph, let the length of the tunnel be 4ℓ miles, and let d miles be the distance from the front of the train to the start of the tunnel when the engineer gets the warning; then $\dfrac{3\ell}{10} = \dfrac{4\ell + d}{s}$ and $\dfrac{\ell}{10} = \dfrac{d}{s}$.

ANSWER: 20

12. Multiplying the second equation by M and substituting from the first equation, we obtain $240 + M^2 = 46M$, so that $M = 6$ or $M = 40$. We find two values for S in a similar way. Then we find C by using the first equation, together with the fact that S, M and C are integers.

ANSWER: 20

13. The two numbers are not equal, so let them be a and b, where $a > b$; then $\frac{a}{b} = \frac{a+b}{a-b}$, and hence $\left(\frac{a}{b}\right)^2 - 2 \times \frac{a}{b} - 1 = 0$.

ANSWER: $1 + \sqrt{2} : 1$

14. ☛ *Corresponding angles on parallel lines are equal.*

☛ *When two angles of one triangle are equal to two angles of a second triangle the triangles are similar* [AA test for similar triangles].

☛ *The opposite sides of a parallelogram are equal.*

The triangles RMU, WTM and XYZ are similar (AA); so they have sides in the ratio 4 : 3 : 2. Also $UMVZ$ and $MTYS$ are parallelograms. Let the length of WT, SV and UR be $4k$; then $TM = 3k$ and $MU = 6k$, so that $YZ = 13k$.

ANSWER: $\frac{12}{13}$

15. Note that $x^3 = px^2 + qx = (p^2 + q)x + pq$.
Setting $p = 1$ and $q = 3$, we get $x^3 = 4x + 3$, for example.

ANSWER: $8x + 5$

16. ☛ *For any c and d:* $(c + d)^2 = c^2 + 2cd + d^2$.

Squaring the required fraction, we get

$$\left(\frac{a+b}{a-b}\right)^2 = \frac{a^2 + 2ab + b^2}{a^2 - 2ab + b^2} = \frac{(a^2 + b^2) + 2ab}{(a^2 + b^2) - 2ab},$$

ANSWER: $\sqrt{2}$

17. ☛ *For any c and d:* $(c+d)^2 = c^2 + 2cd + d^2$.

Note that $x^2 + y^2 + 2xy + 6x + 6y + 4 = (x+y)^2 + 6(x+y) + 4$, which may be written $\left[(x+y)+3\right]^2 - 9 + 4$.

ANSWER: −5

18. Replacing $x+3$ by a and $y-3$ by b, we get $(a+b)^2 = ab$, so that $a^2 + ab + b^2 = 0$. In other words, the sum of three non-negative numbers is equal to zero.

ANSWER: One

19. ☛ *For any c and d:* $(c+d)^2 = c^2 + 2cd + d^2$.

Note that $x^2 + \left(\frac{1}{x}\right)^2 = \left(x + \frac{1}{x}\right)^2 - 2$.

ANSWER: 7

20. Replacing $x+4$ by a and $y-4$ by b, we get $(a+b)^2 = ab$, so that $a^2 + ab + b^2 = 0$. In other words, the sum of three non-negative numbers is equal to zero.

ANSWER: One

Exercise 21

1. ☛ *The angle in a semicircle is 90°* [Thales' Theorem].

☛ *Pythagoras' Theorem.*

Note that $60^2 + 25^2 = 52^2 + SP^2$.

ANSWER: 39

2. ☛ *Pythagoras' Theorem.*

Let the radius of the arc with centre Q be r cm; then

$$(17 - r) + (15 - r) = 8.$$

ANSWER: 12 cm

3. ☛ *The converse*† *of Pythagoras' Theorem.*

☛ *The base angles of an isosceles triangle are equal.*

☛ *The angles in a triangle add up to 180°.*

☛ *The length of the circumference of a circle of radius r is equal to $2\pi r$.*

Join the centres of the circles, as shown in the diagram alongside.

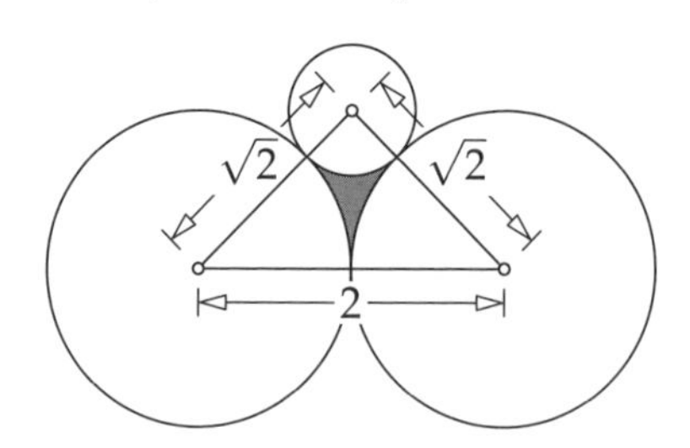

ANSWER: $\frac{1}{2}\sqrt{2}\pi$

4. ☛ *The area of a circle of radius r is equal to πr^2.*

Let the outer radius of a roll containing 80 m of tape be r cm; then $r^2 - 3^2 = 4 \times \left(4^2 - 3^2\right)$.

ANSWER: 6 cm

†The converse of a theorem is the statement obtained by interchanging what is given and what follows.

5. ☛ *The length of the arc with angle $\theta°$ at the centre of a circle of radius r is equal to $\dfrac{\theta}{360} \times 2\pi r$.*

Let the radii of the arcs AA' and BB' be a and b respectively; then

$$\frac{x}{360} \times 2\pi a = \frac{x}{360} \times 2\pi b + 2(a - b).$$

ANSWER: $\dfrac{360}{\pi}$

6. ☛ *Pythagoras' Theorem.*

Join the centres of the circles to form a square, as shown in the diagram alongside. The length of each diagonal of the square is equal to 2.

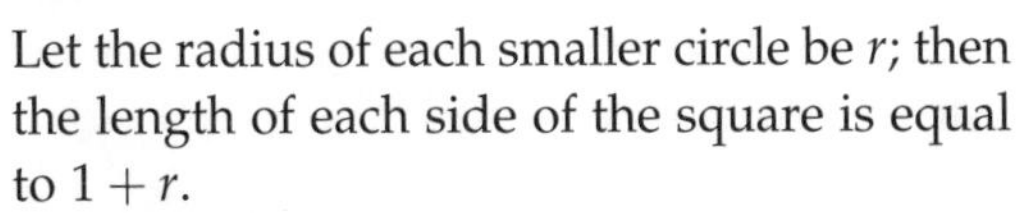

Let the radius of each smaller circle be r; then the length of each side of the square is equal to $1 + r$.

ANSWER: $\sqrt{2} - 1$

7. ☛ *Pythagoras' Theorem.*

Join the centres of the four quarter-circles to form a square with sides of length 2, as shown in the diagram alongside. Thus the length of a diagonal of this square is equal to $\sqrt{2} \times 2$.

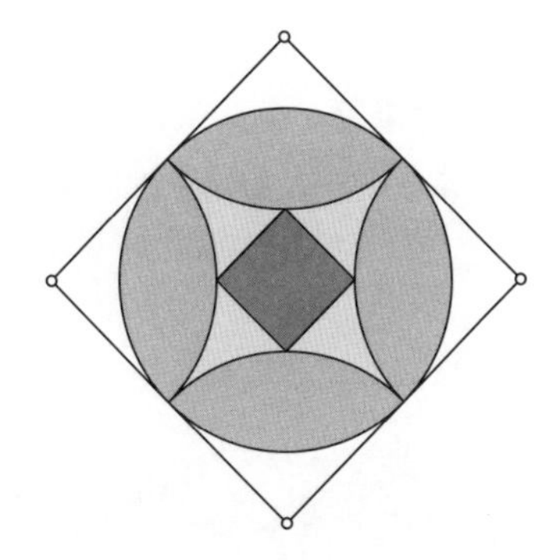

Let the length of each side of the given square be s; then

$$2 + \sqrt{2} \times s = \sqrt{2} \times 2.$$

ANSWER: $2 - \sqrt{2}$

8. ☛ *The base angles of an isosceles triangle are equal.*

☛ *The angles on a straight line add up to 180°.*

☛ *The angle between a tangent and a chord is equal to the angle in the alternate segment* [alternate segment theorem].

☛ *An exterior angle of a triangle is equal to the sum of the interior opposite angles.*

Note that $\angle LMN = \theta$ (alternate segment theorem) and $\angle LMN = \phi + \angle RNM$.

ANSWER: $3\theta - 180°$

9. ☛ *Pythagoras' Theorem.*

Join the centres of the semicircles, as shown in the diagram alongside.

Let r be the radius of the smaller semicircle, and consider the hatched triangle shown.

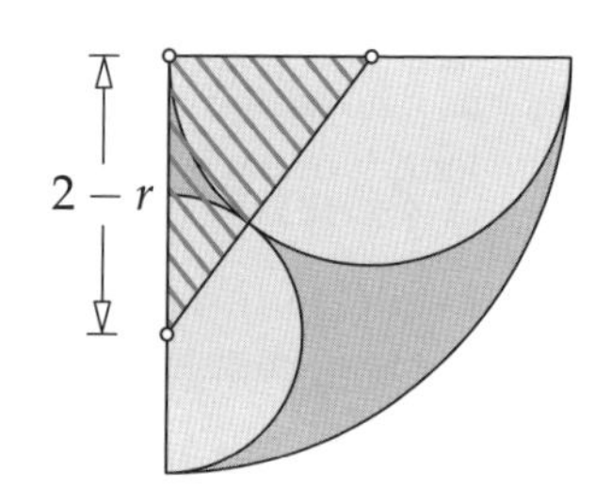

ANSWER: $\frac{2}{3}$

10. ☛ *The angle between a tangent and a chord is equal to the angle in the alternate segment* [alternate segment theorem].

☛ *The angles in a triangle add up to 180°.*

Join S to U, and consider the hatched triangle in the diagram alongside.

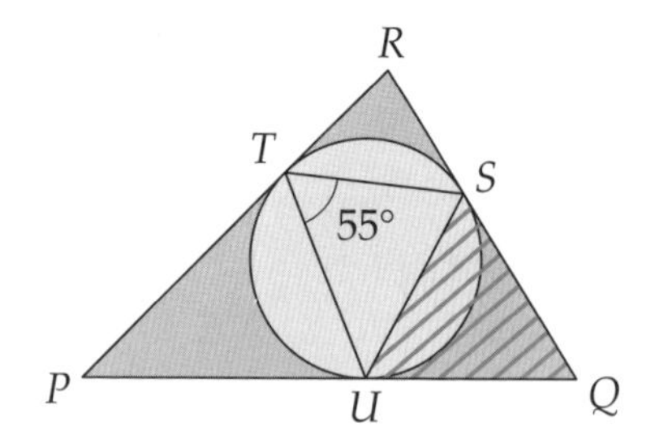

ANSWER: $70°$

11. ☛ *The angle at the centre of a circle is equal to twice the angle at the circumference.*

☛ *An exterior angle of a triangle is equal to the sum of the interior opposite angles.*

Join A to C, and consider the hatched triangle in the diagram alongside.

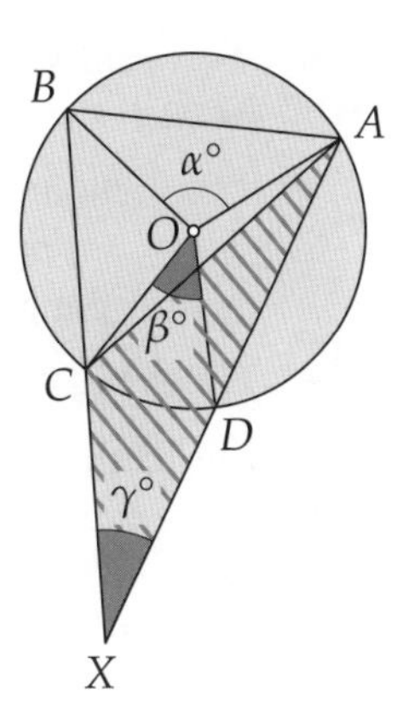

ANSWER: $\frac{1}{2}\alpha - \frac{1}{2}\beta$

12. ☛ *Pythagoras' Theorem.*

Consider the circle shown in the diagram alongside.

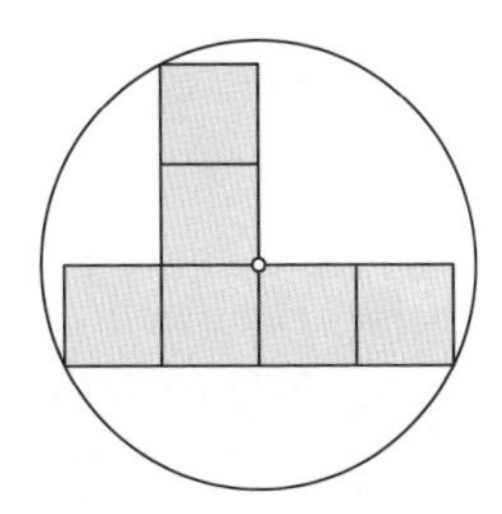

ANSWER: $2\sqrt{5}$

13. ☛ *The two tangents drawn from a point to a circle are equal.*

☛ *The area of a trapezium with height h and parallel sides of length a and b is equal to* $\frac{1}{2}h(a+b)$.

Note that $PQ + RS = SP + QR$, so that the height of the trapezium is equal to $2 \times 600 \div 50$.

ANSWER: 12 cm

14. ☛ *The opposite angles of a cyclic quadrilateral add up to 180°.*

Join W to Z, as shown in the diagram alongside.

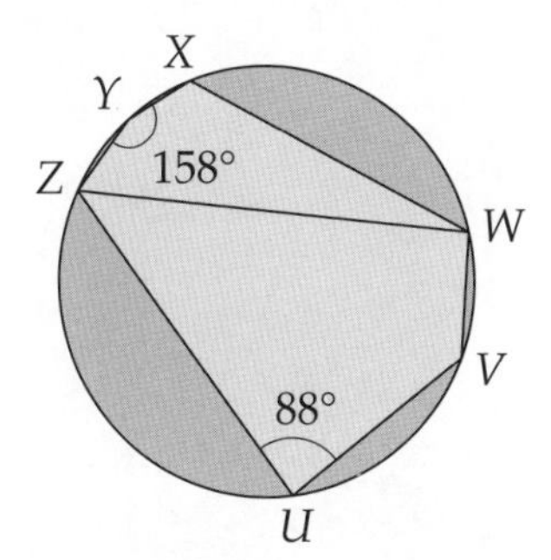

ANSWER: 114°

15. ☛ *A tangent to a circle is perpendicular to the radius through the point of contact.*

☛ *Two right-angled triangles are congruent when the hypotenuse and a side of one are equal to the hypotenuse and a side of the other* [RHS test for congruency].

☛ *The angles of a quadrilateral add up to 360°.*

Join O to the points of contact of the three tangents, as shown in the diagram alongside. The hatched and cross-hatched triangles are congruent (RHS).

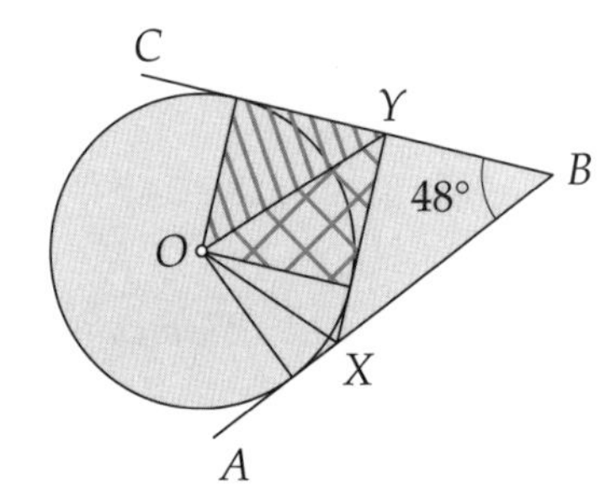

ANSWER: 66°

16. ☛ *The length of the circumference of a circle of radius r is equal to* $2\pi r$.

The two hatched circles in the diagram alongside touch, so that the distance between their centres is $\frac{1}{2}$.

ANSWER: $\frac{5}{2}\pi$

17. ☛ *The two tangents drawn from a point to a circle are equal.*

☛ *An exterior angle of a triangle is equal to the sum of the interior opposite angles.*

☛ *The base angles of an isosceles triangle are equal.*

☛ *The angles in a triangle add up to 180°.*

Extend the tangents QP and SR until they meet, as shown in the diagram below; then the hatched triangle is isosceles, with vertex angle equal to $40° - 30°$.

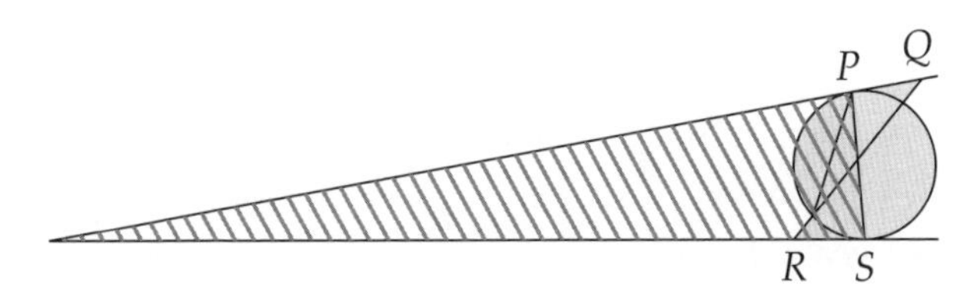

ANSWER: 35

18. ☛ *The converse of Pythagoras' Theorem.*

☛ *The base angles of an isosceles triangle are equal.*

☛ *The angles in a triangle add up to 180°.*

☛ *A tangent to a circle is perpendicular to the radius through the point of contact.*

☛ *Sides opposite equal angles of a triangle are equal.*

☛ *Pythagoras' Theorem.*

☛ *For any a and b:* $a^2 - b^2 = (a - b)(a + b)$ [difference of two squares].

Let the radius of the semicircle be r, as shown in the diagram alongside; then consider the hatched right-angled isosceles triangle.

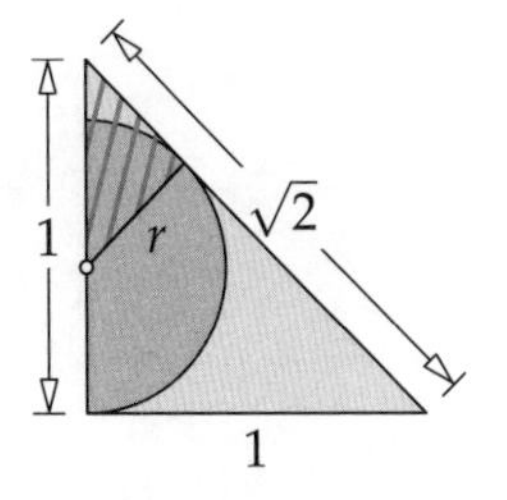

ANSWER: $\sqrt{2} - 1$

19. ☛ *Pythagoras' Theorem.*

☛ *For any positive a, the height of an equilateral triangle of side 2a is equal to $\sqrt{3}a$.*

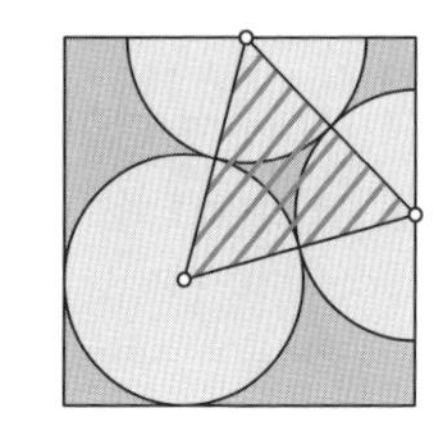

Join the centres of the circle and semicircles, as shown in the diagram alongside; then the hatched triangle is equilateral, and the diagonal of the square has length $\sqrt{2} + \sqrt{3} + 1$.

ANSWER: $4 + 2\sqrt{6} + 2\sqrt{2}$

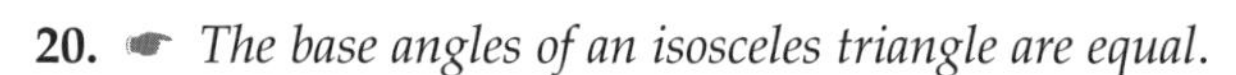

20. ☛ *The base angles of an isosceles triangle are equal.*

☛ *Sides opposite equal angles of a triangle are equal.*

☛ *Pythagoras' Theorem.*

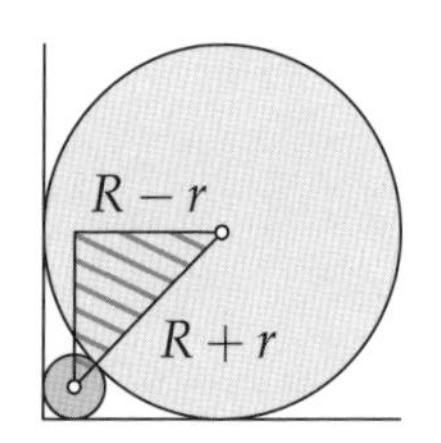

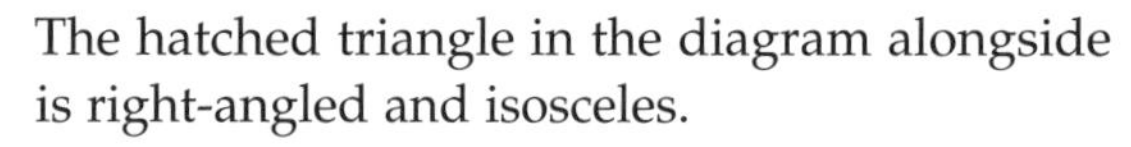

The hatched triangle in the diagram alongside is right-angled and isosceles.

ANSWER: $3 + 3\sqrt{2}$

21. ☛ *The two tangents drawn from a point to a circle are equal.*

☛ *Pythagoras' Theorem.*

Let the sides of the square have length 2, and let $RT = x$; then $TU = (2 - x) + 1$.

ANSWER: $4 : 3$

22. ☛ *A tangent to a circle is perpendicular to the radius through the point of contact.*

☛ *Corresponding angles on parallel lines are equal.*

☛ *When two angles of one triangle are equal to two angles of a second triangle the triangles are similar* [AA test for similar triangles].

☛ *A right-angled triangle in which the length of the hypotenuse is twice the length of one of the other sides is half an equilateral triangle.*

☛ *Each angle in an equilateral triangle is equal to 60°.*

Let the radii of the circles be 1, r and s, from smallest to largest, so that $1 + 2r + s = 16$.

The two hatched triangles in the diagram below are similar (AA), so that $\dfrac{r-1}{r+1} = \dfrac{s-r}{s+r}$.

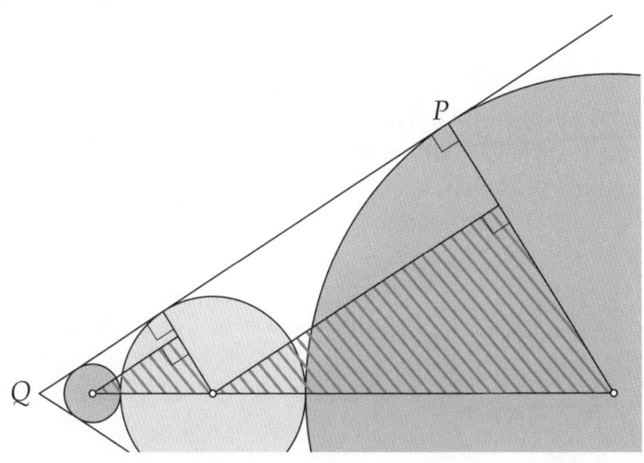

ANSWER: 009

23. ☛ *A tangent to a circle is perpendicular to the radius through the point of contact.*

☛ *Pythagoras' Theorem.*

Let the radius of the largest circle which can be placed in the shaded region be r. Consider the hatched triangle in the diagram alongside.

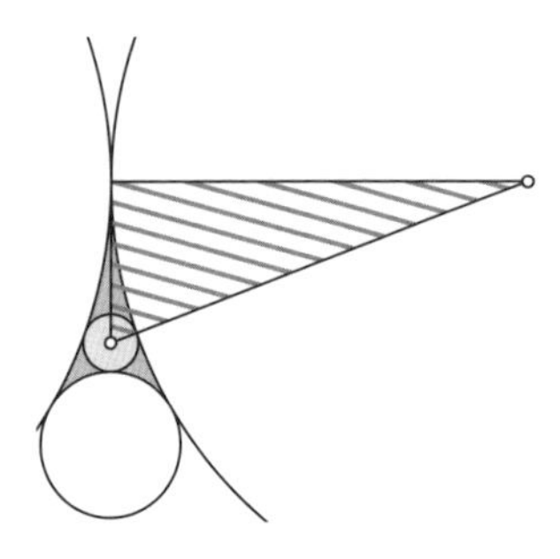

ANSWER: 9

24. ☛ *A tangent to a circle is perpendicular to the radius through the point of contact.*

☛ *Pythagoras' Theorem.*

Join the centre of the circle radius R to its points of contact with OA and OB, and draw the radius through the centres of the circles, as shown in the diagram alongside.

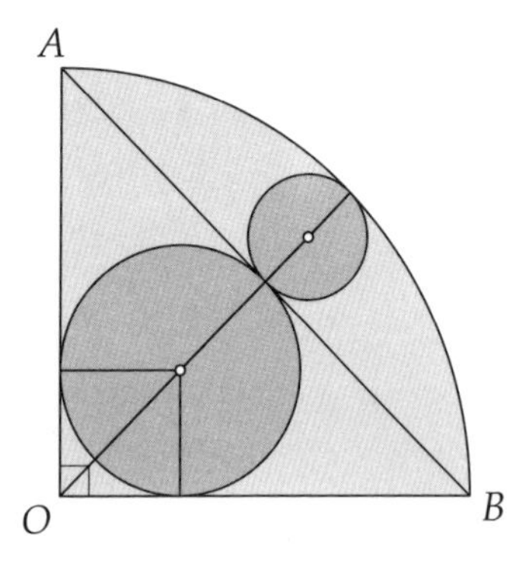

Then

$$R + \sqrt{2}R = \frac{1}{\sqrt{2}} \quad \text{and}$$

$$2r + \frac{1}{\sqrt{2}} = 1.$$

ANSWER: 2

25. ☛ *A tangent to a circle is perpendicular to the radius through the point of contact.*

☛ *Pythagoras' Theorem.*

Let the radius of circle C_1 be r, that of circle C_2 be s, and that of circle C_3 be R.

Join the centres of the circles, and join each circle to its points of contact with ℓ_1, ℓ_2, as shown in the diagram alongside.

Considering the three hatched right-angled triangles shown, we have

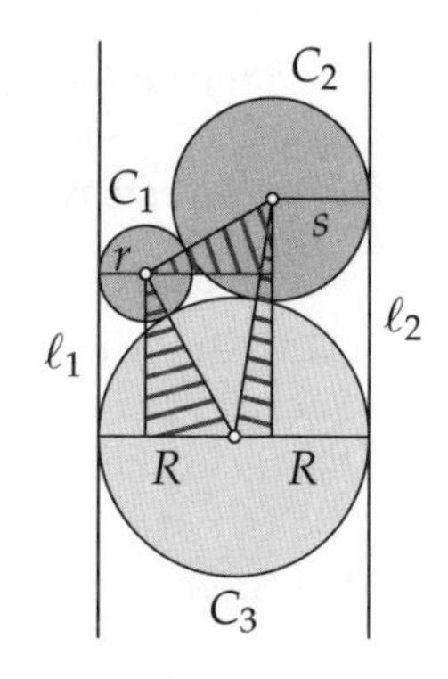

$$(r+s)^2 = (2R-r-s)^2 + \left(2\sqrt{Rs} - 2\sqrt{Rr}\right)^2.$$

ANSWER: $2\sqrt{rs}$

Exercise 22

1. ☛ *The number of different ways of placing n different objects in order is equal to $n!$.*

☛ *Suppose there are m ways of making one choice and, whichever first choice is made, n ways of making a second choice, then there are $m \times n$ ways of making both choices in succession* [multiplication principle].

There are 3! ways of arranging the blue Fnargs.

Note that the colours alternate. Suppose that the heads of the blue Fnargs are in the order 234 (from left to right), for example. Then the heads of the red Fnargs are either in the order 342 (with the red 3 at the left of the line), or in the order 423 (with the red 3 at the right of the line).

ANSWER: Twelve

2. ☛ *Suppose there are m ways of making one choice and, whichever first choice is made, n ways of making a second choice, then there are $m \times n$ ways of making both choices in succession* [multiplication principle].

Suppose that there is no restriction on the maximum number of substitutes. Then the team at the end of the game comprises:

- one goalkeeper chosen from two;
- four defenders chosen from five;
- four midfielders chosen from five; and
- two forwards chosen from three.

However, some of these teams have four substitutes.

ANSWER: 118

3. ☛ *Suppose there are m ways of making one choice and, whichever first choice is made, n ways of making a second choice, then there are* $m \times n$ *ways of making both choices in succession* [multiplication principle].

The middle digit may be anything from 2 to 8.

If the middle digit is 6, for example, then the leftmost digit may be anything from 1 to 5 and the rightmost digit may be anything from 7 to 9.

ANSWER: 84

4. ☛ *Suppose there are m ways of making one choice and, whichever first choice is made, n ways of making a second choice, then there are* $m \times n$ *ways of making both choices in succession* [multiplication principle].

Note that the leftmost digit is never 0.

The rightmost three digits may be in increasing order, with the leftmost digit breaking the pattern, or *vice versa*. In the first case, there are 8 choices for the rightmost three digits—012, 123, 234, and so on. For all but two of these, there are 8 choices for the leftmost digit; for 012 and 123, there are 9 choices.

ANSWER: 130

5. ☛ *Suppose there are m ways of making one choice and, whichever first choice is made, n ways of making a second choice, then there are* $m \times n$ *ways of making both choices in succession* [multiplication principle].

☛ *Pythagoras' Theorem.*

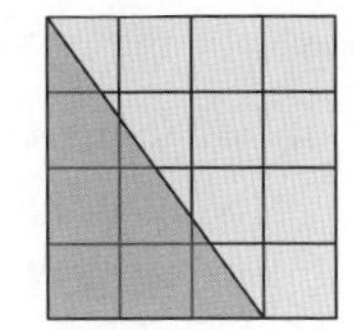

Each of the 25 vertices in the diagram is an integer distance away from any other vertex in the same row or column. Taking the pair 'point A, point B' to be the same as the pair 'point B, point A', this gives $\frac{1}{2} \times 25 \times 8$ pairs.

There are also pairs of vertices at the corners of 3-4-5 triangles, such as that shown in the diagram alongside.

ANSWER: 108

6. ☛ *The number of different ways of placing n different objects in order is equal to n!.*

☛ *Suppose there are m ways of making one choice and, whichever first choice is made, n ways of making a second choice, then there are $m \times n$ ways of making both choices in succession* [multiplication principle].

Since $2+3+4+5+6+7+8$ is equal to 35, the only digit that may be placed in the square where the row and column cross is 7.

Only 7, 4 and 2 may be placed in the same line as 8; there are 3! ways of placing 2, 4 and 8.

ANSWER: 72

7. Note that a bracelet may be turned round or turned over.

The red beads appear in consecutive groups, either 4, $3+1$, $2+2$, $2+1+1$, or $1+1+1+1$; in the second case, for example, the two possible bracelets are shown in the diagrams below, where red beads are dark grey and yellow beads are light grey.

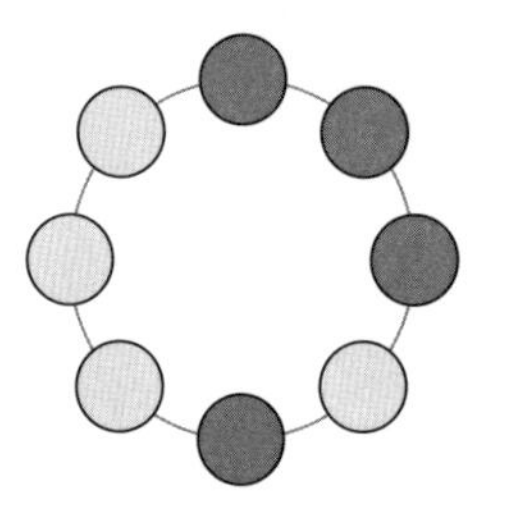

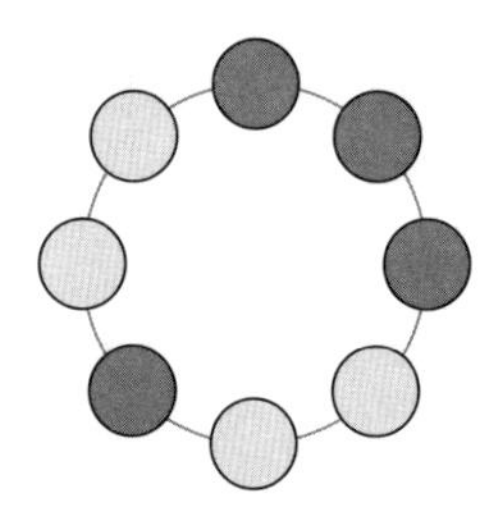

ANSWER: Eight

8. ☛ *Suppose there are m ways of making one choice and, whichever first choice is made, n ways of making a second choice, then there are $m \times n$ ways of making both choices in succession* [multiplication principle].

Taking the choice 'house A, house B' to be the same as 'house B, house A', there are $\frac{1}{2} \times 5 \times 4$ ways of choosing the two houses that receive the correct letter.

ANSWER: 20

9. ☛ *The first n odd integers add up to n^2.*

Suppose that the number of £2 coins that you use is 36, for example; then the number of £1 coins that you use could be 0, 1, 2, ..., 28, with the rest of the £100 made up from 50p coins. In other words, when the number of £2 coins that you use is 36, there are 29 possible ways to make a sum of £100.

ANSWER: 2601

10. ☛ *Suppose there are m ways of making one choice and, whichever first choice is made, n ways of making a second choice, then there are $m \times n$ ways of making both choices in succession* [multiplication principle].

Jessica has 3 choices for the first line of her route; then, whichever line is chosen, she has 3 choices for the station at which she changes lines. The end of the route is the same as the first part in reverse (consider *starting* at Y), and there is only one way to join these parts up, if required, whichever lines have been chosen.

ANSWER: 81

11. ☛ *The number of different ways of placing n different objects in order is equal to $n!$.*

☛ *Suppose there are m ways of making one choice and, whichever first choice is made, n ways of making a second choice, then there are $m \times n$ ways of making both choices in succession* [multiplication principle].

We may assume that 0 is one of the digits of the number. We may treat 0 like any other digit; if 0 appears as the first digit, then we just ignore it, since this does not change the sum of the digits.

Now the sum of the digits from 1 to 9 is 45, so that the unused (non-zero) digits add up to 9.

There are three cases, determined by the number of unused non-zero digits, which may be one, two or three.

For example, there are four ways in which two non-zero digits may be unused: $1 + 8$, $2 + 7$, $3 + 6$ and $4 + 5$. In each case the number has 8 digits (remember, 0 is one of them), so altogether there are $4 \times 8!$ such numbers.

ANSWER: 107

12. Let the number of digits of N be d, where $d < 2002$; then

$$10N + 1 = 3 \times (10^d + N),$$

so that $N = \dfrac{3 \times 10^d - 1}{7}$.

ANSWER: 333

Exercise 23

1. ☛ *The ratio of the areas of similar shapes is equal to the square of the ratio of corresponding lengths.*

   The similar cones have corresponding lengths in the ratio $a : a+b : a+b+c$.

   ANSWER: $5 : 7$

2. ☛ *Pythagoras' Theorem.*

   The rectangular cut with largest area is like that shown in the diagram alongside.

   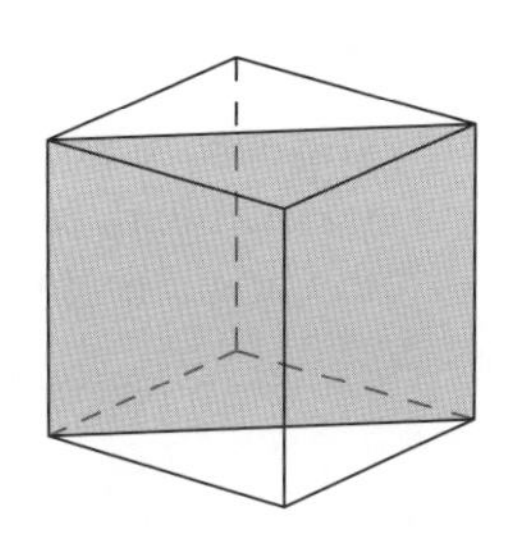

   ANSWER: $\frac{1}{3}\sqrt{2}$

3. ☛ *Pythagoras' Theorem.*

   The longest unbroken line that Beatrix can draw on the cube is like that shown in the diagram alongside.

   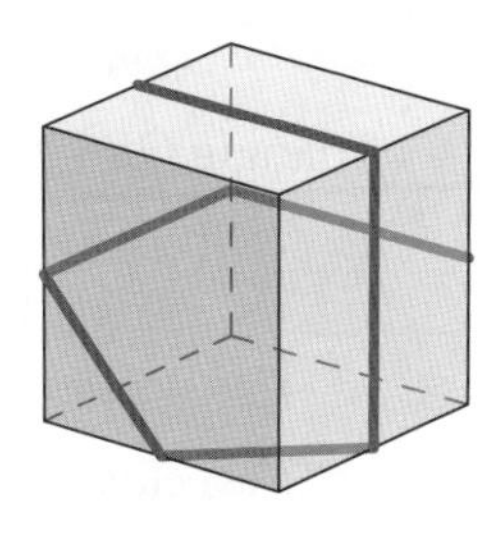

   ANSWER: $8 + 2\sqrt{2}$

4. ☛ *Pythagoras' Theorem.*

   The total surface area of the two prisms is equal to the surface area of the cube plus twice the area of the rectangle.

   ANSWER: $8(3 + \sqrt{2})\ \text{cm}^2$

5. ☛ *The ratio of the volumes of similar shapes is equal to the cube of the ratio of corresponding lengths.*

   ☛ *Pythagoras' Theorem.*

   The ratio of the radii of the spheres is equal to $1 : \sqrt{3}$.

   ANSWER: $1 : 3\sqrt{3}$

6. ☛ *The area of a circle of radius r is equal to* πr^2.

☛ *The curved surface area of a cylinder of radius r and height h is equal to* $2\pi rh$.

ANSWER: $30\pi r^2$

7. ☛ *The angles in a triangle add up to 180°.*

☛ *Sides opposite equal angles of a triangle are equal.*

☛ *Pythagoras' Theorem.*

Suppose that a point on the curve has coordinates (x, y) (each in metres) with respect to horizontal and vertical axes in the wall, where the origin is at the point where DCB meets the wall; then $x^2 + y^2 = 2^2$.

ANSWER: The curve is a circle.

8. ☛ *The area of a triangle is equal to* $\frac{1}{2} \times$ *base* $\times$ *height.*

☛ *Pythagoras' Theorem.*

Triangle QRS has sides of length $\sqrt{5}\,\text{cm}$, $\sqrt{5}\,\text{cm}$ and $2\sqrt{2}\,\text{cm}$.

ANSWER: $\sqrt{6}\,\text{cm}^2$

9. ☛ *The volume of a sphere of radius r is equal to* $\frac{4}{3}\pi r^3$.

☛ *The volume of a cylinder of radius r and height h is equal to* $\pi r^2 h$.

☛ *The volume of a cone of radius r and height h is equal to* $\frac{1}{3}\pi r^2 h$.

ANSWER: $\frac{7}{3}r$

10. ☛ *Pythagoras' Theorem.*

Let the sides of the cube have length x m; then $x^2 + x^2 + x^2 = 1$.

ANSWER: $2\,\text{m}^2$

11. ☛ *Pythagoras' Theorem.*

☛ *The area of a circle of radius r is equal to* πr^2.

The slant length of the original cone is equal to 10 cm.
Let the top radius of the frustum be $3r$ cm, so that the slant length of the removed cone is $5r$ cm; then $36 + (3r)^2 = 6 \times 10 - 3r \times 5r$.

ANSWER: 4 cm

12. ☛ *Pythagoras' Theorem.*

Let the radius of the sphere be r; then $r^2 = 11^2 + 1^2 + 5^2$.

ANSWER: 14

13. None of the hatched faces in the diagram on the left below can be 1, so that 1 has to appear on the two faces indicated in the diagram on the right below.

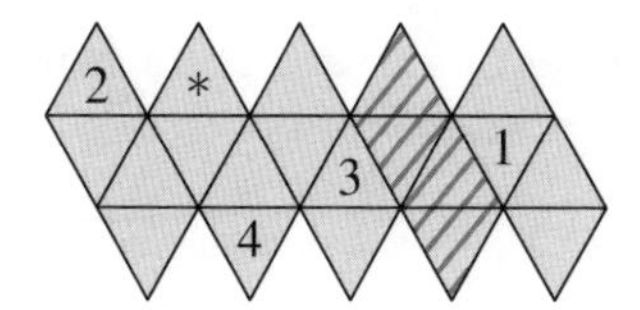

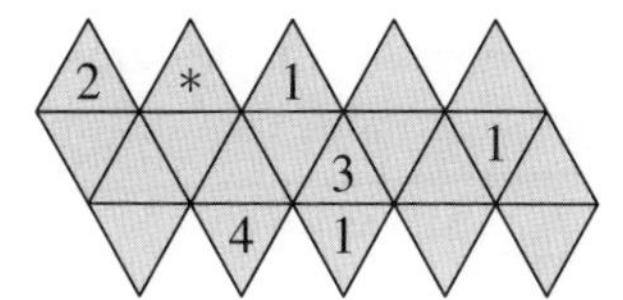

ANSWER: 4

14. ☛ *Pythagoras' Theorem.*

☛ *For any a, b and c:* $(a + b + c)^2 = a^2 + b^2 + c^2 + 2(ab + bc + ca)$.

Let the cuboid have sides of length a cm, b cm and c cm; then

$$x = 4(a + b + c) \text{ and } y^2 = a^2 + b^2 + c^2.$$

ANSWER: $\frac{x^2}{16} - y^2$

15. ☛ *The volume of a pyramid is equal to $\frac{1}{3}$ × base area × height.*

The diagram alongside shows the two planes. The piece containing corner A is a pyramid with base $ADTX$ and vertex B.

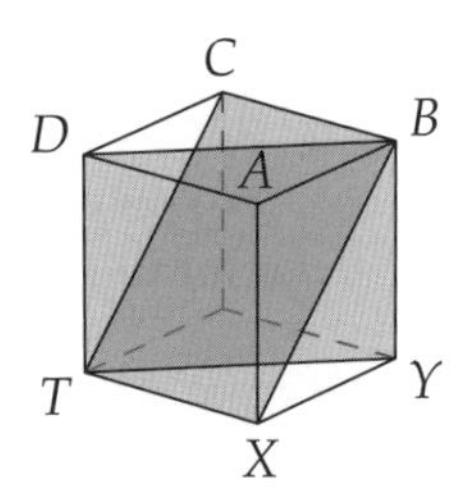

ANSWER: 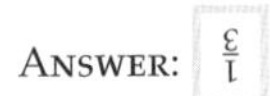 $\frac{1}{3}$

16. ☛ *For any positive a, the height of an equilateral triangle of side 2a is equal to $\sqrt{3}a$.*

☛ *The medians of a triangle meet at a point which is $\frac{2}{3}$ of the way along each median.*

☛ *The volume of a cylinder of radius r and height h is equal to $\pi r^2 h$.*

☛ *The volume of a sphere of radius r is equal to $\frac{4}{3}\pi r^3$.*

The centres of the spheres form an equilateral triangle with sides of length 2, so that the radius of the cylinder is equal to $1 + \frac{2}{3}\sqrt{3}$.

ANSWER: $7 + 4\sqrt{3} : 6$

17. ☛ *Pythagoras' Theorem.*

The length of the diagonal of the cube is equal to $2\sqrt{3}$. Each corner piece is a pyramid, whose 'height' is equal to $\frac{1}{6}$ of the diagonal length of the cube.

ANSWER: $\frac{4}{3}\sqrt{3}$

18. ☛ *Pythagoras' Theorem.*

☛ *For any positive a, the height of an equilateral triangle of side 2a is equal to $\sqrt{3}a$.*

The cut passes through the centre of the cube, and is a regular hexagon whose edges have length $\sqrt{\left(\frac{1}{2}\right)^2 + \left(\frac{1}{2}\right)^2}$.

ANSWER: $\frac{3}{2}\sqrt{3}\text{cm}^2$

19. ☛ *Pythagoras' Theorem.*

☛ *The volume of a pyramid is equal to $\frac{1}{3}$ × base area × height.*

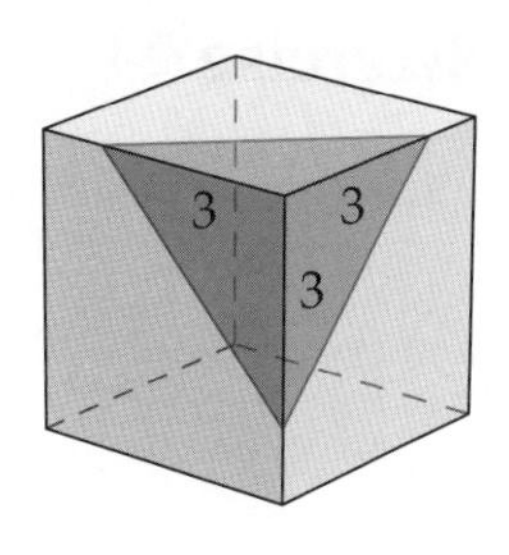

The two cubes intersect in two equal pyramids, each like that shown in the diagram alongside.

ANSWER: 82

20. ☛ *A tangent to a circle is perpendicular to the radius through the point of contact.*

☛ *The volume of a sphere of radius r is equal to $\frac{4}{3}\pi r^3$.*

☛ *The volume of a cone of radius r and height h is equal to $\frac{1}{3}\pi r^2 h$.*

Let the radius of the sphere be r; then the height of the cone is equal to $\dfrac{r}{\sin\alpha} + r$.

ANSWER: $\dfrac{4\sin\alpha(1-\sin\alpha)^3}{\cos^4\alpha}$

Exercise 24

1. When rounded to 3 significant figures, 1002.67, for example, is equal to 1000.

ANSWER: $999.5 \leq x < 1005$

2. ☛ *Pythagoras' Theorem.*

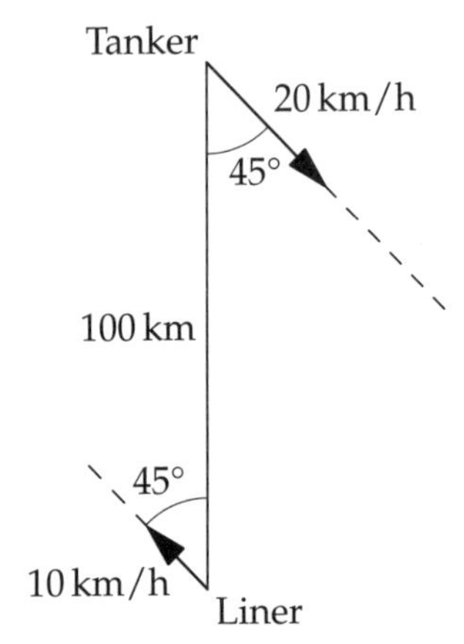

The dashed lines in the diagram alongside represent the paths of the two ships.

At some time (which need not be found) the tanker is NE of the liner.

ANSWER: $50\sqrt{2}$ km

3. The sum of the digits of '200d', where d is a digit, is equal to $2 + d$; on their birthday in 2008, someone born in '200d' was aged $8 - d$.

ANSWER: 18

4. ☛ *Pythagoras' Theorem.*

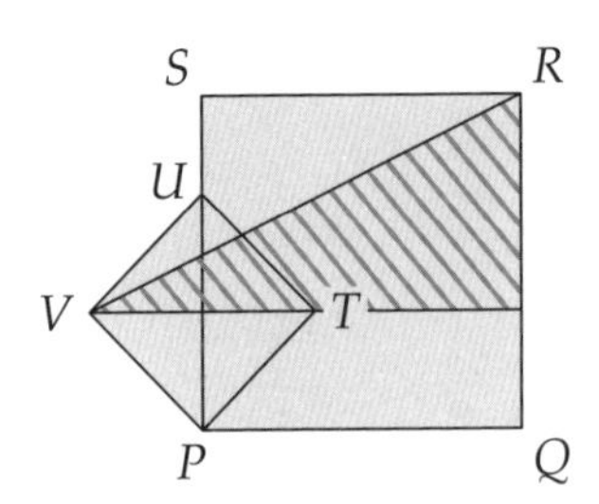

The hatched triangle in the diagram alongside is right-angled.

ANSWER: 6 cm

5. Let the average pocket money per week in the rest of the UK be £x; then

$$0.9 \times x + 0.1 \times 5.35 = 3.1.$$

ANSWER: £2.85

6. ☛ *The area of a square is equal to half the square of the length of a diagonal.*

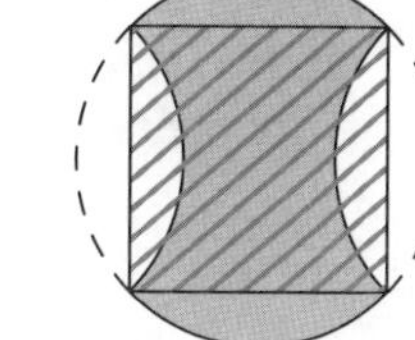

Consider the hatched square in the diagram alongside.

ANSWER: 2

7. The three smallest possible integers in S are 1, 2 and 3. In that case the next integer in S is at least 6.

ANSWER: 11

8. Notice that $\lfloor x \rfloor$, $\lfloor y \rfloor$ and $\lfloor z \rfloor$ are non-negative integers.
Consider what happens when the three given equations are added.

ANSWER: 0.7

9. ☛ *For any positive a, the height of an equilateral triangle of side $2a$ is equal to $\sqrt{3}a$.*

☛ *The area of a triangle is equal to $\frac{1}{2} \times$ base $\times$ height.*

The area of one pane is equal to $6000\,\text{m}^2 \div 3312$.

ANSWER: 2

10. ☛ *The sum of the integers from 1 up to n is equal to $\frac{1}{2}n(n+1)$.*

The sequence has one 1, two 2s, three 3s, and so on. Thus there are $\frac{1}{2}n(n+1)$ terms in the sequence up to and including the last n.
Now $\frac{1}{2} \times 62 \times (62+1)$ is less than 1999, whereas $\frac{1}{2} \times 63 \times (63+1)$ is greater than 1999.

ANSWER: 63

11. ☛ *The area of a triangle is equal to $\frac{1}{2}$ × base × height.*

☛ *The sum of the lengths of two sides of a triangle is greater than the length of the third side* [triangle inequality].

The ratio of the lengths of the three sides of the triangle is equal to

$$\frac{1}{h_1} : \frac{1}{h_2} : \frac{1}{h_3}.$$

When $h_1 : h_2 : h_3 = 2 : 3 : 4$, for example, then the sides are in the ratio 6 : 4 : 3.

ANSWER: 2 : 4 : 5

12. The two fractions

$$\frac{1}{\frac{2008}{1998} - 1} \quad \text{and} \quad b + \frac{1}{c + \frac{1}{d}}$$

are equal.

ANSWER: 4

13. ☛ *When two angles of one triangle are equal to two angles of a second triangle the triangles are similar* [AA test for similar triangles].

Reflect the first part of the ball's path (and the table) in the side PQ, and reflect the last part of the ball's path (and the table) in the side QR, as shown in the diagram below.

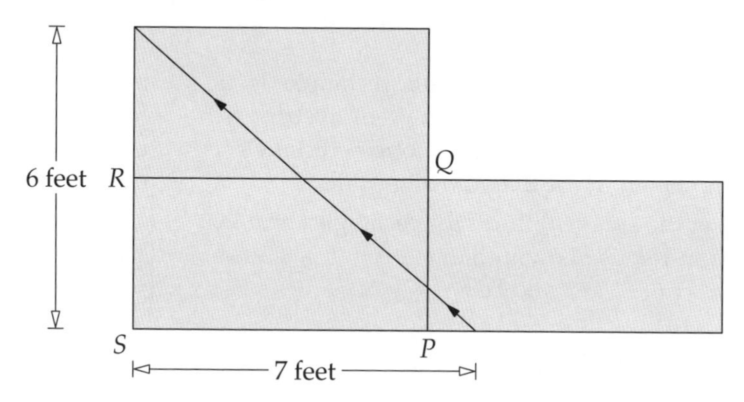

ANSWER: $\frac{6}{7}$

14. ☛ *The ratio of the areas of two triangles with the same height is equal to the ratio of their bases.*

☛ *The area of a triangle with sides a, b and included angle C is equal to* $\frac{1}{2}ab\sin C$.

Consider the diagram alongside. The ratio $RS : SP$ is equal to the ratio of the areas of triangles RSQ and SPQ.

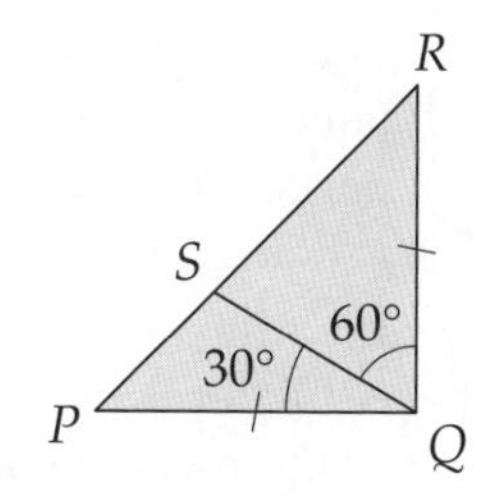

ANSWER: $\sqrt{3} : 1$

15. The statement represented by the expression $3 \boxplus 5 \rightarrow 4$, for example, is correct (as shown in the diagram alongside).

ANSWER: $3 \boxplus 8 \rightarrow 4$

16. Because the central small rectangle is a square, we may remove the central strips to obtain a square divided into four rectangles, as shown in the diagram alongside.

Let the side-lengths of the rectangles be a, b, c and d, as shown; then $a + c = b + d$, and $ad = 6$, $cd = 3$ and $bc = 1$.

ANSWER: $\frac{11}{3}\sqrt{3}$

17. Suppose, for example, that Cam is telling the truth, so that neither Ben nor Dan is telling the truth. Then both the statements made by Ben and Dan are true, which is a contradiction.

ANSWER: Only Cam is lying.

18. ☛ *For any positive a, the height of an equilateral triangle of side $2a$ is equal to $\sqrt{3}a$.*

The diagram alongside shows each pentagon divided into its constituent parts. The hatched right-angled triangle is half an equilateral triangle.

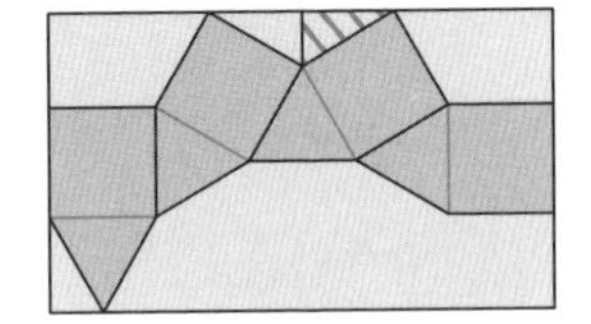

Let the side-length of the square and equilateral triangle be $2a$; then the height of the rectangle is equal to $2\sqrt{3}a + 2a$.

ANSWER: $\sqrt{3} : 1$

19. ☛ *When two angles of one triangle are equal to two angles of a second triangle the triangles are similar* [AA test for similar triangles].

Let O be the point of intersection of the diagonals of the trapezium, as shown in the diagram alongside.

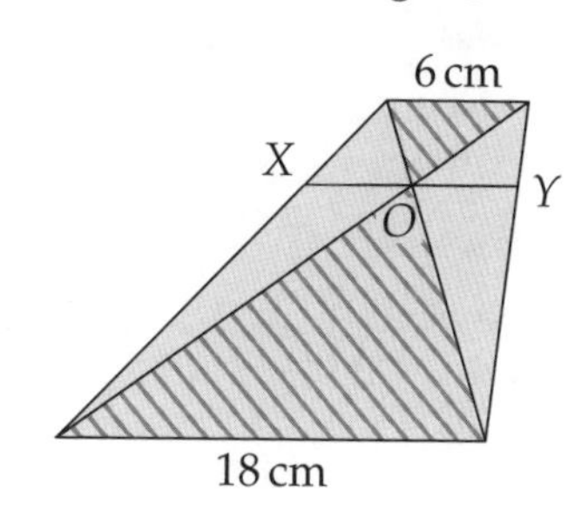

The two hatched triangles are similar (AA), and there are more pairs of similar triangles involving XO and OY.

ANSWER: 9 cm

20. Since neither x nor $x + y$ is equal to zero, we may rearrange to obtain the quadratic equation $y^2 + xy - x = 0$.

When $x = -6$, for example, the discriminant of this quadratic is equal to $(-6)^2 - 4 \times 1 \times (-6)$, which is positive, so that the corresponding values of y are real numbers.

ANSWER: -3

21. ☛ *For any positive a, the height of an equilateral triangle of side $2a$ is equal to $\sqrt{3}a$.*

☛ *The medians of a triangle meet at a point which is $\frac{2}{3}$ of the way along each median.*

☛ *Pythagoras' Theorem.*

Let the length of a side of the smaller triangle be 2, and that of the bigger triangle be $2a$; then the radius of the circle is equal to $\frac{2}{3}\sqrt{3}a$. The hatched triangle in the diagram alongside is right-angled and has sides of length $\frac{2}{3}\sqrt{3}a$, $\frac{1}{3}\sqrt{3}a + \sqrt{3}$ and 1.

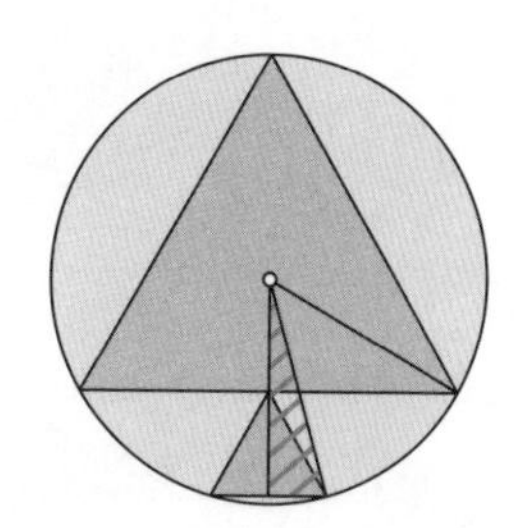

ANSWER: 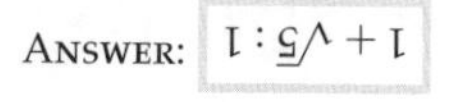

22. The five integers 1, 13, 17, 19 and 23 do not have a prime factor in common with any other integer from 1 to 25, so that none of them can appear in Peter's row. Hence N is at most 20.

There are many ways to place the other 20 cards, other than these five, in a row.

ANSWER: 20

23. Notice that $f(2008) = \dfrac{f(2005) - 1}{f(2005) + 1}$, and that $f(2005) = \dfrac{f(2002) - 1}{f(2002) + 1}$.

ANSWER: -1

24.
- *The angles on a straight line add up to 180°.*
- *The angles at a point add up to 360°.*
- *The angles of a quadrilateral add up to 360°.*

A polygon with at most 12 vertices is obtained, such as that shown in the diagram on the left below. When either the smaller marked angle is equal to 60°, or the larger is equal to 120°, then one of the vertices of the original quadrilateral is not a vertex of the final polygon.

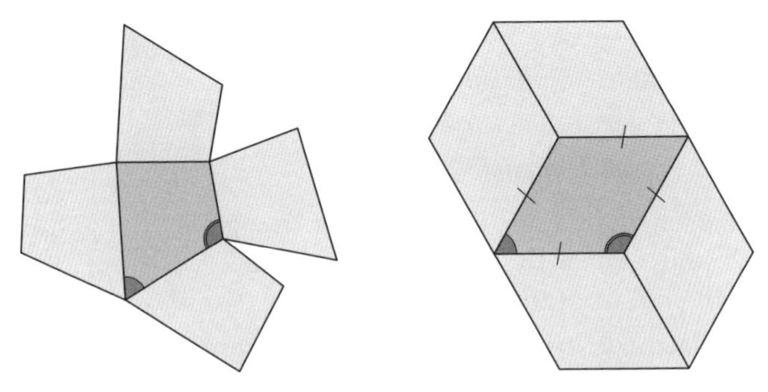

The diagram on the right above shows the hexagon that is obtained by starting with a rhombus, two of whose angles are 60° and 120°.

ANSWER: Six

25. ☛ *The angles on a straight line add up to 180°.*

☛ *The exterior angles of a polygon add up to 360°.*

Each exterior angle of the 'star polygon' is equal to either $180° - 83\frac{1}{3}°$ or $-83\frac{1}{3}°$, where clockwise angles are taken to be negative.

ANSWER: 54

26. Every digit of each of the integers

$$\begin{aligned} Y_1 &= p + q + r, \\ \text{and} \quad Y_{11} &= p \times 11^2 + q \times 11 + r \end{aligned} \qquad (*)$$

is equal to 1. Now $p > 0$ and from equation (*) we cannot have $p = 1$, $q = 0$ and $r = 0$ so that $Y_1 > 1$ and $Y_{11} \geq 11$. It follows that $Y_{11} - Y_1$, that is, $120p + 10q$, is a multiple of 100. Hence $12p + q$ is a multiple of 10, so that q is even.

ANSWER: 2

27. Let

$$S = \frac{1}{2} + \frac{1}{4} + \frac{2}{8} + \frac{3}{16} + \frac{5}{32} + \frac{8}{64} + \frac{13}{128} + \frac{21}{256} + \frac{34}{512} + \cdots;$$

then

$$\tfrac{1}{2}S = \frac{1}{4} + \frac{1}{8} + \frac{2}{16} + \frac{3}{32} + \frac{5}{64} + \frac{8}{128} + \frac{13}{256} + \frac{21}{512} + \cdots$$

and

$$\tfrac{1}{4}S = \frac{1}{8} + \frac{1}{16} + \frac{2}{32} + \frac{3}{64} + \frac{5}{128} + \frac{8}{256} + \frac{13}{512} + \cdots.$$

Therefore

$$\tfrac{1}{2}S + \tfrac{1}{4}S = S - \frac{1}{2}.$$

ANSWER: 2

Exercise 25

1. ☛ *A tangent to a circle is perpendicular to the radius through the point of contact.*

☛ *For any positive a, the height of an equilateral triangle of side 2a is equal to $\sqrt{3}a$.*

☛ *The area of a circle of radius r is equal to πr^2.*

Each side of the hatched triangle in the diagram alongside has length 6, so the triangle is equilateral.

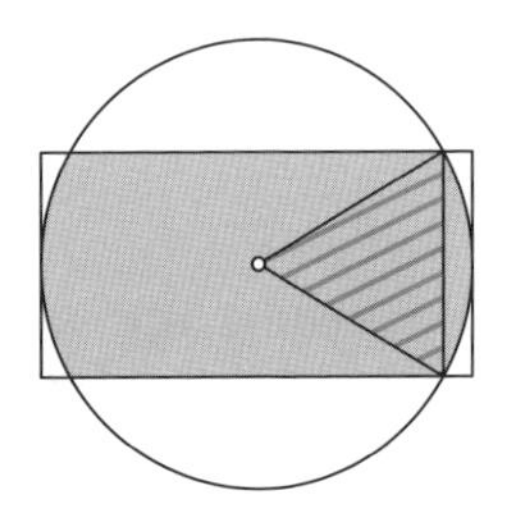

ANSWER: $12\pi + 18\sqrt{3}$

2. ☛ *The area of a triangle is equal to $\frac{1}{2} \times$ base $\times$ height.*

Since the area of triangle QRT is $\frac{1}{5}$ of the area of $PQRS$, it follows that $RT = \frac{2}{5}RS$. Hence $TS = \frac{3}{5}RS$.

Since the area of triangle TSU is $\frac{1}{8}$ of the area of $PQRS$, it follows that $SU = \dfrac{5}{12}SP$.

ANSWER: $\dfrac{23}{60}$

3. ☛ *Two triangles are congruent when two angles and a side of one are equal to two angles and the corresponding side of the other* [AAS test for congruency].

Draw the height of each triangle, as shown in the diagrams below.

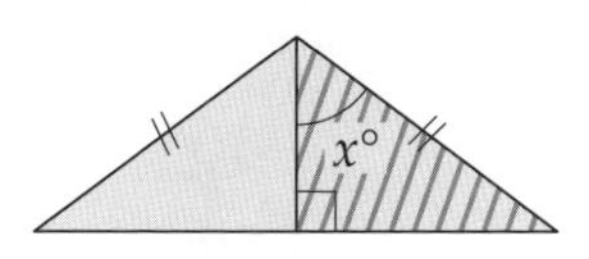

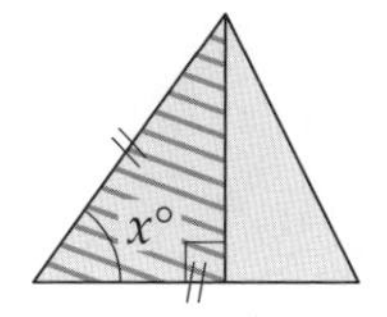

The two hatched triangles are congruent, so that the two unhatched triangles have equal area.

ANSWER: 60

4. ☛ *The exterior angle of a regular octagon is 45°.*

☛ *Pythagoras' Theorem.*

The star comprises a square, and four right-angled isosceles triangles, as shown in the diagram alongside.

ANSWER: $8+4\sqrt{2}$

5. ☛ *Pythagoras' Theorem.*

☛ *The converse of Thales' Theorem.*

☛ *The area of a circle of radius r is equal to πr^2.*

XY and YZ are perpendicular, so that the radius of the circle through the points X, Y and Z is equal to $\frac{1}{2}ZX$.

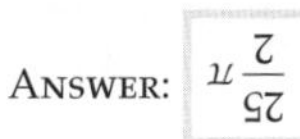

ANSWER: $\frac{25}{2}\pi$

6. ☛ *A tangent to a circle is perpendicular to the radius through the point of contact.*

☛ *Pythagoras' Theorem.*

☛ *The area of a circle of radius r is equal to πr^2.*

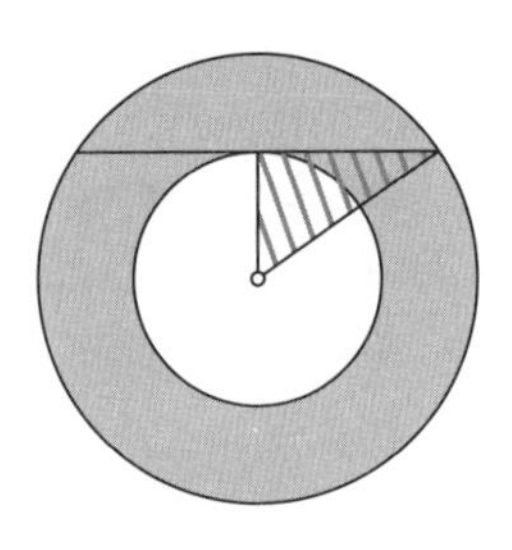

The hatched triangle in the diagram alongside is right-angled.

ANSWER: πp^2

7. ☛ *Pythagoras' Theorem.*

☛ *The exterior angle of a square is 90°.*

☛ *The angle between the side of a square and a diagonal is 45°.*

☛ *The angles in a triangle add up to 180°.*

☛ *Sides opposite equal angles of a triangle are equal.*

Each square has sides of length 1, and diagonals of length $\sqrt{2}$.

The hatched triangle in the diagram alongside is both right-angled and isosceles, in other words, it is half a square.

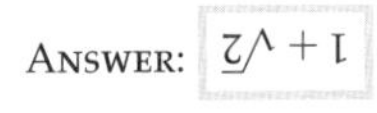

8. ☛ *When two angles of one triangle are equal to two angles of a second triangle the triangles are similar* [AA test for similar triangles].

☛ *Triangles with the same height and equal bases have equal areas.*

The area of each rhombus may be found by adding lines to each diagram, as shown below.

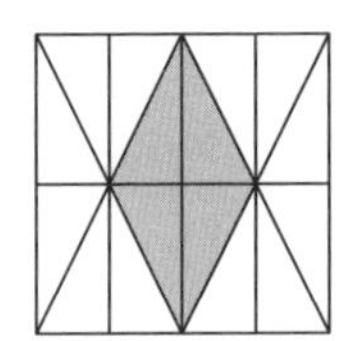

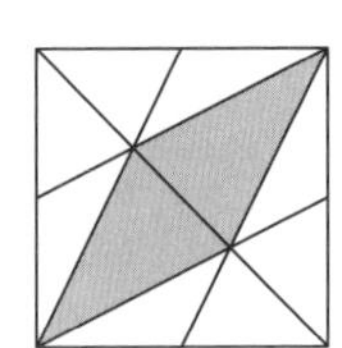

ANSWER: 3

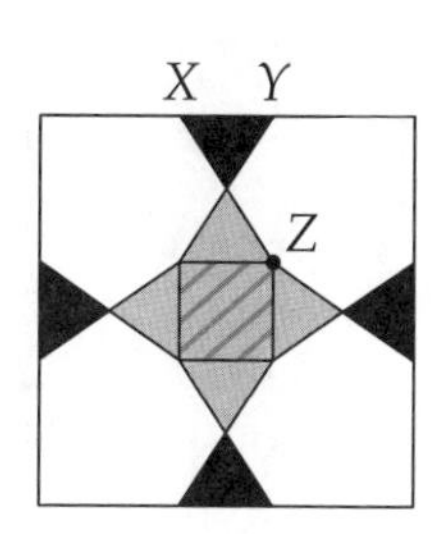

9. ☛ *The area of a triangle is equal to $\frac{1}{2}$ × base × height.*

The central grey octagon comprises the hatched square shown in the diagram alongside, and four triangles.

Each triangle has base equal to the length XY, and height equal to $\frac{1}{2}(8\,\text{cm} - XY)$.

ANSWER: $10\,\text{cm}^2$

10. ☛ *Pythagoras' Theorem.*

☛ *The area of a circle of radius r is equal to πr^2.*

The diagram alongside shows the original and final positions of the pad.

ANSWER: $(1 + \pi)\,\text{cm}^2$

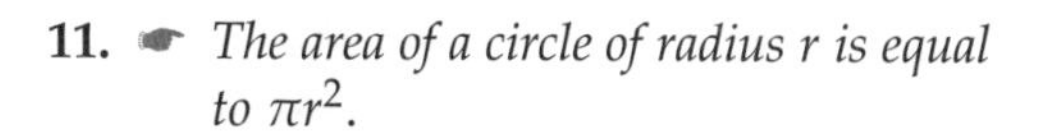

11. ☛ *The area of a circle of radius r is equal to πr^2.*

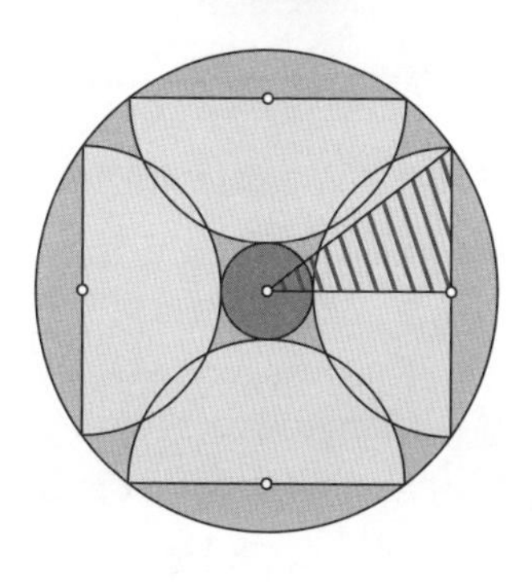

The hatched triangle in the diagram alongside is right-angled.

ANSWER: 100

12. ☛ *Pythagoras' Theorem.*

☛ *The area of a triangle is equal to $\frac{1}{2} \times$ base $\times$ height.*

Let $ABCD$ be the rectangle, with CD longer than BC, and let the corner AXY be cut off, as shown in the diagram alongside. Notice that triangle AXY is right-angled and the lengths of its sides are integers.

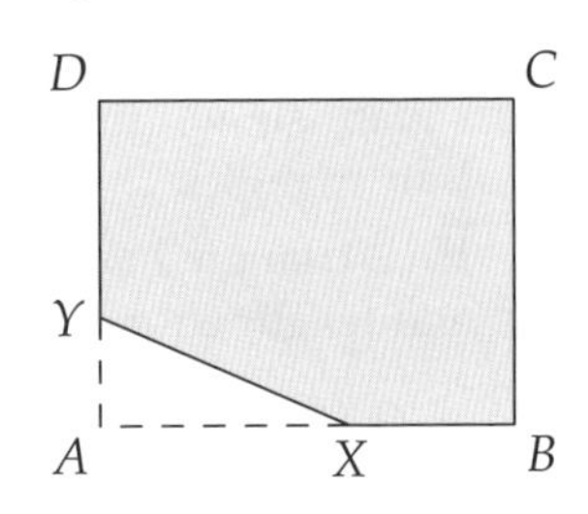

The longest side of the pentagon is either XY or CD.

But when $XY = 20$ then $CD = 15$, because it is longer than any of the other sides of the pentagon apart from XY. The remaining choices for XB are 8, 10 and 13, none of which give an integer length for YA. Therefore $CD = 20$.

Now the choices for the length of XB are 8, 10, 13 or 15.

When $XB = 15$, for example, then $AX = 5$ and none of the remaining choices for XY (8, 10 or 13) gives an integer value for the length of AY.

ANSWER: 270

13. ☛ *For any positive a, the height of an equilateral triangle of side 2a is equal to $\sqrt{3}a$.*

☛ *The area of a square is equal to half the square of the length of a diagonal.*

The hexagon may be divided into six equilateral triangles, as shown in the diagram alongside.

The length of a diagonal of the square is equal to $2 \times \left(\frac{1}{2}\sqrt{3} + \frac{1}{2}\right)$.

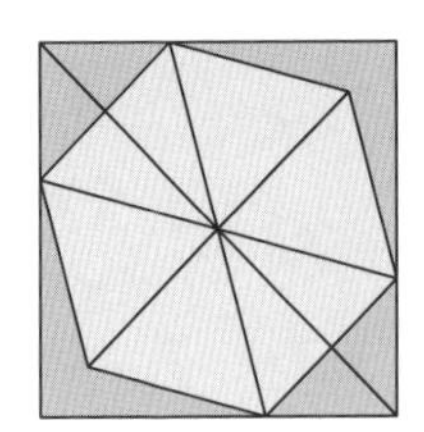

14. ☛ *The area of a triangle with sides a, b and included angle C is equal to* $\frac{1}{2}ab\sin C$.

Label the outer equilateral triangle ABC, as shown in the diagram alongside; then the ratio of the areas of triangles APR and ABC is equal to $\frac{1}{4} \times \frac{3}{4} : 1 \times 1$.

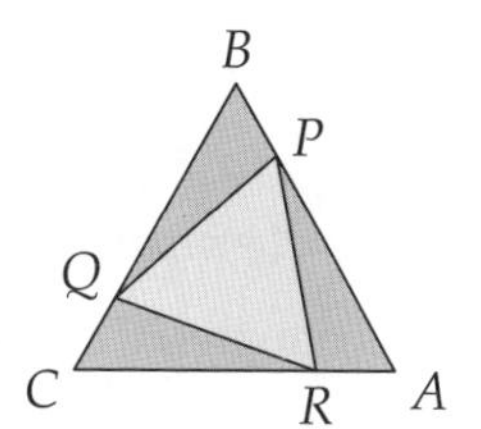

ANSWER: $\frac{7}{16}$

15. ☛ *A tangent to a circle is perpendicular to the radius through the point of contact.*

☛ *When two angles of one triangle are equal to two angles of a second triangle the triangles are similar* [AA test for similar triangles].

☛ *The area of a triangle is equal to* $\frac{1}{2} \times$ *base* $\times$ *height.*

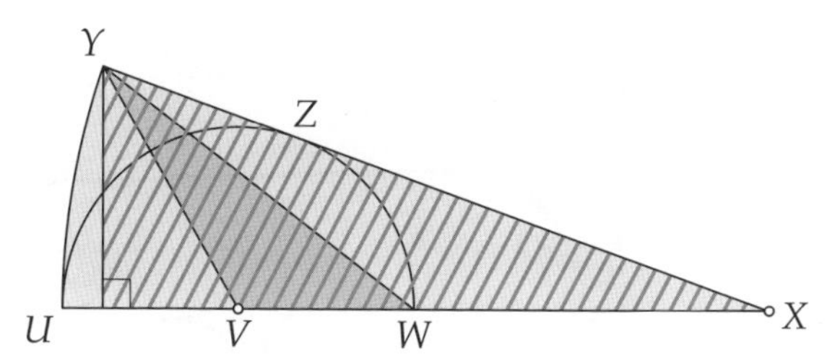

Triangle VXZ is similar to the hatched triangle in the above diagram (AA).

ANSWER: $\frac{2}{3}r^2$

16. ☛ *The area of a parallelogram is equal to base* $\times$ *height.*

☛ *The area of a triangle is equal to* $\frac{1}{2} \times$ *base* $\times$ *height.*

The area of triangle NGM is equal to a quarter of the area of the parallelogram $EFGH$.

ANSWER: 32 cm^2

17. ☛ *When two angles of one triangle are equal to two angles of a second triangle the triangles are similar* [AA test for similar triangles].

☛ *The ratio of the areas of similar shapes is equal to the square of the ratio of corresponding lengths.*

☛ *The area of a quadrilateral with perpendicular diagonals is equal to half the product of the lengths of the diagonals.*

Triangle PTS is similar to triangle PQR (AA).

ANSWER: 64

18. ☛ *The ratio of the areas of similar shapes is equal to the square of the ratio of corresponding lengths.*

☛ *Pythagoras' Theorem.*

☛ *For any a and b:* $a^2 - b^2 = (a - b)(a + b)$ [difference of two squares].

Double each semicircle in order to consider large circles of area 4, as shown in the diagrams below.

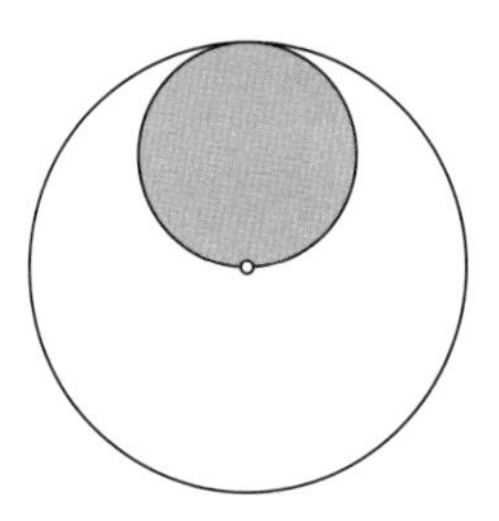

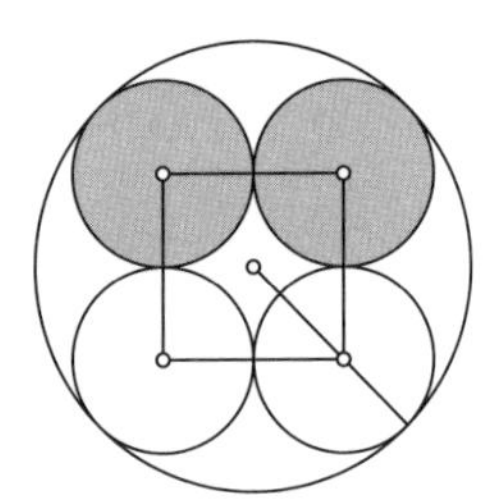

In the left-hand diagram, the area of the shaded region is a quarter of the area of the large circle.

The centres of the small circles in the right-hand diagram form a square. The ratio of the radius of a small circle to the radius of the large circle is equal to $1 : 1 + \sqrt{2}$.

ANSWER: $23 - 16\sqrt{2}$

19. ☛ *When two angles of one triangle are equal to two angles of a second triangle the triangles are similar* [AA test for similar triangles].

☛ *The ratio of the areas of two triangles with the same height is equal to the ratio of their bases.*

Triangles WQT and WSP are similar (AA), so that W lies $\frac{1}{3}$ of the way along QS.

Hence triangle PWV is $\frac{1}{3} \times \frac{1}{2}$ of the area of the square $PQRS$.

ANSWER: $\frac{1}{3}$

20. ☛ *A tangent to a circle is perpendicular to the radius through the point of contact.*

☛ *The angles in a triangle add up to 180°.*

☛ *Sides opposite equal angles of a triangle are equal.*

☛ *Pythagoras' Theorem.*

☛ *The area of a circle of radius r is equal to* πr^2.

☛ *For any a and b:* $a^2 - b^2 = (a-b)(a+b)$ [difference of two squares].

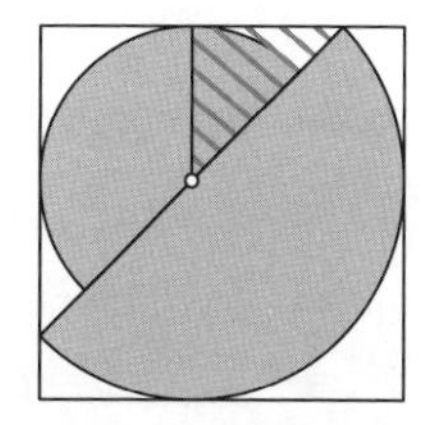

The hatched triangle in the diagram alongside is right-angled and isosceles.

Let the radius of the smaller semicircle be r; then the radius of the larger semicircle is equal to $\sqrt{2}r$. Hence $\sqrt{2}r + r = 2$.

ANSWER: 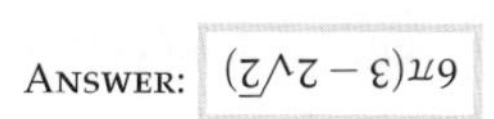

21. ☛ *For any positive a, the height of an equilateral triangle of side 2a is equal to $\sqrt{3}a$.*

☛ *The medians of a triangle meet at a point which is $\frac{2}{3}$ of the way along each median.*

☛ *A tangent to a circle is perpendicular to the radius through the point of contact.*

☛ *The area of a circle of radius r is equal to πr^2.*

Let the radius of the smaller circles be a and the radius of the larger circle be b; then b is equal to $\frac{1}{2}\sqrt{3}$.

Each of the two hatched triangles in the diagrams below is half an equilateral triangle, so that $2b = 2a + a + b$.

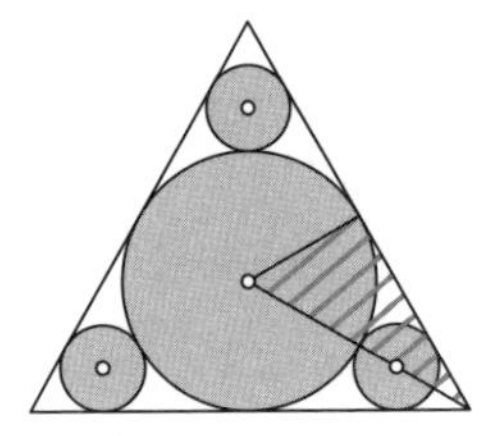

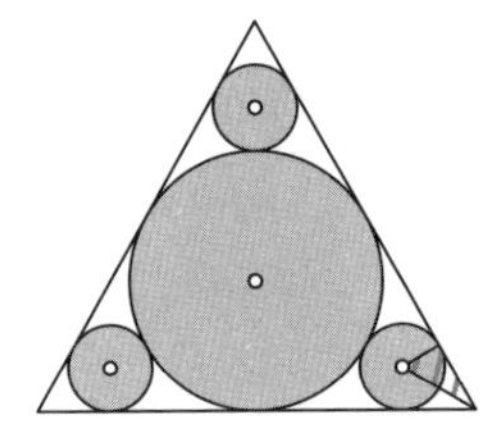

ANSWER: π

22. ☛ *The interior angle of a square is 90°.*

☛ *The converse of Thales' Theorem.*

☛ *Pythagoras' Theorem.*

☛ *The area of a square is equal to half the square of the length of a diagonal.*

The diagram alongside shows the configuration. Notice that ABY is a straight line.

Consider the hatched triangle in the diagram.

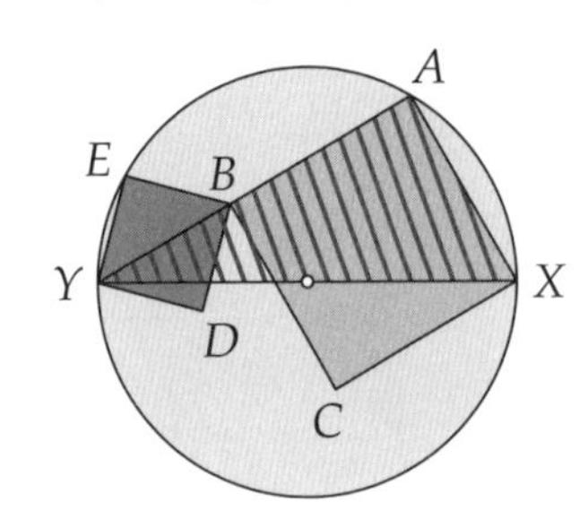

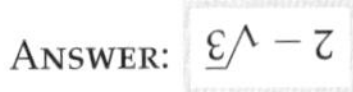

ANSWER: $2 - \sqrt{3}$

23. ☛ *A tangent to a circle is perpendicular to the radius through the point of contact.*

☛ *The ratio of the areas of similar shapes is equal to the square of the ratio of corresponding lengths.*

Let the radius of the smaller circles be a and the radius of the larger circle be b; then b is equal to $\frac{1}{2}\sqrt{3}$.

Each of the two hatched triangles in the diagrams below is half an equilateral triangle, so that $2b = 2a + a + b$.

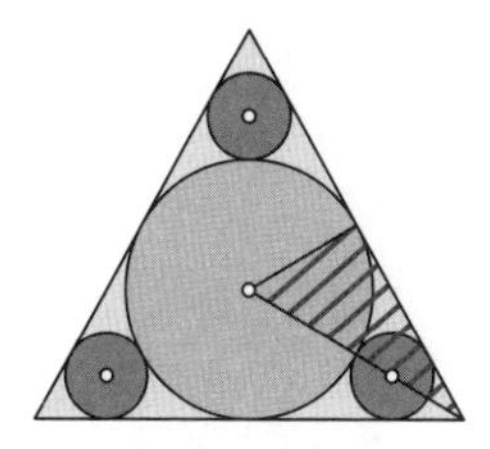

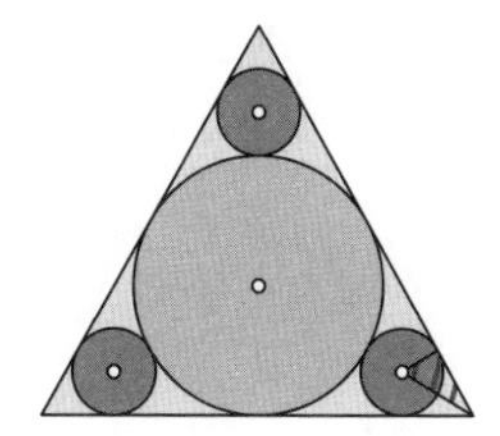

ANSWER: $1 : 9$

24. ☛ *Vertically opposite angles are equal.*

☛ *Two triangles are congruent when two angles and a side of one are equal to two angles and the corresponding side of the other* [AAS test for congruency].

☛ *For any positive a, the height of an equilateral triangle of side $2a$ is equal to $\sqrt{3}a$.*

☛ *The area of a triangle is equal to $\frac{1}{2} \times$ base $\times$ height.*

☛ *The ratio of the areas of similar shapes is equal to the square of the ratio of corresponding lengths.*

The hatched triangles in the left-hand diagram below are congruent (AAS).

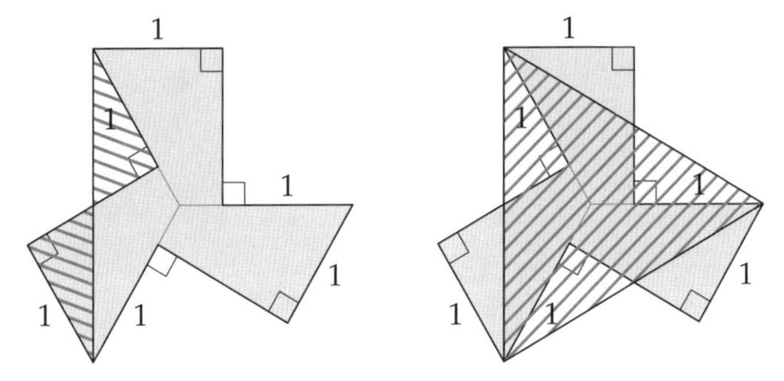

It follows that the area of the tile is equal to the area of the hatched equilateral triangle in the right-hand diagram above.

Each of the congruent triangles is half an equilateral triangle. The height of this triangle is equal to 1, and the sides have half the length of the hatched equilateral triangle.

ANSWER: $\frac{3}{4}\sqrt{3}$

25. ☛ *Vertically opposite angles are equal.*

☛ *Two triangles are congruent when two angles and a side of one are equal to two angles and the corresponding side of the other* [AAS test for congruency].

☛ *The area of a triangle is equal to $\frac{1}{2} \times$ base $\times$ height.*

The two hatched triangles in the diagram alongside are congruent (AAS), so that the area of the dashed square is equal to 5.

The area of each congruent triangle is equal to $\frac{1}{4}$, so the 'height' is equal to $\dfrac{1}{\sqrt{5}}$.

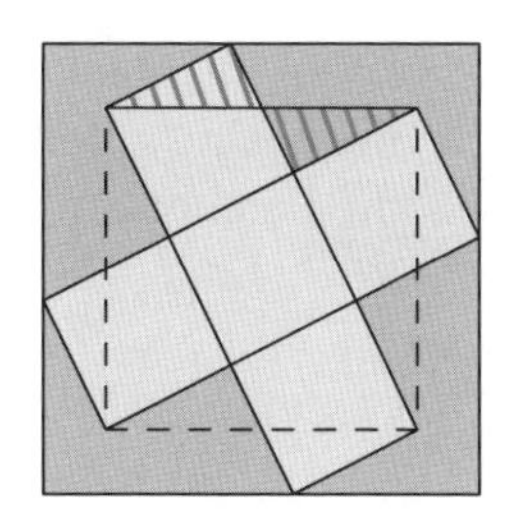

ANSWER: $\dfrac{49}{5}$

26. ☛ *For any positive a, the height of an equilateral triangle of side 2a is equal to $\sqrt{3}a$.*

☛ *The medians of a triangle meet at a point which is $\frac{2}{3}$ of the way along each median.*

☛ *The area of a circle of radius r is equal to πr^2.*

The triangle ABC, shown hatched in the diagram alongside, is equilateral with sides of length 3 cm.

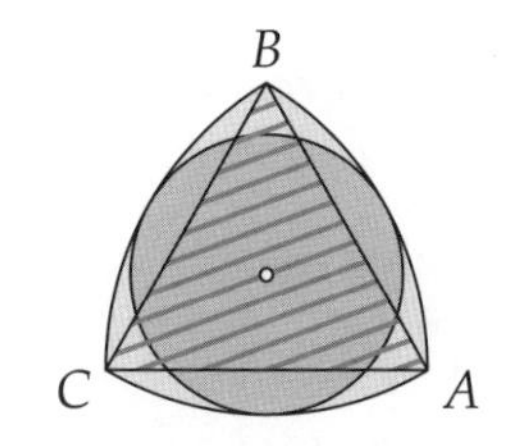

ANSWER: $6\pi(2 - \sqrt{3})$ cm^2

27. ☛ *The interior angle of a square is 90°.*

☛ *The angles at a point add up to 360°.*

☛ *With the standard notation for a triangle:* $c^2 = a^2 + b^2 - 2ab\cos C$ [cosine rule].

☛ *For any angle* θ: $\cos(180° - \theta) = -\cos\theta$.

Label the black triangle ABC, as shown in the diagram below. Using the cosine rule for one of the grey triangles, we find that the area of the hatched square is equal to $a^2 + b^2 - 2ab\cos(180° - C)$.

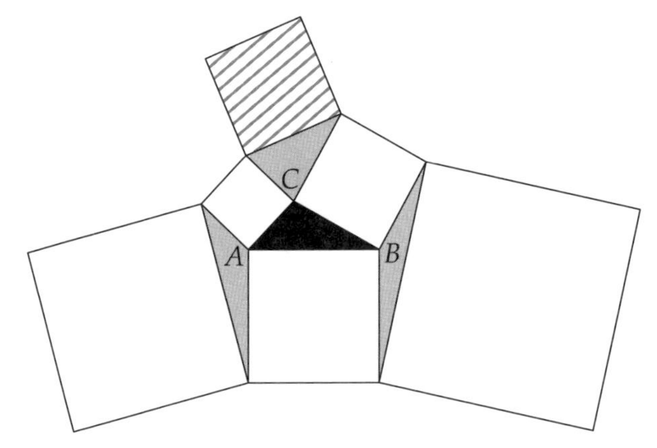

But $\cos(180° - C) = -\cos C$, so that the area of the hatched square is equal to $2a^2 + 2b^2 - c^2$, using the cosine rule for the black triangle.

ANSWER: 3

28. ☛ *Pythagoras' Theorem.*

☛ *The area of a circle of radius r is equal to πr^2.*

☛ *The area of a triangle is equal to $\frac{1}{2}$ × base × height.*

The octagon in the diagram alongside is regular.

The 'height' of the hatched triangle is equal to $\frac{1}{2}\sqrt{2}$. Let the radius of the circle be r; then $r^2 = (1 + \frac{1}{2}\sqrt{2})^2 + \left(\frac{1}{2}\sqrt{2}\right)^2$.

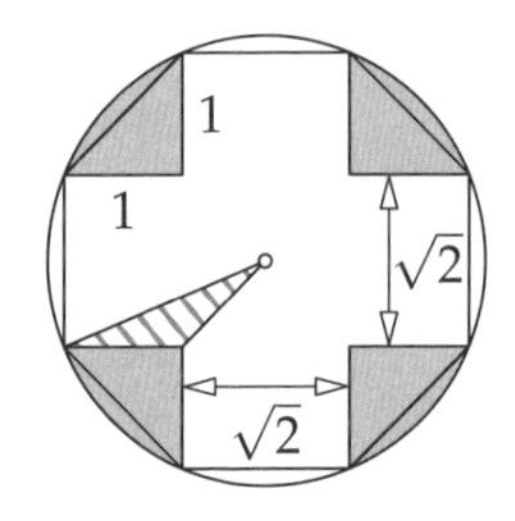

ANSWER: $\frac{1}{2}\pi(2+\sqrt{2}) - 2\sqrt{2}$

Exercise 26

1. ☛ *For any positive a and b:* $\sqrt{ab} = \sqrt{a} \times \sqrt{b}$.

☛ *For any a:* a^1 *is equal to a.*

☛ *For any positive a:* $a^{\frac{1}{2}}$ *is equal to* $\sqrt{a}$.

☛ *For any positive a and any powers p and q:* $a^p \times a^q = a^{p+q}$.

Notice that $\sqrt{56}$, for example, is equal to $2\sqrt{14}$.

ANSWER: $\frac{3}{2}$

2. ☛ *For any positive a:* $a^{\frac{1}{2}}$ *is equal to* $\sqrt{a}$.

☛ *For any positive a and any powers p and q:* $(a^p)^q$ *is equal to* a^{pq}.

The given expression is equal to $\left(9^{16x^2}\right)^{\frac{1}{2}}$.

ANSWER: 9^{8x^2}

3. ☛ *For any a:* a^1 *is equal to a.*

☛ *For any positive a and any powers p and q:* $a^p \times a^q = a^{p+q}$.

The expression 2^{2003}, for example, is equal to $2^{2000} \times 2^3$.

ANSWER: 2^{2000}

4. ☛ *For any positive a and any powers p and q:* $(a^p)^q$ *is equal to* a^{pq}.

☛ *For any positive a and any powers p and q:* $a^p \div a^q = a^{p-q}$.

☛ *For any a:* a^1 *is equal to a.*

When n is equal to 81, then n^{20} is equal to $\left(3^4\right)^{20}$.

ANSWER: $\frac{1}{3}$

5. Adding $\sqrt{11}$ to each side of the given equation and then squaring, we get

$$m = n + 2\sqrt{11n} + 11, \qquad (*)$$

so that $\sqrt{11n}$ is an integer. Therefore $n = 11b^2$ for some integer b.

Now $m = 11(1+b)^2$ from equation (*), and so $\dfrac{m}{n} = \left(1 + \dfrac{1}{b}\right)^2$, which is greatest when $b = 1$.

ANSWER: 4

6. Notice that $17 + 12\sqrt{2}$, for example, is equal to $\left(3 + 2\sqrt{2}\right)^2$.

ANSWER: $54 + 12\sqrt{2}$

7. ☛ *For any a and b:* $a^2 - b^2 = (a-b)(a+b)$ [difference of two squares].

Notice that $f(x) = \dfrac{(x - \sqrt{x^2+1}) \times (x + \sqrt{x^2+1}) + 1}{x - \sqrt{x^2+1}}$.

ANSWER: 0

8. The inequalities $2x < 2^x < x^2$, for example, are true when $x = 3$.

ANSWER: $2^x < x^2 < 2x$ and $2^x < 2x < x^2$

9. ☛ *For any positive a and b:* $\sqrt{ab} = \sqrt{a} \times \sqrt{b}$.

☛ *For any a and b:* $a^2 - b^2 = (a-b)(a+b)$ [difference of two squares].

Notice that $7 - 4\sqrt{3}$, for example, is equal to $7 - \sqrt{48}$, which in turn is equal to $\dfrac{1}{7 + \sqrt{48}}$, whose denominator is just less than 14.

ANSWER: $10 - 3\sqrt{11}$

10. ☛ *The first n odd integers add up to* n^2.

The length of the hypotenuse is equal to 13, so that the other two sides are 5 and 12 (in some order).

ANSWER: 32

11. Notice that when $\sqrt{m}$ is equal to $(k+1)\sqrt{17}$ and $\sqrt{n}$ is equal to $k\sqrt{17}$ then the equation is satisfied for any value of k.

ANSWER: There are infinitely many pairs.

12. ☛ *For any a and b:* $a^2 - b^2 = (a-b)(a+b)$ [difference of two squares].

Notice that $2005 + \sqrt{2005^2 - 1}$ is equal to

$$1002 + 2 \times \sqrt{1002} \times \sqrt{1003} + 1003,$$

which is equal to $\left(\sqrt{1002} + \sqrt{1003}\right)^2$.

ANSWER: $\sqrt{1003} - \sqrt{1002}$

13. ☛ *For any a and b:* $a^2 - b^2 = (a-b)(a+b)$ [difference of two squares].

Squaring the given equation, we get

$$p + \tfrac{1}{2}\sqrt{q} - 2\sqrt{(p + \tfrac{1}{2}\sqrt{q}) \times (p - \tfrac{1}{2}\sqrt{q})} + p - \tfrac{1}{2}\sqrt{q} = 1,$$

so that

$$2p - 1 = \sqrt{4p^2 - q}.$$

Hence

$$(2p-1)^2 = 4p^2 - q,$$

and so

$$q = 4p - 1.$$

Because we have squared twice we may have introduced spurious answers, so we now need to check that $q = 7$, $p = 2$ is indeed a solution of the given equation.

But when $p = 2$ then $2p > 1$, and when $q = 7$ then $p + \frac{1}{2}\sqrt{q}$ is greater than $p - \frac{1}{2}\sqrt{q}$. Therefore we have always squared terms that are positive, so that the above argument is reversible when $p = 2$ and $q = 7$.

ANSWER: 7

Exercise 27

1. Damien needs to check every prime that is less than $\sqrt{457}$, and no others.

   ANSWER: Eight

2. Since puzzle number 351 is in volume 5, there are at most $351 \div 4$ puzzles in each volume.

   ANSWER: 87

3. Consider 10! when it is written as a product of prime factors.

   ANSWER: 720

4. Notice that $2 \times 3 \times 12 \times 14 \times 15 \times 20 \times 21 = 2520^2$, and it is possible to divide the given numbers into two appropriate sets.

   ANSWER: 2520

5. ☛ *For any a and b:* $a^2 - b^2 = (a-b)(a+b)$ [difference of two squares].

   Notice that 199 is prime. Suppose that $199p + 1$ is equal to m^2 for some integer m; then $199p = (m-1)(m+1)$. It follows that either $m - 1 = 199$ or $m + 1 = 199$. In the first case $p = 201$, which is divisible by 3; in the second case $p = 197$.

   ANSWER: One

6. For example, 2002 is equal to $2 \times 7 \times 11 \times 13$, so can only be written as a product of *four* distinct primes.

   ANSWER: 2006

7. Written as a product of prime factors, 396 is equal to $2^2 \times 3^2 \times 11$.

   ANSWER: 726

8. Consider the lsist with greatest product.

Notice that $2^3 < 3^2$, so that $3+3$ is 'better' than $2+2+2$—in other words, the list includes 3s rather than 2s, where possible.

The list does not contain any 1s, because $1 \times n < (n+1)$, where n is a positive integer, so that using $(n+1)$ as a single number is 'better' than using 1 and n separately.

The list does not contain any 5s, for example, because $2+3$ is 'better' than 5.

ANSWER: $2^2 \times 3^{32}$

9. Notice that $\dfrac{n^2-9}{n-1}$ is equal to $n+1-\dfrac{8}{n-1}$.

ANSWER: 8

10. ☛ *For any a and b:* $a^2 - b^2 = (a-b)(a+b)$ [difference of two squares].

☛ *A positive integer is a multiple of 5 when the rightmost digit is either 0 or 5, and not otherwise.*

☛ *A positive integer is a multiple of 11 when the 'alternating sum' of its digits is a multiple of 11, and not otherwise. For example, 86 691 is a multiple of 11, because* $8-6+6-9+1=0$, *which is* 0×11.

The units digit of $1001^2 + 1003^2$, for example, is 0, so it is not prime.

ANSWER: $1000^2 + 111^2$

11. The numbers in the sequence 11, 21, 31, 41, ..., 981, 991 which are *not* grime numbers are 11×11, 11×21, ..., 11×81, 21×21, 21×31, 21×41 and 31×31.

ANSWER: 87

12. Notice that $\dfrac{k}{n^3} + \dfrac{n^3-k}{n^3}$ is equal to 1, so that the left-hand side of the equation has 60 pairs of terms. Hence $(n^3-3)-3 = 120-1$.

ANSWER: 5

13. ☛ *The sum of the integers from 1 up to n is equal to* $\frac{1}{2}n(n+1)$.

Notice that

$$\begin{aligned} S &= 81 \times m + \tfrac{1}{2} \times 100 \times 101 - \tfrac{1}{2} \times 19 \times 20 \\ &= 81(m+60). \end{aligned}$$

ANSWER: 4

14. ☛ *For any a:* a^1 *is equal to a.*

☛ *For any non-zero a:* a^0 *is equal to 1.*

☛ *For any positive a, and power p:* $a^{\frac{p}{2}}$ *is equal to* $(\sqrt{a})^p$.

Notice that $4^{\frac{n-1}{n+1}}$ is an integer precisely when $\dfrac{n-1}{n+1} = 1 - \dfrac{2}{n+1}$ is half a positive integer.

ANSWER: Five

15. Let the four digits be a, b, c and d; then each digit occurs six times in each column of the sum of the 24 integers, so that the sum is equal to $6(a+b+c+d) \times 1111$. Notice that $1111 = 11 \times 101$ and that $a+b+c+d < 101$.

ANSWER: 101

16. ☛ *The sum of the integers from 1 up to n is equal to* $\frac{1}{2}n(n+1)$.

Note that $\frac{1}{2} \times 62 \times 63$ is less than 2011, but that $\frac{1}{2} \times 63 \times 64$ is greater than 2011.

The numbers on the number line that *Lumber9* visits (starting from 0) are 1, -1, 2, -2, and so on. After 2011 paces, the robot is 58 paces forwards from -31.

ANSWER: 27

17. ☛ *A positive integer is a multiple of 2 when the rightmost digit is even, and not otherwise.*

☛ *A positive integer is a multiple of 3 when its digits add up to a multiple of 3, and not otherwise.*

Notice that 2004 is a multiple of 6, and that (by dividing them by 7) each of the 6-digit integers 222 222 and 888 888 is a multiple of 7.

ANSWER: 2 or 9

18. ☛ *Suppose there are m ways of making one choice and, whichever first choice is made, n ways of making a second choice, then there are $m \times n$ ways of making both choices in succession* [multiplication principle].

Notice that $n + 2n < 20$, so that n is at most 6. Noting that the match 'player A *versus* player B' is the same as the match 'player B *versus* player A', the total number of matches played was $\frac{1}{2} \times 3n \times (3n - 1)$, which is therefore a multiple of $3 + 4$.

ANSWER: 5

19. Notice that $\dfrac{2n+m}{n-2} = 2 + \dfrac{m+4}{n-2}$, so that $\dfrac{2n+m}{n-2}$ is an integer precisely when $m + 4$ is a multiple of $n - 2$. This happens exactly four times when $m + 4$ is prime, and not otherwise.

ANSWER: Seven

20. Notice that, for example, 124! ends in 28 zeros, whereas 125! ends in 31 zeros.

ANSWER: Nine

21. The smallest multiple of 7 that has 2016 digits is 1 followed by 2014 digits 0 followed by 2.

ANSWER: 6

22. Notice that $f(40) = f(2) + f(2) + f(10)$ so that $f(2) = 3$,. Therefore $f(5) = 11$ because $f(10) = f(2) + f(5)$. Finally, $f(500) = f(5) + 2f(10)$.

ANSWER: 39

23. Notice that

$$(a+1)(b+1)(c+1)(d+1) = 2010.$$

ANSWER: 73

24. Notice that $(3m-19)(3n-38) = 19 \times 38$ so that $3m-19$ and $3n-38$, which are integers, multiply to give $2 \times 19 \times 19$.

ANSWER: Three

There is nothing special about the prime 19. The answer is also three when 19 is replaced by any other prime greater than 3.

Appendix

Sources of the problems

The problems are taken from the SMC papers for the years 1997–2016. The wording of some problems has been edited, and in every case the multiple-choice options have been removed.

The following tables give the sources of all the problems in the book.

Exercise 1

1. 2015 01
2. 2014 01
3. 2013 01
4. 2008 01
5. 2005 01
6. 1997 01
7. 2008 02
8. 2004 02
9. 2000 02
10. 2012 03
11. 2009 03
12. 2008 03
13. 2007 03
14. 2003 03
15. 2012 04
16. 2006 04
17. 2008 05
18. 2003 05
19. 2006 06
20. 2001 06
21. 2016 07
22. 1998 08
23. 2010 09
24. 2000 09
25. 1999 10
26. 2010 11
27. 1997 11
28. 1997 12

Exercise 2

1. 2011 01
2. 2003 01
3. 2000 01
4. 2009 02
5. 2001 02
6. 2010 04
7. 2002 04
8. 2014 05
9. 2012 06
10. 2007 07
11. 2014 09
12. 2008 09
13. 2009 10
14. 2010 13
15. 2003 13
16. 2005 14

Exercise 3

1. 2001 01
2. 2013 02
3. 2007 02
4. 1999 02
5. 2014 03
6. 2009 04
7. 2006 05
8. 1999 05
9. 2014 07
10. 2004 07
11. 2002 08
12. 2007 10
13. 1998 10
14. 2008 12
15. 1999 12
16. 2007 13

Exercise 4

1. 2009 01
2. 2007 01
3. 2006 01
4. 2016 02
5. 2011 02
6. 2015 03
7. 2005 03
8. 2014 04
9. 1999 04
10. 2000 06
11. 1999 06
12. 2015 07
13. 1998 07
14. 2009 08
15. 2006 08
16. 2013 09
17. 2007 09
18. 2005 09
19. 2003 09
20. 2008 10
21. 1997 10
22. 1998 11
23. 2002 12
24. 2000 13

Exercise 5

1. 2012 02
2. 2010 03
3. 2006 03
4. 2016 04
5. 2007 04
6. 2011 05
7. 1999 07
8. 2008 08
9. 2015 12
10. 1998 12
11. 2005 13
12. 2016 15

Exercise 6

1. 2016 01
2. 2010 01
3. 2013 03
4. 2011 04
5. 2008 04
6. 2016 05
7. 2012 05
8. 2014 06
9. 2002 07
10. 2004 09
11. 2012 10
12. 2006 10
13. 2001 10
14. 2007 12
15. 2004 13
16. 2001 15
17. 2000 15

Exercise 7

1. 1998 01
2. 2015 02
3. 2006 02
4. 1997 02
5. 2004 03
6. 2000 03
7. 2015 05
8. 2013 05
9. 2004 05
10. 2013 06
11. 2012 07
12. 2010 08
13. 2003 08
14. 1999 08
15. 1998 09
16. 2015 10
17. 2014 10
18. 2005 10
19. 2016 11
20. 2006 11
21. 2001 11
22. 2014 12
23. 2009 13
24. 1998 13
25. 2014 14
26. 2011 15
27. 2006 14

Exercise 8

1. 2002 01
2. 2002 02
3. 2016 03
4. 2002 03
5. 1999 03
6. 1998 03
7. 1997 04
8. 2007 05
9. 2015 06
10. 2011 07
11. 1997 06
12. 2003 07
13. 1997 07
14. 2012 08
15. 2004 08
16. 1997 08
17. 2009 09
18. 2010 10
19. 2002 10
20. 2000 10
21. 2009 11
22. 2003 12
23. 2012 13
24. 2011 14
25. 2009 14
26. 2003 14
27. 2001 14
28. 2008 15

Exercise 9

1. 2012 01
2. 1999 01
3. 2002 05
4. 2001 05
5. 2004 06
6. 2014 11
7. 2011 12
8. 2013 15
9. 2010 15
10. 1999 15

Exercise 10

1. 2014 02
2. 2001 03
3. 2013 04
4. 2009 06
5. 2008 06
6. 2005 06
7. 2003 06
8. 2011 08
9. 2010 07
10. 2009 07
11. 2016 08
12. 2015 08
13. 2014 08
14. 2015 09
15. 2015 11
16. 1999 11
17. 2013 12
18. 2012 12
19. 2011 13
20. 2006 13
21. 2014 15
22. 2007 15

Exercise 11

1. 2003 02
2. 1997 03
3. 2005 04
4. 2000 05
5. 1998 05
6. 2016 06
7. 2000 07
8. 2013 08
9. 2001 08
10. 2011 10
11. 2002 09
12. 2011 11
13. 2008 11
14. 2010 12
15. 2001 12
16. 1999 13
17. 2015 14
18. 2013 14
19. 2006 15

Exercise 12

1. 2004 01
2. 2010 02
3. 2005 02
4. 2004 04
5. 2001 04
6. 2011 06
7. 2005 05
8. 2007 06
9. 1998 06
10. 2013 07
11. 2005 07
12. 2001 07
13. 2005 08
14. 1999 09
15. 2016 10
16. 2013 10
17. 2000 11
18. 2016 12
19. 2005 12
20. 2000 12
21. 2008 13
22. 1997 13
23. 1997 14
24. 2009 15
25. 2003 15
26. 2002 15

Exercise 13

1. 2000 04
2. 2010 05
3. 2010 06
4. 2008 07
5. 2007 08
6. 2000 08
7. 2004 11
8. 2013 13
9. 2001 13
10. 2012 15
11. 1998 15

Exercise 14

1. 2015 04
2. 1998 04
3. 2009 05
4. 2006 09
5. 2004 10
6. 2003 10
7. 2013 11
8. 2002 11
9. 2016 13
10. 2007 14
11. 2002 14
12. 1998 14
13. 2004 15

Exercise 15

1. 1997 05
2. 2006 07
3. 2011 09
4. 1997 09
5. 2012 11
6. 2007 11
7. 2005 11
8. 2003 11
9. 2004 12
10. 2014 13
11. 2004 14
12. 2000 14
13. 2015 15

Exercise 16

1. 1998 02
2. 2003 04
3. 2002 06
4. 2012 09
5. 2001 09
6. 2006 12
7. 2015 13
8. 2016 14
9. 2005 15
10. 2013 16
11. 2011 17
12. 2006 18
13. 2011 21
14. 2001 24

Exercise 17

1. 2009 12
2. 2010 14
3. 2008 14
4. 1997 15
5. 2006 16
6. 2013 17
7. 2012 18
8. 1998 19
9. 2016 21
10. 2011 22
11. 1997 22
12. 2013 24

Exercise 18

1. 2016 09
2. 1999 14
3. 2012 16
4. 2006 17
5. 2004 17
6. 2009 18
7. 2001 18
8. 2000 18
9. 1997 18
10. 2005 19
11. 2003 19
12. 2002 20
13. 2014 21
14. 2008 25
15. 2007 25

Exercise 19

1. 2002 13
2. 2012 14
3. 1998 16
4. 2010 20
5. 2009 20
6. 2014 22
7. 1998 22
8. 2012 23

Exercise 20

1. 2009 16
2. 2008 16
3. 2003 16
4. 2000 17
5. 1999 17
6. 1998 17
7. 1997 17
8. 2011 18
9. 2015 19
10. 2009 19
11. 2006 19
12. 2004 19
13. 2013 20
14. 2015 21
15. 2010 22
16. 2000 22
17. 2011 23
18. 2008 23
19. 1998 24
20. 2012 25

Exercise 21

1. 2010 16
2. 2004 16
3. 2002 16
4. 2000 16
5. 1997 16
6. 2015 17
7. 2012 17
8. 2004 18
9. 2014 19
10. 2007 19
11. 2000 19
12. 2014 20
13. 2012 20
14. 2003 20
15. 2001 20
16. 2013 21
17. 2002 21
18. 2000 21
19. 2006 23
20. 1998 23
21. 2016 24
22. 2011 24
23. 2004 24
24. 2003 24
25. 2000 25

Exercise 22

1. 2015 16
2. 2005 16
3. 2016 17
4. 2007 18
5. 2013 19
6. 2012 19
7. 2007 21
8. 2001 21
9. 2003 22
10. 2013 25
11. 2010 25
12. 2002 25

Exercise 23

1. 2001 16
2. 2009 17
3. 2014 18
4. 2010 18
5. 2005 18
6. 1998 18
7. 2002 19
8. 1999 19
9. 1997 19
10. 1998 20
11. 2009 21
12. 2016 23
13. 2009 23
14. 2007 23
15. 2003 23
16. 2010 24
17. 2007 24
18. 2006 24
19. 2011 25
20. 1997 25

Exercise 24

1. 1999 16
2. 2014 17
3. 2008 17
4. 2003 17
5. 2001 17
6. 2016 18
7. 2016 19
8. 2006 20
9. 2005 20
10. 1999 20
11. 1997 20
12. 2008 21
13. 2006 21
14. 2004 21
15. 1998 21
16. 1997 21
17. 2016 22
18. 2008 22
19. 2004 22
20. 2002 22
21. 2001 23
22. 2015 24
23. 2002 24
24. 1999 24
25. 2014 25
26. 2006 25
27. 1999 25

Exercise 25

1.	2014	16
2.	2011	16
3.	2007	17
4.	2005	17
5.	2008	18
6.	1999	18
7.	2011	19
8.	2010	19
9.	2016	20
10.	2015	20
11.	2008	20
12.	2007	20
13.	2010	21
14.	2003	21
15.	2012	22
16.	2009	22
17.	2007	22
18.	1999	22
19.	2013	23
20.	2010	23
21.	2005	23
22.	2002	23
23.	1997	23
24.	2012	24
25.	2009	24
26.	1997	24
27.	2001	25
28.	1998	25

Exercise 26

1.	2016	16
2.	2010	17
3.	2003	18
4.	2002	18
5.	2011	20
6.	2012	21
7.	2015	22
8.	2014	23
9.	2014	24
10.	2008	24
11.	2000	24
12.	2005	25
13.	2004	25

Exercise 27

1.	2007	16
2.	2002	17
3.	2015	18
4.	2013	18
5.	2008	19
6.	2001	19
7.	2004	20
8.	2000	20
9.	2005	21
10.	1999	21
11.	2013	22
12.	2006	22
13.	2005	22
14.	2001	22
15.	2015	23
16.	2011	03
17.	2004	23
18.	2000	23
19.	1999	23
20.	2005	24
21.	2016	25
22.	2015	25
23.	2009	25
24.	2003	25

Index

Mostly, only terms from the problems appear in the index. Please also refer to the table of contents.